Students and External Readers	Staff & Research Students
DATE DUE FOR RETURN	**DATE OF ISSUE**
15 MAR. 1968	
30. JUN 92 9 2	

Any book which you borrow remains your responsibility
until the loan slip is cancelled

GILBERT
ON THE MAGNET

The Collector's

Series in Science

VOLUMES IN THE COLLECTOR'S SERIES
John Baptista Porta, *Natural Magick*
William Gilbert, *On the Magnet*

EDITED BY

DEREK J. PRICE

Institute for Advanced Study

Basic Books, Inc., New York

ON THE MAGNET

BY

William Gilbert

William Gilbert and His
De Magnete

"GILBERT shall live till loadstones cease to draw." Thus spoke the poet Dryden of a man who was a contemporary of Drake and Shakespeare. The Elizabethan contributions to sea-power and to literature have often been explored, but few are familiar at first hand with the book which has the unique honor of being the earliest contribution to modern physics.

De Magnete has always been a difficult book to obtain. Galileo puts into the mouth of Salviati the cry that "the book of Gilbert might never have come into my hands, if a Peripatetic philosopher of great fame, to free his library from contagion, as I believe, had not given it to me." To reprint the original Latin edition today would do service to few, but by rare good fortune this is one case in which there exists an almost perfect English translation—so perfect, indeed, that to all intents and purposes it is as the book would appear if it had been composed in the vernacular and printed and arranged by the same London printer that issued it in 1600.

William Gilbert, Physician to the Queen, was the first man to raise himself from the Aristotelian morass and work scientifically through an entire field of inquiry. In his time, other writers either were concerned as encyclopedists with the whole content of the universe or were practitioners, dealing only with the application of science to such practical purposes as navigation, surveying, or other arts. Of all the sciences only astronomy had been so perfected by the Greeks that it could serve as a secure foundation for the new discoveries and improvements made during the Renaissance. This, however, was a self-contained subject, throwing little light on the nature of terrestrial phenomena. The other branches of science were therefore in the position of starting afresh and being delayed rather than helped by most of the "knowledge" accumulated before that time. At this time, too, it must be remembered, even the basic rules and methods for the conduct of scientific inquiry had not yet been formulated by Francis Bacon.

In this context, one might well feel that Gilbert had invented the whole process of modern science rather than merely discovering the basic laws of magnetism and of static electricity. Certainly he was the first to have the tenacity to work through a whole segment of physics methodically, appealing to experiment and reason throughout. Gilbert's work formed the pattern for the subsequent treatment of other parts of physics, and much later for chemistry and for biological subjects.

The publication of this book was a most auspicious beginning for the glorious seventeenth century of the scientific revolution. It was incidentally, the first great book of modern science to be published in England and the first to be written by an Englishman.

The Author

Who was this man who managed to shake off the old tradition and to think in a new manner that was destined to be recognized as truly scientific? William Gilbert was born on May 24, 1544, as the eldest son of Jerome Gilbert (Hierom Gilberd or Gylberd), a Suffolk gentleman who had become recorder of the town of Colchester in Essex. It was a thriving provincial town, and the post of recorder was the most distinguished political appointment it had to offer. William's mother had three more children in three more years; then she died and Jerome married again and sired seven further additions to his family. One of these seven, also called William (the younger, of Melford), was responsible for the posthumous publication of a second book by his namesake half-brother. With Ambrose, another of the seven, he erected a memorial tablet to (the elder) William Gilbert in Holy Trinity Church, Colchester, from which an erroneous birthdate of 1540 has been taken to the continued confusion of biographers.

William was sent to Cambridge at the usual age of 14, where he entered St. John's College and followed the normal courses, gaining his bachelor's degree in two years and his master's four years after that. He remained at college for five years more, becoming a medical doctor and senior fellow, and acting as mathematical examiner in 1565 and 1569. At the end of this he went, as was also customary, to the finishing school of grand travel on the Continent. He seems to have spent most of four years in Italy, afterwards returning to London, where he set up house and began to practice medicine in 1573.

In this practice, Gilbert soon won great renown, attaining membership in the Royal College of Physicians and being appointed to a succession of offices of that body, from Censor in 1581 to President in 1599. In 1601 he reached the highest post in his profession, as physician to Queen Elizabeth. There is a legend that when the queen died just two years later, her only personal legacy was to Gilbert, for the furthering of his researches. But Gilbert outlived her by but eight months, continuing as Royal Physician until carried off by the plague on November 30 (New Style, December 10) 1603. He died a bachelor, leaving all his books and scientific instruments to the Royal College of Physicians, where they were destroyed in 1666 by the great fire of London.

Gilbert's investigations of magnetism seem to date from about 1581, when he was just firmly established as a leading physician. Like Giambattista della Porta in Italy (with whom he had several controversies), he became the leader of a little group of men who met at his house to carry out experiments and discuss scientific matters—an unofficial scientific academy which preceded by many decades the Invisible College and its matured successor, the Royal Society. Although the scientists themselves were not yet formally organized or even aware of being something more than simply men of general culture or professional teachers at universities, the artisans of science were already well established. During the last two decades of the sixteenth century, professional surveyors, navigators, makers of mathematical instruments, and teachers of their uses became very numerous and enjoyed considerable status, especially in the metropolitan seaport of London.

In this atmosphere of practitioneering, Gilbert spent some 17 or 18 years working on the topics of his book, luxuriating in the availability of new instruments and specimens of loadstones. Like Edison, he methodically and exhaustively tried all possibilities within range, sometimes repeating experiments to the point of tedium. When he investigated the tale that diamond could act like loadstone in magnetizing an iron needle (Book 3, Chap. 13), he "made the experiment ourselves with seventy-five diamonds in the presence of witnesses." We know, incidentally, that he spent £5,000 of his own money on such experiments—no small sum for the times.

It is evident from his style that Gilbert saw clearly that he was making a radical break with the past in examining the phenomena of electricity and magnetism by an experimental method. Like a true man of his period, he frequently vituperates against the asinine errors of men who believe differently. Perhaps it is to his credit that he was probably the first in England to advocate the new Copernican doctrine and hold that the fixed stars were at various distances rather than on a great sphere or shell spinning around the sun. It must be remembered, though, that at this time, before the telescopic observations of Galileo, there was little or no evidence on which one might accept or reject such Copernican ideas. Astronomers knew that they could measure no stellar parallax, and therefore it was meaningless to talk about the distances of the stars. These ideas had but the status of ultimately successful guesses and Gilbert can get little credit for deciding correctly.

We should also remember, throughout any reading of this book, that Gilbert was writing within the matrix of Aristotelian thought and, though he escapes from it miraculously from time to time, much of the book, in both language and content, is embedded in Aristotelian terminology and ideas. If Gilbert's basic theories of magnetism and electricity seem almost theological, it is for this reason, and we must therefore view with even greater respect the firm foundations on which he placed so many phenomena. It was no light matter, and the year of publication of this book was also that in which Giordano Bruno was burned at the stake for perhaps lesser scientific heresies.

In addition to establishing a new science and its method, Gilbert publishes in this book several new discoveries, sufficient in themselves for any later writer to have established an independent reputation. In particular, Gilbert discusses the magnetism of the earth by making a model—a spherical piece of loadstone called a *terrella* (little earth). This led him to many new, useful, and striking ideas, notably that the magnetism could be an explanation for gravitational forces—Gilbert's was, after all, the first experimental investigation that could deal with "forces acting at a distance." In his second and posthumous book, *De Mundo Nostro Sublunari Philosophia Nova* (new philosophy of our sublunary world), published in Amsterdam in 1651, he suggested that it was magnetic force in the solar system and in the moon that kept the same face of that body constantly turned toward the earth though all else was in a state of rotation.

Anticipating the Baconian "New Philosophy" in yet another way, Gilbert is also very much aware of the emphasis to be laid on the practical as well as the philosophical benefits of his establishment of this science. He points out the use of the magnetic needle in navigation, in mining, and in the military applications of finding the directions in which to point guns and dig tunnels toward an enemy. Unfortunately his great discovery that magnetic variations could be used to find the longitude at sea proved a useless chimera, but only after inspiring much research useful in other ways.

Almost all of Gilbert's scientific work was published in this book. He had intended to add a small section of six or eight leaves describing new instruments (so he wrote to Barlow in 1601) but he was probably hindered by his new appointment as Royal Physician, and the instruments were described a year later in a book by Thomas Blundeville, *The Theoriques of the Seven Planets* . . . (London 1602). In the same way he was probably hindered during his lifetime from publishing his second and still neglected book on the sublunary world.

THE BOOK

The first edition of *De Magnete* was printed in London in 1600 by the house of Peter Short, whose trademark, a serpent draped over a Greek *Tau*, appears large on the title page. Its long descriptive title was, of course, in the usual style of its time; in full, it reads, *Guilielmi Gilberti Colcestrensis, Medici Londinensis, De Magnete, magneticisque Corporibus, et de magno Magnete Tellure; Physiologia nova, plurimis & argumentis & experimentis demonstrata.* A not so common, but rather charming, practice is Gilbert's use (see Preface, p. ii *verso*) of large and small asterisks to indicate the passages describing and enunciating the important new discoveries and experiments of great and greatest merit. There are, in all, 178 small and 21 large asterisks—five for every six pages of text of the book.

De Magnete cannot have been printed in a very large edition, for copies have now become very rare and valuable, distinctly more rare, for example, than the First Folio Shakespeare. Even allowing for abnormally high loss—copies in Italy are frequently found with the sixth book (dealing with the rotation of the Earth) mutilated or removed—the original printing must have been small, probably less than the three or four hundred copies printed for the first edition of Newton's *Principia* much later in the seventeenth century. Certainly there were not sufficient copies to make it a hardship for somebody to make three or four small ink corrections of typographical errors in almost all known copies.

A second and third Latin edition were brought out in 1628 and 1633 respectively by Wolfgang Lochmann in Stettin; both are now rare, the 1628 edition especially so. This latter is also known with a new title page bearing an imprint, "Frankfort a/m 1629." The second Stettin edition is, incidentally, the only one having an engraved title-page (see frontispiece). It shows, of course, loadstones, compasses, and a terrella; also in a vignette is a ship, apparently sailing away from a floating bowl compass with a terrella at the center. A photo-zincographic facsimile of the first London edition was published in 1892 by Mayer and Mueller of Berlin.

THE TRANSLATION

Soon after publication of the first Latin edition of *De Magnete,* a need was felt for an English version. William Barlow (1544-1625), Archdeacon of Salisbury and friend and contemporary of Gilbert, wrote in his *Magneticall Advertisements* (London, 1616) as follows:

"Many of our nation, both Gentlemen and others of excellent witts and lovers of these knowledges, not able to read Doctor Gilbert's booke in Latin have bin (ever since the first publishing thereof) exceeding desirous to have it translated into English, but hitherto no man hath done it, neither as yet goeth about any such matter, whereof one principall cause is that there are very few that understande his booke, because they have not load-stones of divers forms, but especially round ones. . . ."

As knowledge of magnetism grew, this excuse became less tenable, but still there was no man to go about the matter. Toward the end of the nineteenth century, after the science of electricity and magnetism had changed the face of the world and produced men of excellent witt who were highly successful electrical engineers and scientists, there were some who looked more kindly on the project. It was an easily remembered anniversary that *De Magnete* would be just 300 years old as mankind moved forward into the first year of the twentieth century. The movement seems to have started about 1889 with the formation of a "Gilbert Club" having Sir William Thomson (Lord Kelvin) as its president and Conrad W. Cooke as its honorary secretary. The chief object was the preparation of a tercentenary translation made as perfectly as possible to correspond with the original in all but language. It was to be set in type of the original face, using precisely the same printer's ornaments and decorative colophons, each page contain exactly the same sentences. One small but necessary change was the omission of the list of printer's errors in the Latin edition, since these were no longer relevant; another change was the addition of a most useful modern index.

It is recorded that the actual labor of translation and revision was carried out by ten people; Rev. A. W. Howard, Mr. G. T. Dickin, Mr. Edward Little, Prof. R. A. Sampson, Prof. Meldola, Mr. Latimer Clark, Sir B. W. Richardson, Rev. W. C. Howell, Dr. Joseph Larmor, and Prof. Silvanus P. Thompson. Of these, it is evident that the last-named became the guiding light and undertook the lion's share of this work and also of the preparation of the set of valuable notes; these were printed in the year after the translation, and bound up with it, at the end of the volume. The translation was privately printed in 1900 by the Chiswick Press, well known for its typographical artistry, and was distributed in a limited numbered edition of 250 copies, bound in vellum and tied with green tapes. Appearance was delayed for at least a year by the inclusion of Silvanus Thompson's volume of notes.

The translation is not only a labor of love but a work of art, similar in its status to the translation of a poem from one language to another without loss, improvement, or change of feeling. Where the Latin is grave or animated, clear or obscure, so is the English version. It is a masterpiece of translation, having the flavor and appearance of the original in all but the tongue, and marred only by the fault that very few copies were printed. Thus history repeated itself: the book was unobtainable by the general public and the quite large number of people who had now begun to take a serious interest in the history of science.

The unavailability of the Thompson translation was all the more unfortunate because it had been preceded, by some seven years, by a more workaday version by Paul Fleury Mottelay (New York, 1893; reprinted 1952 as part of Vol. 28, *Great Books of the Western World*, Encyclopaedia Britannica). Mottelay was a brilliant bibliographer of electricity and magnetism, and his translation might have seemed adequate and competent enough if it were not for the meticulous luxury and inspired sensitivity of the Gilbert Club edition. The ever-increasing number of persons wishing to read Gilbert in translation have therefore very often been forced to use the inferior edition, being unable to have access to the rare Latin edition or to the almost as rare Gilbert Club translation. Now, too, even the Mottelay translation is not always easy to obtain for one's own bookshelf.

SILVANUS P. THOMPSON

The existence of this fine facsimile translation is due, as we have noted, to one member of the Gilbert Club who shouldered most of the burden and spent much of his life in enthusiastic and painstaking research on Gilbert and the other men and events that were important in the early history of electricity and magnetism. Silvanus Phillips Thompson (1851-1916) spent the greater part of his life as Principal of the Technical College in Finsbury, London. Being a Quaker and therefore not admissible to Cambridge or Oxford, he had been educated in the University of London, quickly showing considerable scientific talent and an outstanding facility for clear and powerful exposition that made him one of the most popular scientific lecturers and writers of his day. In addition to carrying a heavy teaching load, he wrote many scientific papers (mostly of rather secondary research value), several textbooks, better than anything hitherto available and providing inspiration for such men as Lord Rutherford, and excellent biographies of Philipp Reis, Michael Faraday, and Lord Kelvin. He was a very keen bibliophile and book-collector, taking a professional interest in the minutae of this field and attaining great skill in the sleuthlike building of a clear case from tiny clues. In addition, he frequently worked as a consultant physicist in electrical engineering and did much to advance this new profession and enhance its status.

His books were his friends and if any one book should be singled out, it was his *De Magnete*, on which he lavished the most of his literary and scientific affection. Gilbert was his life's hobby, and this translation stands now as a rare product of sympathetic magic in contact between an author of genius and his dedicated exponent and translator.

Institute for Advanced Study   DEREK J. DE S. PRICE
Princeton, New Jersey.

April 7, 1958

SUGGESTED FURTHER READING

RUFUS SUTER, "A Biographical Sketch of Dr. William Gilbert of Colchester," *Osiris*, Vol. 10 (1952), pp. 368-384.

BERN DIBNER, *Dr. William Gilbert*, Burndy Library, 1947, 16 pp.

(Both the treatments above include good bibliographies of other modern writings about Gilbert and his work.)

J. S. THOMPSON and H. G. THOMPSON, *Silvanus Phillips Thompson, His Life and Letters*, New York, 1920.

GEORGE SARTON, *Six Wings, Men of Science in the Renaissance*, Indiana University Press, 1957, pp. 94-98.

FRANCIS R. JOHNSON, *Astronomical Thought in Renaissance England*, Johns Hopkins University Press, 1937, 215*ff.*

A. WOLF, *A History of Science, Technology, and Philosophy in the 16th and 17th Centuries*, London (2d. ed.), 1950, pp. 293-297.

ACKNOWLEDGMENT

The portrait (p. iii), the frontispiece (p. xii), and the copy from which this facsimile was made were borrowed from the Burndy Library by the kind permission of Mr. Bern Dibner.

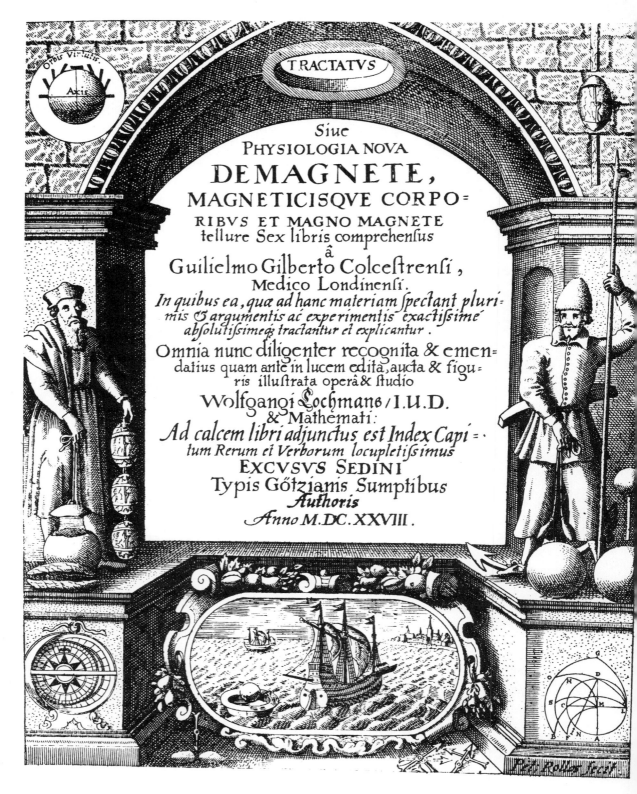

Title page of the second edition of *De Magnete* (see editor's introduction, p. ix).

VVILLIAM GIL-
BERT OF COLCHES-
TER, PHYSICIAN OF
LONDON.

ON THE MAGNET, MAGNE-
TICK BODIES ALSO, AND ON

the great magnet the earth; a new Physi-
ology, demonſtrated by many ar-
guments & experiments.

LONDON

IMPRINTED AT THE CHISWICK PRESS ANNO
MCM.

PREFACE TO THE CANDID
READER, STUDIOUS OF
THE MAGNETICK
PHILOSOPHY.

LEARER proofs, in the difcovery of fecrets, and in the inveftigation of the hidden caufes of things, being afforded by truftworthy experiments and by demonftrated arguments, than by the probable gueffes and opinions of the ordinary profeffors of philofophy : fo, therefore, that the noble fubftance of that great magnet, our common mother (the earth), hitherto quite unknown, and the confpicuous and exalted powers of this our globe, may be the better underftood, we have propofed to begin with the common magnetick, ftony, and iron material, and with magnetical bodies, and with the nearer parts of the earth which we can reach with our hands and perceive with our fenfes ; then to proceed with demonftrable magnetick experiments ; and fo penetrate, for the firft time, into the innermoft parts of the earth. For after we had, in order finally to learn the true fubftance of the globe, feen and thoroughly examined many of thofe things which have been obtained from mountain heights or ocean depths, or from the profoundeft caverns and from hidden mines: we applied much prolonged labour on inveftigating the magnetical forces ; fo wonderful indeed are they, compared with the forces of all other minerals, furpaffing even the virtues of all other bodies about us. Nor have we found this our labour idle or unfruitful ; fince daily during our experimenting, new and unexpected properties came to light ; and our Philofophy hath grown fo much from the things diligently obferved, that we have attempted to expound the interior parts of the terrene globe, and its native fubftance, upon magnetick principles ; and to reveal to men the earth (our common mother), and to point it out as if with the finger, by real demonftrations and by

* ij   experiments

experiments manifeftly apparent to the fenfes.   And as geometry afcends from fundry very fmall and very eafy principles to the greateft and moft difficult ; by which the wit of man climbs above the firmament : fo our magnetical doctrine and fcience firft fets forth in convenient order the things which are lefs obfcure ; from thefe there come to light others that are more remarkable ; and at length in due order there are opened the concealed and moft fecret things of the globe of the earth, and the caufes are made known of thofe things which, either through the ignorance of the ancients or the neglect of moderns, have remained unrecognized and overlooked. But why fhould I, in fo vaft an Ocean of Books by which the minds of ftudious men are troubled and fatigued, through which very foolifh productions the world and unreafoning men are intoxicated, and puffed up, rave and create literary broils, and while profeffing to be philofophers, phyficians, mathematicians and aftrologers, neglect and defpife men of learning : why fhould I, I fay, add aught further to this fo-perturbed republick of letters, and expofe this noble philofophy, which feems new and incredible by reafon of fo many things hitherto unrevealed, to be damned and torn to pieces by the maledictions of thofe who are either already fworn to the opinions of other men, or are foolifh corruptors of good arts, learned idiots, grammatifts, fophifts, wranglers, and perverfe little folk ? But to you alone, true philofophizers, honeft men, who feek knowledge not from books only but from things themfelves, have I addreffed thefe magnetical principles in this new fort of Philofophizing. But if any fee not fit to affent to thefe felf-fame opinions and paradoxes, let them neverthelefs mark the great array of experiments and dif-coveries (by which notably every philofophy flourifheth), which have been wrought out and demonftrated by us with many pains and vigils and expenfes. In thefe rejoice, and employ them to better ufes, if ye fhall be able. I know how arduous it is to give frefhnefs to old things, luftre to the antiquated, light to the dark, grace to the defpifed, credibility to the doubtful ; fo much the more by far is it difficult to win and eftablifh fome authority for things new and unheard-of, in the face of all the opinions of all men. Nor for that do we care, fince philofophizing, as we deemed, is for the few.   To our own difcoveries and experiments we have affixed afterifks, larger and fmaller, according to the importance and fub-tlety of the matter. Whofo defireth to make trial of the fame experiments, let him handle the fubftances, not negligently and careleffly, but prudently, deftly, and in the proper way ; nor let him (when a thing doth not fucceed) ignorantly denounce our dif-coveries : for nothing hath been fet down in thefe books which hath not been explored and many times performed and repeated amongft us.   Many things in our reafonings and hypothefes will, perchance, at firft fight, feem rather hard, when they are foreign to the commonly

monly received opinion; yet I doubt not but that hereafter they will yet obtain authority from the demonftrations themfelves. Wherefore in magnetical fcience, they who have made moft pro- grefs, truft moft in and profit moft by the hypothefes; nor will anything readily become certain to any one in a magnetical philo- fophy in which all or at leaft moft points are not afcertained. This nature-knowledge is almoft entirely new and unheard-of, fave what few matters a very few writers have handed down concerning cer- tain common magnetical powers. Wherefore we but feldom quote antient Greek authors in our fupport, becaufe neither by ufing greek arguments nor greek words can the truth be demonftrated or elucidated either more precifely or more fignificantly. For our doctrine magnetical is at variance with moft of their principles and dogmas. Nor have we brought to this work any pretence of eloquence or adornments of words; but this only have we done, that things difficult and unknown might be fo handled by us, in fuch a form of fpeech, and in fuch words as are needed to be clearly underftood: Sometimes therefore we ufe new and unufual words, not that by means of foolifh veils of vocabularies we fhould cover over the facts with fhades and mifts (as Alchemifts are wont to do) but that hidden things which have no name, never having been hitherto perceived, may be plainly and correctly enunciated. After defcribing our magnetical experiments and our information of the homogenick parts of the earth, we proceed to the general nature of the whole globe; wherein it is permitted us to philofophize freely and with the fame liberty which the Egyptians, Greeks, and Latins formerly ufed in publifhing their dogmas: whereof very many errors have been handed down in turn to later authors: and in which fmatterers ftill perfift, and wander as though in perpetual darknefs. To thofe early forefathers of philofophy, Ariftotle, Theophraftus, Ptolemy, Hippocrates, and Galen, let due honour be ever paid: for by them wifdom hath been diffufed to pofterity;

but our age hath detected and brought to light very many facts which they, were they now alive, would gladly have accepted. Wherefore we alfo have not hefi- tated to expound in demonftrable hypothefes thofe things which we have difcovered by long experience. Farewell.

TO

Dr. William Gilbert,

a diſtinguiſhed Doctor of Medicine amongſt the
Londoners, and Father of Magnetick Philoſophy,
an Encomiaſtic Preface of Edward Wright
on the ſubject of theſe books
Magnetical.

SHOULD *there by chance be any one, moſt eminent Sir, who reckons as of ſmall account theſe magnetical books and labours of yours, and thinks theſe ſtudies of yours of too little moment, and by no means worthy enough of the attention of an eminent man devoted to the weightier ſtudy of Medicine: truly he muſt deſervedly be judged to be in no common degree void of underſtanding. For that the uſe of the magnet is very important and wholly admirable is better known for the moſt part to men of even the loweſt claſs than to need from me at this time any long addreſs or commendation. Nor truly in my judgment could you have choſen any topick either more noble or more uſeful to the human race, upon which to exerciſe the ſtrength of your philoſophic intellect; ſince indeed it has been brought about by the divine agency of this ſtone, that continents of ſuch vaſt circuit, ſuch an infinite number of lands, iſlands, peoples, and tribes, which have remained unknown for ſo many ages, have now only a ſhort time ago, almoſt within our own memory, been quite eaſily diſcovered and quite frequently explored, and that the circuit of the whole terreſtrial globe alſo has been more than once circumnavigated by our own countrymen, Drake and Cavendiſh; a fact which I wiſh to mention to the laſting memory of theſe men. For by the pointing of the iron touched by a loadſtone, the points of South, North, Eaſt, and Weſt, and the other quarters of the world are made known to navigators even under an overcaſt ſky and in the darkeſt night; ſo that thus they always very eaſily underſtand to which point of the world they ought to direct their ſhip's courſe; which before the diſcovery of this wonderful virtue of the magnetick* βορεοδείξις *was clearly impoſſible. Hence in old times (as is eſtabliſhed in hiſtories), an incredible anxiety and immenſe danger was continually threatening ſailors; for at the coming on of a tempeſt and the obſcuring of the view of ſun and ſtars, they were left entirely in ignorance whither they were making; nor could they find out this by any reaſoning or ſkill. With what joy then may we ſuppoſe them to have been filled, to what feelings of delight muſt all ſhipmaſters have given utterance, when that index magnetical firſt offered itſelf to them as a moſt ſure guide, and as it were a Mercury, for their journey? But neither was this ſufficient for this magnetical Mercury; to indicate, namely, the right way, and to point, as it were, a finger in the direction toward which the courſe muſt be*
                                                                    directed;

directed; it began also long ago to show distinctly the distance of the place toward which it points. For since the index magnetical does not always in every place look toward the same point of the North, but deviates from it often, either toward the East or toward the West, yet always has the same deviation in the same place, whatever the place is, and steadily preserves it; it has come about that from that deviation, which they call variation, carefully noticed and observed in any maritime places, the same places could afterwards also be found by navigators from the drawing near and approach to the same variation as that of these same places, taken in conjunction with the observation of the latitude. Thus the Portuguese in their voyages to the East Indies had the most certain indications of their approach to the Cape of Good Hope; as appears from the narrations of Hugo van Lynschoten and of the very learned Richard Hakluyt, our countryman. Hence also the experienced skippers of our own country, not a few of them, in making the voyage from the Gulf of Mexico to the islands of the Azores, recognized that they had come as near as possible to these same islands; although from their sea-charts they seemed to be about six hundred British miles from them. And so, by the help of this magnetick index, it would seem as though that geographical problem of finding the longitude, which for so many centuries has exercised the intellects of the most learned Mathematicians, were going to be in some way satisfied; because if the variation for any maritime place whatever were known, the same place could very readily be found afterward, as often as was required, from the same variation, the latitude of the same place being not unknown.

It seems, however, that there has been some inconvenience and hindrance connected with the observation of this variation; because it cannot be observed excepting when the sun or the stars are shining. Accordingly this magnetick Mercury of the sea goes on still further to bless all shipmasters, being much to be preferred to Neptune himself, and to all the sea-gods and goddesses; not only does it show the direction in a dark night and in thick weather, but it also seems to exhibit the most certain indications of the latitude. For an iron index, suspended on its axis (like a pair of scales), with the most delicate workmanship so as to balance in æquilibrio, and then touched and excited by a loadstone, dips to some fixed and definite point beneath the horizon (in our latitude in London, for example, to about the seventy-second degree), at which it at length comes to rest. But under the æquator itself, from that admirable agreement and congruency which, in almost all and singular magnetical experiments, exists between the earth itself and a terrella (that is, a globular loadstone), it seems exceedingly likely (to say the very least), and indeed more than probable, that the same index (again stroked with a loadstone) will remain in æquilibrio in an horizontal position. Whence it is evident that this also is very probable, that in an exceedingly small progress from the South toward the North (or contrariwise), there will be at least a sufficiently perceptible change in that

* iiij
declination;

declination; so that from that declination in any place being once carefully observed along with the latitude, the same place and the same latitude may be very easily recognized afterward, even in the darkest night and in the thickest mist by a declination instrument. Wherefore to bring our oration at length back to you, most eminent and learned Dr. Gilbert (whom I gladly recognize as my teacher in this magnetick philosophy), if these books of yours on the Magnet had contained nothing else, excepting only this finding of latitude from magnetick declination, by you now first brought to light, our shipmasters, Britains, French, Belgians, and Danes, trying to enter the British Channel or the Straits of Gibraltar from the Atlantick Ocean in dark weather, would still most deservedly judge them to be valued at no small sum of gold. But that discovery of yours about the whole globe of the earth being magnetical, although perchance it will seem to many " most paradoxical," producing even a feeling of astonishment, has yet been so firmly defended by you at all points and confirmed by so many experiments so apposite and appropriate to the matter in hand, in Bk. 2, chap. 34; Bk. 3, chap. 4 and 12; and in almost the whole of the fifth book, that no room is left for doubt or contradiction. I come therefore to the cause of the magnetick variation, which hitherto has distracted the minds of all the learned; for which no mortal has ever adduced a more probable reason than that which has now been set forth by you for the first time in these books of yours on the Magnet. The ὀρθοβορεοδείξις of the index magnetical in the middle of the ocean, and in the middle of continents (or at least in the middle of their stronger and more lofty parts), its inclining near the shore toward those same parts, even by sea and by land, agreeing with the experiments Bk. 4, chap. 2, on an actual terrella (made after the likeness of the terrestrial globe, uneven, and rising up in certain parts, either weak or wanting in firmness, or imperfect in some other way),—this inclination having been proved, very certainly demonstrates the probability that that variation is nought else than a certain deviation of the magnetick needle toward those parts of the earth that are more vigorous and more prominent. Whence the reason is readily established of that irregularity which is often perceived in the magnetick variations, arising from the inæquality and irregularity of those eminences and of the terrestrial forces. Nor of a surety have I any doubt, that all those even who have either imagined or admitted points attractive or points respective in the sky or the earth, and those who have imagined magnetick mountains, or rocks, or poles, will immediately begin to waver as soon as they have perused these books of yours on the Magnet, and willingly will march with your opinion. Finally, as to the views which you discuss in regard to the circular motion of the earth and of the terrestrial poles, although to some perhaps they will seem most supposititious, yet I do not see why they should not gain some favour, even among the very men who do not recognize a sphærical motion of the earth; since not even they can easily clear themselves from many difficulties, which necessarily follow from the daily motion of the
whole

whole sky. For in the first place it is against reason that that should be effected by many causes, which can be effected by fewer; and it is against reason that the whole sky and all the sphæres (if there be any) of the stars, both of the planets and the fixed stars, should be turned round for the sake of a daily motion, which can be explained by the mere daily rotation of the earth. Then whether will it seem more probable, that the æquator of the terrestrial globe in a single second (that is, in about the time in which any one walking quickly will be able to advance only a single pace) can accomplish a quarter of a British mile (of which sixty equal one degree of a great circle on the earth), or that the æquator of the primum mobile *in the same time should traverse five thousand miles with celerity ineffable; and in the twinkling of an eye should fly through about five hundred British miles, swifter than the wings of lightning, if indeed they maintain the truth who especially assail the motion of the earth). Finally, will it be more likely to allow some motion to this very tiny terrestrial globe; or to build up with mad endeavour above the eighth of the fixed sphæres those three huge sphæres, the ninth (I mean), the tenth, and the eleventh, marked by not a single star, especially since it is plain from these books on the magnet, from a comparison of the earth and the terrella, that a circular motion is not so alien to the nature of the earth as is commonly supposed. Nor do those things which are adduced from the sacred Scriptures seem to be specially adverse to the doctrine of the mobility of the earth; nor does it seem to have been the intention of Moses or of the Prophets to promulgate any mathematical or physical niceties, but to adapt themselves to the understanding of the common people and their manner of speech, just as nurses are accustomed to adapt themselves to infants, and not to go into every unnecessary detail. Thus in* Gen. i. v. 16, *and* Psal. 136, *the moon is called a great light, because it appears so to us, though it is agreed nevertheless by those skilled in astronomy that many of the stars, both of the fixed and wandering stars, are much greater. Therefore neither do I think that any solid conclusion can be drawn against the earth's mobility from* Psal. 104, v. 5; *although God is said to have laid the foundations of the earth that it should not be removed for ever; for the earth will be able to remain evermore in its own and self-same place, so as not to be moved by any wandering motion, nor carried away from its seat (wherein it was first placed by the Divine artificer). We, therefore, with devout mind acknowledging and adoring the inscrutable wisdom of the triune Divinity (having more diligently investigated and observed his admirable work in the magnetical motions), induced by philosophical experiments and reasonings not a few, do deem it to be probable enough that the earth, though resting on its centre as on an immovable base and foundation, nevertheless is borne around circularly.*

But passing over these matters (concerning which I believe no one has ever demonstrated anything with greater certainty), without any doubt those matters which you have discussed concerning the causes of

the

the variation and of the magnetick dip below the horizon, not to mention many other matters, which it would take too long to speak of here, will gain very great favour amongst all intelligent men, and especially (to speak after the manner of the Chemists) amongst the sons of the magnetick doctrine. Nor indeed do I doubt that when you have published these books of yours on the Magnet, you will excite all the diligent and industrious shipmasters to take no less care in observing the magnetick declination beneath the horizon than the variation. Since (if not certain) it is at least probable, that the latitude itself, or rather the effect of the latitude, can be found (even in very dark weather) much more accurately from that declination alone, than can either the longitude or the effect of the longitude from the variation, though the sun itself is shining brightly or all the stars are visible, with the most skilful employment likewise of all the most exact instruments. Nor is there any doubt but that those most learned men, Peter Plancius (not more deeply versed in Geography than in observations magnetical), and Simon Stevinus, the most distinguished mathematician, will rejoice in no moderate degree, when they first see these magnetical books of yours, and observe their λιμενευρετική, or Haven-finding Art, *enlarged and enriched by so great and unexpected an addition ; and without doubt they will urge all their own shipmasters (as far as they can) to observe also everywhere the magnetick declination below the horizon no less than the variation. May your Magnetical Philosophy, therefore, most learned Dr. Gilbert, come forth into the light under the best auspices, after being kept back not till the ninth year only (as Horace prescribes), but already unto almost a second nine, a philosophy rescued at last by so many toils, studyings, watchings, with so much ingenuity and at no moderate expense maintained continuously through so many years, out of darkness and dense mist of the idle and feeble philosophizers, by means of endless experiments skilfully applied to it ; yet without neglecting anything which has been handed down in the writings of any of the ancients or of the moderns, all which you did diligently peruse and perpend. Do not fear the boldness or the prejudice of any supercilious and base philosophaster, who by either enviously calumniating or stealthily arrogating to himself the investigations of others seeks to snatch a most empty glory. Verily*

Envy detracts from great Homer's genius ;
but

Whoever thou art, Zoilus, thou hast thy name from him.

May your new physiology of the Magnet, I say (kept back for so many years), come forth now at length into the view of all, and your Philosophy, never to be enough admired, concerning the great Magnet (that is, the earth) ; for, believe me

(If there is any truth in the forebodings of seers),

these books of yours on the Magnet will avail more for perpetuating the memory of your name than the monument of any great Magnate placed upon your tomb.

Interpretation

Interpretation of certain words.

TErrella, a globular loadftone.

Verticity, polar vigour, not περιδίνησις, but περιδίνεισιος δύναμις: not a vertex or πόλος, but a turning tendency.

Electricks, things which attract in the fame manner as amber.

Excited Magnetick, that which has acquired powers from the loadftone.

Magnetick Verforium, a piece of iron upon a pin, excited by a loadftone.

Non-magnetick Verforium, a verforium of any metal, ferving for electrical experiments.

Capped loadftone, which is furnifhed with an iron cap, or fnout.

Meridionally, that is, along the projection of the meridian.

Paralleletically, that is, along the projection of a parallel.

Cufp, tip of a verforium excited by the loadftone.

Crofs, fometimes ufed of the end that has not been touched and excited by a loadftone, though in many inftruments both ends are excited by the appropriate termini of the ftone.

Cork, that is, bark of the cork-oak.

Radius of the Orbe of the Loadftone, is a ftraight line drawn from the fummit of the orbe of the loadftone, by the fhorteft way, to the furface of the body, which, continued, will pafs through the centre of the loadftone.

Orbe of Virtue, is all that fpace through which the Virtue of any loadftone extends.

Orbe of Coition, is all that fpace through which the fmalleft magnetick is moved by the loadftone.

Proof, for a demonftration fhown by means of a body.

Magnetick Coition: fince in magnetick bodies, motion does not occur by an attractive faculty, but by a concourfe or concordance of both, not as if there were an ἑλκτική δύναμις of one only, but a συνδρομή of both; there is always a coition of the vigour: and even of the body if its mafs fhould not obftruct.

Declinatorium, a piece of Iron capable of turning about an axis, excited by a loadftone, in a declination inftrument.

INDEX OF CHAPTERS.

Book 1.

INDEX OF CHAPTERS.

Chap.

INDEX OF CHAPTERS.

INDEX OF CHAPTERS.

Book 4.

INDEX OF CHAPTERS.

WILLIAM

WILLIAM GILBERT
ON THE LOADSTONE, BK. I.

CHAP. I.

ANCIENT AND MODERN WRITINGS
on the Loadſtone, with certain matters of mention only,
various opinions, & vanities.

T an early period, while philoſophy lay as yet rude and uncultivated in the miſts of error and ignorance, few were the virtues and properties of things that were known and clearly perceived : there was a briſtling foreſt of plants and herbs, things metallick were hidden, and the knowledge of ſtones was unheeded. But no ſooner had the talents and toils of many brought to light certain commodities neceſſary for the uſe and ſafety of men, and handed them on to others (while at the ſame time reaſon and experience had added a larger hope), than a thorough examination began to be made of foreſts and fields, hills and heights ; of ſeas too, and the depths of the waters, of the bowels of the earth's body ; and all things began to be looked into. And at length by good luck the magnet-ſtone was diſcovered in iron lodes, probably by ſmelters of iron or diggers of metals. This, on being handled by metal folk, quickly diſplayed that powerful and ſtrong attraction for iron, a virtue not latent and obſcure, but eaſily proved by all, and highly praiſed and commended. And in after time when it had emerged, as it were out of darkneſs and deep dungeons, and had become dignified of men on account of its ſtrong and amazing attraction for iron, many philoſophers as well as phyſicians of ancient days diſcourſed of it, in ſhort celebrated, as it were, its memory only ; as for inſtance Plato in the *Io,* Ariſtotle in the *De Anima,* in Book I. only, Theophraſtus the Leſbian, Dioſcorides, C. Plinius Secundus, and Julius Solinus. As handed down by them the loadſtone merely attracted iron, the reſt of its virtues were all undiſcovered. But that the ſtory of the load-

ſtone

ftone might not appear too bare and too brief, to this fingular and fole known quality there were added certain figments and falfehoods, which in the earlieft times, no lefs than nowadays, ufed to be put forth by raw fmatterers and copyifts to be fwallowed of men.   As for inftance, that if a loadftone be anointed with garlick, or if a diamond be near, it does not attraft iron.   Tales of this fort occur in Pliny, and in Ptolemy's *Quadripartitum;* and the errors have been feduloufly propagated, and have gained ground (like ill weeds that grow apace) coming down even to our own day, through the writings of a hoft of men, who, to fill out their volumes to a proper bulk, write and copy out pages upon pages on this, that, and the other fubjeft, of which they knew almoft nothing for certain of their own experience.   Such fables of the loadftone even Georgius Agricola himfelf, moft diftinguifhed in letters, relying on the writings of others, has embodied as aftual hiftory in his books *De Natura Foffilium.* Galen noted its medicinal power in the ninth book of his *De Simplicium Medicamentorum Facultatibus,* and its natural property of attrafting iron in the firft book of *De Naturalibus Facultatibus;* but he failed to recognize the caufe, as Diofcorides before him, nor made further inquiry.   But his commentator Matthiolus repeats the ftory of the garlick and the diamond, and moreover introduces Mahomet's fhrine vaulted with loadftones, and writes that, by the exhibition of this (with the iron coffin hanging in the air) as a divine miracle, the public were impofed upon.   But this is known by travellers to be falfe.   Yet Pliny relates that Chinocrates the architeft had commenced to roof over the temple of Arfinoe at Alexandria with magnet-ftone, that her ftatue of iron placed therein might appear to hang in fpace.   His own death, however, intervened, and alfo that of Ptolemy, who had ordered it to be made in honour of his fifter.   Very little was written by the ancients as to the caufes of attraftion of iron ; by Lucretius and others there are fome fhort notices ; others only make flight and meagre mention of the attraftion of iron : all of thefe are cenfured by Cardan for being fo carelefs and negligent in a matter of fuch importance and in fo wide a field of philofophizing ; and for not fupplying an ampler notion of it and a more perfeft philofophy : and yet, beyond certain received opinions and ideas borrowed from others and ill-founded conjeftures, he has not himfelf any more than they delivered to pofterity in all his bulky works any contribution to the fubjeft worthy of a philofopher. Of modern writers fome fet forth its virtue in medicine only, as Antonius Mufa Brafavolus, Baptifta Montanus, Amatus Lufitanus, as before them Oribafius in his thirteenth chapter *De Facultate Metallicorum,* Aetius Amidenus, Avicenna, Serapio Mauritanus, Hali Abbas, Santes de Ardoynis, Petrus Apponenfis, Marcellus, Arnaldus.   Bare mention is made of certain points relating to the loadftone in very few words by Marbodeus Gallus, Albertus,
Matthæus

Matthæus Silvaticus, Hermolaus Barbarus, Camillus Leonhardus, Cornelius Agrippa, Fallopius, Johannes Langius, Cardinal Cufan, Hannibal Rofetius Calaber; by all of whom the fubject is treated very negligently, while they merely repeat other people's fictions and ravings. Matthiolus compares the alluring powers of the loadftone which pafs through iron materials, with the mifchief of the torpedo, whofe venom paffes through bodies and fpreads imperceptibly; Guilielmus Puteanus in his *Ratio Purgantium Medicamentorum* difcuffes the loadftone briefly and learnedly. Thomas Eraftus, knowing little of magnetical nature, finds in the loadftone weak arguments againft Paracelfus; Georgius Agricola, like Encelius and other metallurgifts, merely ftates the facts; Alexander Aphrodifeus in his *Problemata* confiders the queftion of the loadftone inexplicable; Lucretius Carus, the poet of the Epicurean fchool, confiders that an attraction is brought about in this way: that as from all things there is an efflux of very minute bodies, fo from the iron atoms flow into the fpace emptied by the elements of the loadftone, between the iron and the loadftone, and that as foon as they have begun to ftream towards the loadftone, the iron follows, its corpufcles being entangled. To much the fame effect Johannes Coftæus adduces a paffage from Plutarch; Thomas Aquinas, writing briefly on the loadftone in Chapter VII. of his *Phyfica*, touches not amifs on its nature, and with his divine and clear intellect would have publifhed much more, had he been converfant with magnetick experiments. Plato thinks the virtue divine. But when three or four hundred years afterwards, the magnetick movement to North and South was difcovered or again recognized by men, many learned men attempted, each according to the bent of his own mind, either by wonder and praife, or by fome fort of reafonings, to throw light upon a virtue fo notable, and fo needful for the ufe of mankind. Of more modern authors a great number have ftriven to fhow what is the caufe of this direction and movement to North and South, and to underftand this great miracle of nature, and to difclofe it to others: but they have loft both their oil and their pains; for, not being practifed in the fubjects of nature, and being mifled by certain falfe phyfical fyftems, they adopted as theirs, from books only, without magnetical experiments, certain inferences bafed on vain opinions, and many things that are not, dreaming old wives' tales. Marfilius Ficinus ruminates over the ancient opinions, and in order to fhow the reafon of the direction feeks the caufe in the heavenly conftellation of the Bear, fuppofing the virtue of the Bear to prevail in the ftone and to be transferred to the iron. Paracelfus afferted that there are ftars, endowed with the power of the loadftone, which attract to themfelves iron. Levinus Lemnius defcribes and praifes the compafs, and infers its antiquity on certain grounds; he does not divulge the hidden miracle which he propounds. In the kingdom

of

of Naples the Amalfians were the firſt (ſo it is ſaid) to conſtruct the mariners' compaſs : and as Flavius Blondus ſays the Amalfians boaſt, not without reaſon, that they were taught by a certain citizen, Johannes Goia, in the year thirteen hundred after the birth of Chriſt. That town is ſituated in the kingdom of Naples not far from Salerno, near the promontory of Minerva ; and Charles V. beſtowed that principality on Andrea Doria, that great Admiral, on account of his ſignal naval ſervices.   Indeed it is plain that no invention of man's device has ever done more for mankind than the compaſs : ſome notwithſtanding conſider that it was diſcovered by others previouſly and uſed in navigation, judging from ancient writings and certain arguments and conjectures.   The knowledge of the little mariners' compaſs ſeems to have been brought into Italy by Paolo, the Venetian, who learned the art of the compaſs in the Chinas about the year MCCLX. ; yet I do not wiſh the Amalfians to be deprived of an honour ſo great as that of having firſt made the conſtruction common in the Mediterranean Sea.   Goropius attributes the diſcovery to the Cimbri or Teutons, forſooth becauſe the names of the thirty-two winds inſcribed on the compaſs are pronounced in the German tongue by all ſhip-maſters, whether they be French, Britiſh, or Spaniards ; but the Italians deſcribe them in their own vernacular.   Some think that Solomon, king of Judæa, was acquaint with the uſe of the mariners' compaſs, and made it known to his ſhip-maſters in the long voyages when they brought back ſuch a power of gold from the Weſt Indies : whence alſo, from the Hebrew word *Parvaim*, Arias Montanus maintains that the gold-abounding regions of Peru are named.   But it is more likely to have come from the coaſt of lower Æthiopia, from the region of Cephala, as others relate.   Yet that account ſeems to be leſs true, inaſmuch as the Phœnicians, on the frontier of Judæa, who were moſt ſkilled in navigation in former ages (a people whoſe talents, work, and counſel Solomon made uſe of in conſtructing ſhips and in the actual expeditions, as well as in other operations), were ignorant of magnetick aid, the art of the mariners' compaſs :   For had it been in uſe amongſt them, without doubt the Greeks and alſo Italians and all barbarians would have underſtood a thing ſo neceſſary and made famous by common uſe ; nor could matters of much repute, very eaſily known, and ſo highly requiſite ever have periſhed in oblivion ; but either the learning would have been handed down to poſterity, or ſome memorial of it would be extant in writing.   Sebaſtian Cabot was the firſt to diſcover that the magnetick iron varied. Gonzalus Oviedus is the firſt to write, as he does in his *Hiſtoria*, that in the ſouth of the Azores it does not vary.   Fernelius in his book *De Abditis Rerum Cauſis* ſays that in the loadſtone there is a hidden and abſtruſe cauſe, elſewhere calling it celeſtial ; and he brings forth nothing but the unknown by means of what is ſtill more unknown.

For

For clumfy, and meagre, and pointlefs is his inquiry into hidden caufes. The ingenious Fracaftorio, a diftinguifhed philofopher, in feeking the reafon for the direction of the loadftone, feigns Hyperborean magnetick mountains attracting magnetical things of iron: this view, which has found acceptance in part by others, is followed by many authors and finds a place not in their writings only, but in geographical tables, marine charts, and maps of the globe: dreaming, as they do, of magnetick poles and huge rocks, different from the poles of the earth. More than two hundred years earlier than Fracaftorio there exifts a little work, fairly learned for the time, going under the name of one Peter Peregrinus, which fome confider to have originated from the views of Roger Bacon, the Englifhman of Oxford: In which book caufes for magnetick direction are fought from the poles of the heaven and from the heaven itfelf. From this Peter Peregrinus, Johannes Taifnier of Hainault extracted materials for a little book, and publifhed it as new. Cardan talks much of the rifing of the ftar in the tail of the Greater Bear, and has attributed to its rifing the caufe of the variation: fuppofing that the variation is always the fame, from the rifing of the ftar. But the difference of the variation according to the change of pofition, and the changes which occur in many places, and are even irregular in fouthern regions, preclude the influence of one particular ftar at its northern rifing. The College of Coimbra feeks the caufe in fome part of the heaven near the pole: Scaliger in fection CXXXI. of his *Exercitationes* on Cardan fuggefts a heavenly caufe unknown to himfelf, and terreftrial loadftones nowhere yet difcovered. A caufe not due to thofe fideritic mountains named above, but to that power which fafhioned them, namely that portion of the heaven which overhangs that northern point. This view is garnifhed with a wealth of words by that erudite man, and crowned with many marginal fubtilities; but with reafonings not fo fubtile. Martin Cortes confiders that there is a place of attraction beyond the poles, which he judges to be the moving heavens. One Beffardus, a Frenchman, with no lefs folly notes the pole of the zodiack. Jacobus Severtius, of Paris, while quoting a few points, fafhions new errors as to loadftones of different parts of the earth being different in direction: and alfo as to there being eaftern and weftern parts of the loadftone. Robert Norman, an Englifhman, fixes a point and region refpective, not attractive; to which the magnetical iron is collimated, but is not itfelf attracted. Francifcus Maurolycus treats of a few problems on the loadftone, taking the trite views of others, and avers that the variation is due to a certain magnetical ifland mentioned by Olaus Magnus. Jofephus Acofta, though quite ignorant about the loadftone, neverthelefs pours forth vapid talk upon the loadftone. Livio Sanuto in his Italian *Geographia*, difcuffes at length the queftion whether the prime magnetick

meridian

meridian and the magnetick poles are in the heavens or in the earth; also about an inftrument for finding the longitude: but through not underftanding magnetical nature, he raifes nothing but errors and mifts in that fo important notion. Fortunius Affaytatus philofophizes foolifhly enough on the attraction of iron, and its turning to the poles. Moft recently, Baptifta Porta, no ordinary philofopher, in his *Magia Naturalis*, has made the feventh book a cuftodian and diftributor of the marvels of the loadftone; but little did he know or ever fee of magnetick motions; and fome things that he noted of the powers which it manifefted, either learned by him from the Reverend Maeftro Paolo, the Venetian, or evolved from his own vigils, were not fo well difcovered or obferved; but abound in utterly falfe experiments, as will be clear in due place: ftill I deem him worthy of high praife for having attempted fo great a fubject (as he has done with fufficient fuccefs and no mean refult in many other inftances), and for having given occafion for further refearch. All thefe philofophizers of a previous age, philofophizing about attraction from a few vague and untruftworthy experiments, drawing their arguments from the hidden caufes of things; and then, feeking for the caufes of magnetick directions in a quarter of the heavens, in the poles, the ftars, conftellations, or in mountains, or rocks, fpace, atoms, attractive or refpective points beyond the heavens, and other fuch unproven paradoxes, are whole horizons wrong, and wander about blindly. And as yet we have not fet ourfelves to overthrow by argument thofe errors and impotent reafonings of theirs, nor many other fables told about the loadftone, nor the fuperftitions of impoftors and fabulifts: for inftance, Francifcus Rueus' doubt whether the loadftone were not an impofture of evil fpirits: or that, placed underneath the head of an unconfcious woman while afleep, it drives her away from the bed if an adulterefs: or that the loadftone is of ufe to thieves by its fume and fheen, being a ftone born, as it were, to aid theft: or that it opens bars and locks, as Serapio crazily writes: or that iron held up by a loadftone, when placed in the fcales, added nothing to the weight of the load-ftone, as though the gravity of the iron were abforbed by the force of the ftone: or that, as Serapio and the Moors relate, in India there exift certain rocks of the fea abounding in loadftone, which draw out all the nails of the fhips which are driven toward them, and fo ftop their failing; which fable Olaus Magnus does not omit, faying that there are mountains in the north of fuch great powers of attraction, that fhips are built with wooden pegs, left the iron nails fhould be drawn from the timber as they paffed amongft the magnetick crags. Nor this: that a white loadftone may be procured as a love potion: or as Hali Abbas thoughtleffly reports, that if held in the hand it will cure gout and fpafms: Or that it makes one acceptable and in favour with princes, or eloquent, as Pictorio has
fung;

fung; Or as Albertus Magnus teaches, that there are two kinds of loadftones, one which points to the North, the other to the South: Or that iron is directed toward the Northern ftars by an influence imparted by the polar ftars, even as plants follow the fun, as Helio-trope does: Or that there is a magnet-ftone fituated under the tail of the Greater Bear, as Lucas Gauricus the Aftrologer ftated: He would even affign the loadftone, like the Sardonyx and onyx, to the planet Saturn, yet at the fame time he affigns it with the adamant, Jafper, and Ruby, to Mars; fo that it is ruled by two planets. The loadftone moreover is faid by him to pertain to the fign Virgo; and he covers many fuch fhameful pieces of folly with a veil of mathe-matical erudition. Such as that an image of a bear is engraved on a loadftone when the Moon faces towards the north, fo that when hung by an iron wire it may conciliate the influence of the celeftial Bear, as Gaudentius Merula relates: Or that the loadftone drew iron and directed it to the north, becaufe it is fuperior in rank to iron, at the Bear, as Ficinus writes, and Merula repeats: Or that by day it has a certain power of attracting iron, but by night the power is feeble, or rather null: Or that when weak and dulled the virtue is renewed by goats' blood, as Ruellius writes: Or that Goats' blood fets a loadftone free from the venom of a diamond, fo that the loft power is revived when bathed in goats' blood by reafon of the difcord between that blood and the diamond: Or that it removed forcery from women, and put to flight demons, as Arnaldus de Villanova dreams: Or that it has the power to reconcile hufbands to their wives, or to recall brides to their hufbands, as Marbodeus Gallus, chorus-leader of vanities, teaches: Or that in a loadftone pickled in the falt of a fucking fifh there is power to pick up gold which has fallen into the deepeft wells, according to the narratives of Cælius Calcagninus. With fuch idle tales and trumpery do plebeian philofophers delight themfelves and fatiate readers greedy for hidden things, and unlearned devourers of abfurdities: But after the magnetick nature fhall have been difclofed by the difcourfe that is to follow, and perfected by our labours and experiments, then will the hidden and abftrufe caufes of fo great an effect ftand out, fure, proven, difplayed and demon-ftrated; and at the fame time all darknefs will difappear, and all error will be torn up by the roots and will lie unheeded; and the foundations of a grand magnetick philofophy which have been laid will appear anew, fo that high intellects may be no further mocked by idle opinions. Some learned men there are who in the courfe of long voyages have obferved the differences of magnetick variation: the moft fcholarly Thomas Hariot, Robert Hues, Edward Wright, Abraham Kendall, all Englifhmen; Others there are who have invented and produced magnetical inftruments, and ready methods of obfervation, indifpenfable for failors and to thofe travelling afar:

as

as William Borough in his little book on the *Variation of the
Compaſs* or Magneticall Needle, William Barlowe in his *Supply*,
Robert Norman in his *Newe Attractive*.   And this is that Robert
Norman (a ſkilful ſeaman and ingenious artificer) who firſt diſcovered
the declination of the magnetick needle.   Many others I omit
wittingly ;   modern Frenchmen, Germans, and Spaniards, who in
books written for the moſt part in their native tongues either miſ-
uſe the placets of others, and ſend them forth furbiſhed with new
titles and phraſes as tricky traders do old wares with meretricious
ornaments ;   or offer ſomething not worthy of mention even :   and
theſe lay hands on ſome work filched from other authors and ſolicit
ſome one as their patron, or go hunting after renown for themſelves
among the inexperienced and the young ;   who in all branches of
learning are ſeen to hand on errors and occaſionally add ſomething
falſe of their own.

CHAP. II.

Magnet Stone, of what kind it is, and its
diſcovery.

OADSTONE, the ſtone which is commonly called
the Magnet, derives its name either from the diſ-
coverer (though he was not Pliny's fabulous herdſ-
man, quoted from Nicander, the nails of whoſe ſhoes
and the tip of whoſe ſtaff ſtuck faſt in a magnetick
field while he paſtured his flocks), or from the
region of Magneſia in Macedonia, rich in loadſtones :   Or elſe from
the city Magneſia in Ionia in Aſia Minor, near the river Mæander.
Hence Lucretius ſays,

> *The Magnet's name the obſerving Grecians drew*
> *From the Magnetick region where it grew.*

It is called Heraclean from the city Heraclea, or from the invincible
Hercules, on account of the great ſtrength and domination and
power which there is in iron of ſubduing all things :   it is alſo
called *ſiderite*, as being of iron ;   being not unknown to the moſt
ancient writers, to the Greeks, Hippocrates, and others, as alſo (I
believe) to Jewiſh and Egyptian writers ;   For in the oldeſt mines
of iron, the moſt famous in Aſia, the loadſtone was often dug out
with its uterine brother, iron.   And if the tales be true which are
told of the people of the Chinas, they were not unacquainted in
primitive times with magnetical experiments, for even amongſt
them

them the fineſt magnets of all are ſtill found. The Egyptians, as Manetho relates, gave it the name Os Ori: calling the power which governs the turning of the ſun Orus, as the Greeks call it Apollo. But later by Euripides, as narrated by Plato, it was deſignated under the name of Magnet. By Plato in the *Io*, Nicander of Colophon, Theophraſtus, Dioſcorides, Pliny, Solinus, Ptolemy, Galen, and other inveſtigators of nature it was recognized and commended ; ſuch, however, is the variety of magnets and their points of unlike-neſs in hardneſs, ſoftneſs, heavineſs, lightneſs, denſity, firmneſs, and friability of ſubſtance: ſo great and manifold are the differences in colour and other qualities, that they have not handed down any adequate account of it, which therefore was laid aſide or left im-perfect by reaſon of the unfavourable character of the time ; for in thoſe times varieties of ſpecimens and foreign products never before ſeen were not brought from ſuch diſtant regions by traders and mariners as they have been lately, and now that all over the globe all kinds of merchandiſe, ſtones, woods, ſpices, herbs, metals, and ore in abundance are greedily ſought after : neither was metallurgy ſo generally cultivated in a former age. There is a difference in vigour ; as whether it is male or female : for it was thus that the ancients uſed often to diſtinguiſh many individuals of the ſame ſpecies. Pliny quotes from Sotacus five kinds ; thoſe from Æthiopia, Macedonia, Bœotia, the Troad, and Aſia, which were eſpecially known to the ancients: but we have poſited as many kinds of load-ſtones as there are in the whole of nature regions of different kinds of ſoil. For in all climates, in every province, on every ſoil, the loadſtone is either found, or elſe lies unknown on account of its rather deep ſite and inacceſſible poſition ; or by reaſon of its weaker and leſs obvious ſtrength it is not recognized by us while we ſee and handle it. To the ancients the differences were thoſe of colour, how they are red and black in Magneſia and Macedonia, in Bœotia red rather than black, in the Troad black, without ſtrength : While in Magneſia in Aſia they are white, not attracting iron, and reſemble pumice-ſtone. A ſtrong loadſtone of the kind celebrated ſo often nowadays in experiments preſents the appearance of un-poliſhed iron, and is moſtly found in iron mines : it is even wont to be diſcovered in an unbroken lode by itſelf: Loadſtones of this ſort are brought from Eaſt India, China, and Bengal, of the colour of iron, or of a dark blood or liver colour ; and theſe are the fineſt, and are ſometimes of great ſize, as though broken off a great rock, and of conſiderable weight ; ſometimes ſingle ſtones, as it were, and entire : ſome of theſe, though of only one pound weight, can lift on high four ounces of iron or a half-pound or even a whole pound. Red ones are found in Arabia, as broad as a tile, not equal in weight to thoſe brought from China, but ſtrong and good: they are a little darker in the iſland of Elba in the Tuſcan ſea, and together with

c   theſe thefe alfo grow white ones, like fome in Spain in the mines of Caravaca : but thefe are of leffer power. Black ones alfo are found, of lower ftrength, fuch as thofe of the iron mines in Norway and in fea-coaft places near the ftrait of Denmark. Amongft the blue-black or dufky blue alfo fome are ftrong and highly commended. Other loadftones are of a leaden colour, fiffile and not-fiffile, capable of being fplit like flates in layers. I have alfo fome like gray marble of an afhen colour, and fome fpeckled like gray marble, and thefe take the fineft polifh. In Germany there are fome perforated like honeycombs, lighter than any others, and yet ftrong. Thofe are metallick which fmelt into the beft iron ; others are not eafily fmelted, but are burned up. There are loadftones that are very heavy, as alfo others very light ; fome are very powerful in catching up pieces of iron, while others are weaker and of lefs capacity, others fo feeble and barren that they with difficulty attract ever fo tiny a piece of iron and cannot repel an oppofite magnetick. Others are firm and tough, and do not readily yield to the artificer. Others are friable. Again, there are fome denfe and hard as emery, or loofe-textured and foft as pumice ; porous or folid ; entire and uniform, or varied and corroded ; now like iron for hardnefs, yea, fometimes harder than iron to cut or to file ; others are as foft as clay. Not all magnets can be properly called ftones ; fome rather reprefent rocks ; while others exift rather as metallick lodes ; others as clods and lumps of earth. Thus varied and unlike each other, they are all endowed, fome more, fome lefs, with the peculiar virtue. For they vary according to the nature of the foil, the different admixture of clods and humours, having refpect to the nature of the region and to their fubfidence in this laft-formed cruft of the earth, refulting from the confluence of many caufes, and the per-petual alternations of growth and decline, and the mutations of bodies. Nor is this ftone of fuch potency rare ; and there is no region wherein it is not to be found in fome fort. But if men were to fearch for it more diligently and at greater outlay, or were able, where difficulties are prefent, to mine it, it would come to hand everywhere, as we fhall hereafter prove. In many countries have been found and opened mines of efficacious loadftones unknown to the ancient writers, as for inftance in Germany, where none of them has ever afferted that loadftones were mined. Yet fince the time when, within the memory of our fathers, metallurgy began to flourifh there, loadftones ftrong and efficacious in power have been dug out in numerous places ; as in the Black Foreft beyond Helceburg ; in Mount Mifena not far from Schwartzenberg ; a fairly ftrong kind between Schneeberg and Annaberg in Joachimfthal, as was noticed by Cordus : alfo near the village of Pela in Franconia. In Bohemia it occurs in iron mines in the Leffa diftrict and other places, as Georgius Agricola and feveral other men learned in metallurgy witnefs.

witnefs. In like manner in other countries in our time it is brought to light; for as the ftone remarkable for its virtues is now famous throughout the whole world, fo alfo everywhere every land produces it, and it is, fo to fpeak, indigenous in all lands. In Eaft India, in China, in Bengal near the river Indus it is common, and in certain maritime rocks: in Perfia, Arabia, and the iflands of the Red Sea; in many places in Æthiopia, as was formerly Zimiri, of which Pliny makes mention. In Afia Minor around Alexandria and the Troad; in Macedonia, Bœotia, in Italy, the ifland of Elba, Barbary; in Spain ftill in many mines as aforetime. In England quite lately a huge power of it was difcovered in a mine belonging to Adrian Gilbert, gentleman; alfo in Devonfhire and the Foreft of Dean; in Ireland, too, Norway, Denmark, Sweden, Lapland, Livonia, Pruffia, Poland, Hungary. For although the terreftrial globe, owing to the varied humours and natures of the foil arifing from the continual fucceffion of growth and decay, is in the lapfe of time efflorefcing through all its ambit deeper into its furface, and is girt about with a varied and perifhable covering, as it were with a veil; yet out of her womb arifeth in many places an offspring nigher to the more perfect body and makes its way to the light of day. But the weak and lefs vigorous loadftones, enfeebled by the flow of humours, are vifible in every region, in every ftrath. It is eafy to difcover a vaft quantity of them everywhere without penetrating mountains or great depths, or encountering the difficulties and hardfhips of miners; as we fhall prove in the fequel. And thefe we fhall take pains fo to prepare by an eafy operation that their languid and dormant virtue fhall be made manifeft. It is called by the Greeks ἡράκλιος, as by Theophraftus, and μαγνῆτις; and μάγνης, as by Euripides, as quoted by Plato in the *Io:* by Orpheus too μαγνῆοσα, and σιδερίτης as though of iron: by the Latins *magnes, Herculeus;* by the French *aimant,* corruptly from *adamant;* by the Spaniards *piedramant:* by the Italians *calamita;* by the Englifh **loadftone** and **adamant ftone,** by the Germans *magnefs* and *fiegelftein:* Among Englifh, French, and Spaniards it has its common name from adamant; perhaps becaufe they were at one time mifled by the name *fideritis* being common to both: the magnet is called σιδερίτης from its virtue of attracting iron: the adamant is called σιδερίτης from the brilliancy of polifhed iron. Ariftotle defignates it merely by the name of *the ftone:* Ἔοικε δὲ καὶ Θαλῆς ἐξ ὧν ἀπομνημονεύουσι, κινητικόν τι τὴν ψυχὴν ὑπολαβεῖν, εἴπερ τὸν λίθον ἔφη ψυχὴν ἔχειν, ὅτι τὸν σίδηρον κινεῖ: *De Anima,* Lib. I. The name of magnet is alfo applied to another ftone differing from fiderite, having the appearance of filver; it is like Amianth in its nature; and fince it confifts of laminæ (like fpecular ftone), it differs in form: in German *Katzenfilber* and *Talke.*

CHAP.

CHAP. III.

The Loadſtone has parts diſtinct in their natural
power, & poles conſpicuous for their property.

THE ſtone itſelf manifeſts many qualities which, though known afore this, yet, not having been well inveſtigated, are to be briefly indicated in the firſt place ſo that ſtudents may underſtand the powers of loadſtone and iron, and not be troubled at the outſet through ignorance of reaſonings and proofs. In the heaven aſtronomers aſſign a pair of poles for each moving ſphere : ſo alſo do we find in the terreſtrial globe natural poles pre-eminent in virtue, being the points that remain conſtant in their poſition in reſpect to the diurnal rotation, one tending to the Bears and the ſeven ſtars; the other to the oppoſite quarter of the heaven. In like manner the loadſtone has its poles, by nature northern and ſouthern, being definite and determined points ſet in the ſtone, the primary boundaries of motions and effects, the limits and governors of the many actions and virtues.   However, it muſt be underſtood that the ſtrength of the ſtone does not emanate from a mathematical point, but from the parts themſelves, and that while all thoſe parts in the whole belong to the whole, the nearer they are to the poles of the ſtone the ſtronger are the forces they acquire and ſhed into other bodies: theſe poles are obſervant of the earth's poles, move toward them, and wait upon them.   Magnetick poles can be found in every magnet, in the powerful and mighty (which Antiquity uſed to call the maſculine) as well as in the weak, feeble and feminine ; whether its figure is due to art or to chance, whether long, flat, ſquare, three-cornered, poliſhed ; whether rough, broken, or unpoliſhed ; always the loadſtone contains and ſhows its poles. ✻ But ſince the ſpherical form, which is alſo the moſt perfect, agrees beſt with the earth, being a globe, and is moſt ſuitable for uſe and experiment, we accordingly wiſh our principal demonſtrations by the ſtone to be made with a globe-ſhaped magnet as being more perfect and adapted for the purpoſe.   Take, then, a powerful load-ſtone, ſolid, of a juſt ſize, uniform, hard, without flaw ; make of it a globe upon the turning tool uſed for rounding cryſtals and ſome other ſtones, or with other tools as the material and firmneſs of the ſtone requires, for ſometimes it is difficult to be worked.   The ſtone thus prepared is a true, homogeneous offspring of the earth and of the ſame ſhape with it: artificially poſſeſſed of the orbicular form which nature granted from the beginning to the common mother earth: and it is a phyſical corpuſcle imbued with many virtues, by

means

means of which many abſtruſe and neglected truths in philoſophy buried in piteous darkneſs may more readily become known to men.   This round ſtone is called by us a μικρόγη or *Terrella*.   To find, then, the poles conformable to the earth's, take the round ſtone in hand, and place upon the ſtone a needle or wire of iron: the ends of the iron move upon their own centre and ſuddenly ſtand ſtill.   Mark the ſtone with ochre or with chalk where the wire lies and ſticks: move the middle or centre of the wire to another place, and ſo on to a third and a fourth, always marking on the ſtone along the length of the iron where it remains at reſt: thoſe lines ſhow the meridian circles, or the circles like meridians on the ſtone, or terrella, all of which meet as will be manifeſt at the poles of the ſtone.   By the circles thus continued the poles are made out, the Boreal as well as the ſouthern, and in the middle ſpace betwixt theſe a great circle may be drawn for an æquator, juſt as Aſtronomers deſcribe them in the heavens and on their own globes, or as Geographers do on the terreſtrial globe : for that line ſo drawn on this our terrella is of various uſes in our demonſtrations and experiments magnetical.   Poles are alſo found in a round ſtone by a verſorium, a piece of iron touched with a loadſtone, and placed upon a needle or point firmly fixed on a foot ſo as to turn freely about in the following way :

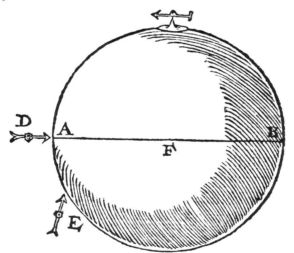

On the ſtone A B the verſorium is placed in ſuch a way that the verſorium may remain in equilibrium : you will mark with chalk the courſe of the iron when at reſt: Move the inſtrument to another ſpot, and again make note of the direction and aſpect: do the ſame thing in ſeveral places, and from the concurrence of the lines of direction you will find one pole at the point A, the other at B.   A verſorium placed near the ſtone alſo indicates the true pole ; when at right angles it eagerly beholds the ſtone and ſeeks the pole itſelf directly, and is turned in a ſtraight line through the axis to the

centre

centre of the ftone. For inftance, the verforium D faces toward
A and F, the pole and centre, whereas E does not exactly refpect
★ either the pole A or the centre F. A bit of rather fine iron wire, of
the length of a barley-corn, is placed on the ftone, and is moved over
the regions and furface of the ftone, until it rifes to the perpendicular: for it ftands erect at the actual pole, whether Boreal or auftral;
the further from the pole, the more it inclines from the vertical.
The poles thus found you fhall mark with a fharp file or gimlet.

CHAP. IIII.

Which pole of the ftone is the Boreal: & how it is
diftinguifhed from the auftral.

NE pole of the earth turns toward the conftellation
of the Cynofure, and conftantly regards a fixed point
in the heaven (except fo far as it changes by the
fixed ftars being fhifted in longitude, which motion
we recognize as exifting in the earth, as we fhall
hereafter prove): While the other pole turns to
the oppofite face of heaven, unknown to the ancients, now vifible
on long voyages, and adorned with multitudinous ftars: In the fame
way the loadftone has the property and power of directing itfelf
North and South (the earth herfelf confenting and contributing
force thereto) according to the conformation of nature, which arranges
the movements of the ftone towards its native fituation. Which
thing is proved thus: Place a magnetick ftone (after finding the
poles) in a round wooden veffel, a Bowl or difh, at the fame time
place it together with the veffel (like a failor in a fkiff) upon water
in fome large veffel or ciftern, fo that it may be able to float freely
in the middle, nor touch the edge of it, and where the air is not difturbed by winds, which would thwart the natural movement of the
ftone. Hereupon the ftone placed as it were in a fhip, in the
middle of the furface of the ftill and unruffled water, will at once
put itfelf in motion along with the veffel that carries it, and revolve
circularly, until its auftral pole points to the north, and its boreal
pole to the fouth. For it reverts from the contrary pofition to the
poles: and although by the firft too-vehement impulfe it over-paffes
the poles; yet after returning again and again, it refts at length at
the poles, or at the meridian (unlefs becaufe of local reafons it is
diverted fome little from thofe points, or from the meridional line,
by fome fort of variation, the caufe of which we will hereafter
ftate). However often you move it away from its place, fo often by
virtue of nature's noble dower does it feek again thofe fure and
                                                        determined

determined goals ; and this is fo, not only if the poles have been difpofed in the veffel evenly with the plane of the horizon, but alfo in the cafe of one pole, whether auftral or boreal, being raifed in the veffel ten, or twenty, or thirty, or fifty or eighty degrees, above the plane of the horizon, or lowered beneath it : Still you fhall fee the boreal part of the ftone feek the fouth, and the auftral part feek the north ; So much fo that if the pole of the ftone fhall be only one degree diftant from the Zenith and higheft point of the heaven, in the cafe of a fpherical ftone, the whole ftone revolves until the pole occupies its own fite ; though not in the abfolutely direct line, it will yet tend toward thofe parts, and come to reft in the meridian of the directive action.   With a like impulfe too it is borne if the auftral pole have been raifed toward the upper quarters, the fame as if the Boreal had been exalted above the Horizon.   But it is always to be noted that, though there are various kinds of unlikenefs in the ftones, and one loadftone may far furpafs another in virtue and efficiency ; yet all hold to the fame limits, and are borne toward the fame points.   Further it is to be remembered that all who before our time wrote of the poles of the ftone, and all the craftfmen and navigators, have been very greatly in error in confidering the part of the ftone which tended to the north as the north pole of the ftone, and that which verged toward the fouth, the fouth pole, which we fhall hereafter prove to be falfe.   So badly hitherto hath the whole magnetick philofophy been cultivated, even as to its foundation principles.

CHAP. V.

Loadftone feems to attract Loadftone when in natural
pofition : but repels it when in a contrary one, and brings
it back to order.

IRST of all we muft declare, in familiar language, what are the apparent and common virtues of the ftone ; afterward numerous fubtilities, hitherto abftrufe and unknown, hidden in obfcurity, are to be laid open, and the caufes of all thefe (by the un-locking of nature's fecrets) made evident, in their place, by fitting terms and devices.   It is trite and commonplace that loadftone draws iron ; in the fame way too does loadftone attract loadftone.   Place the ftone which you have feen to have poles clearly diftinguifhed, and marked auftral and boreal, in its veffel fo as to float ; and let the poles be rightly arranged with refpect to the plane of the horizon, or, at any rate not much raifed or awry : hold in your hand another ftone the poles of which are alfo known ; in
                                                                    fuch

fuch a way that its auftral pole may be toward the boreal pole of
the one that is fwimming, and near it, fideways: for the floating
ftone forthwith follows the other ftone (provided it be within its
force and dominion) and does not leave off nor forfake it until it
adhæres; unlefs by withdrawing your hand, you cautioufly avoid
contact.   In like manner if you fet the boreal pole of the one you
hold in your hand oppofite the auftral pole of the fwimming ftone,
they rufh together and follow each other in turn.   For contrary
poles allure contrary.   If, however, you apply in the fame way
the northern to the northern, and the auftral to the auftral pole,
the one ftone puts the other to flight, and it turns afide as though a
pilot were pulling at the helm and it makes fail in the oppofite ward
as one that ploughs the fea, and neither ftands anywhere, nor halts,
if the other is in purfuit.   For ftone difpofeth ftone; the one turns
the other around, reduces it to range, and brings it back to harmony
with itfelf.   When, however, they come together and are conjoined
according to the order of nature, they cohære firmly mutually.   For
inftance, if you were to fet the boreal pole of that ftone which is in
your hand before the tropic of Capricorn of a round floating loadftone (for it will be well to mark out on the round ftone, that is
the terrella, the mathematical circles as we do on a globe itfelf), or
before any point between the æquator and the auftral pole; at
once the fwimming ftone revolves, and fo arranges itfelf that its
auftral pole touches the other's boreal pole, and forms a clofe union
with it.   In the fame way, again, at the other fide of the æquator,
with the oppofite poles, you may produce fimilar refults; and thus
by this art and fubtilty we exhibit attraction, repulfion, and circular
motion for attaining a pofition of agreement and for declining hoftile
encounters.   Moreover 'tis in one and the fame ftone that we are
thus able to demonftrate all thefe things and alfo how the fame part
of one ftone may on divifion become either boreal or auftral.   Let
A D be an oblong ftone, in which A is the northern, D the fouthern
pole; cut this into two equal parts, then fet part A in its veffel on
the water, fo as to float.

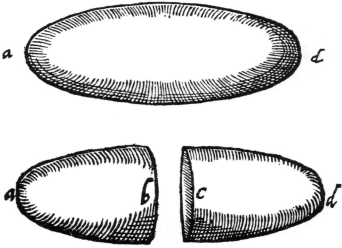

And

And you will then fee that A the northern point will turn to the fouth, as before; in like manner alfo the point D will move to the north, in the divided ftone, as in the whole one.   Whereas, of the parts B and C, which were before continuous, and are now divided, the one is fouthern B, the other northern C.   B draws C, defirous to be united, and to be brought back into its priftine continuity: for thefe which are now two ftones were formed out of one: and for this caufe C of the one turning itfelf to B of the other, they mutually attract each other, and when freed from obftacles and relieved of their own weight, as upon the furface of water, they run together and are conjoined.   But if you direct the part or point A to C in the other ftone, the one repels or turns away from the other: for fo were nature perverted, and the form of the ftone perturbed, a form that ftrictly keeps the laws which it impofed upon bodies: hence, when all is not rightly ordered according to nature, comes the flight of one from the other's perverfe pofition and from the difcord, for nature does not allow of an unjuft and inequitable peace, or compromife: but wages war and exerts force to make bodies acquiefce well and juftly.   Rightly arranged, therefore, thefe mutually attract each other; that is, both ftones, the ftronger as well as the weaker, run together, and with their whole forces tend to unity, a fact that is evident in all magnets, not in the Æthiopian only, as Pliny fuppofed.   The Æthiopian magnets if they be powerful, like thofe brought from China, becaufe all ftrong ones fhow the effect more quickly and more plainly, attract more ftrongly in the parts neareft the pole, and turn about until pole looks directly at pole.   The pole of a ftone more perfiftently attracts and more rapidly feizes the correfponding part (which they term the adverfe part) of another ftone; for inftance, North pulls South; juft fo it alfo fummons iron with more vehemence, and the iron cleaves to it more firmly whether it have been previoufly excited by the magnet, or is untouched.   For thus, not without reafon hath it been ordained by nature, that the parts nearer to the pole fhould more firmly attract: but that at the pole itfelf fhould be the feat, the throne, as it were, of a confummate and fplendid virtue, to which magnetical bodies on being brought are
more vehemently attracted, and from which they are with utmoft
difficulty diflodged.   So the poles are the parts which
more particularly fpurn and thruft away
things ftrange and alien perverfely
fet befide them.

D   CHAP.

CHAP. VI.

Loadftone attracts the ore of iron, as well as iron
proper, fmelted and wrought.

✱ PRINCIPAL and manifeft among the virtues of the magnet, fo much and fo anciently commended, is the attraction of iron; for Plato ftates that the magnet, fo named by Euripides, allures iron, and that it not only draws iron rings but alfo indues the rings with power to do the fame as the ftone; to wit, draw other rings, fo that fometimes a long chain of iron objects, nails or rings is formed, fome hanging from others. The beft iron (like that which is called *acies* from its ufe, or *chalybs* from the country of the Chalybes) is beft and ftrongly drawn by a powerful loadftone; whereas the lefs good fort, which is impure, rufty, and not thoroughly purged from drofs, and not wrought in fecond furnaces, is more feebly drawn; and yet more weakly when covered and defiled with thick, greafy, and fluggifh humours. It alfo draws ores of iron, thofe that are rich and of iron colour; the poorer and not fo productive ores it does not attract, except they be prepared with fome art. A loadftone lofes fome attractive virtue, and, as it were, pines away with age, if expofed too long to the open air inftead of being laid in a cafe with filings or fcales of iron. Whence it fhould be buried in fuch materials; for there is nothing that plainly refifts this exhauftlefs virtue which does not deftroy the form of the body, or corrode it; not even if a thoufand adamants were conjoined. Nor do I confider that there is any fuch thing as the Theamedes, or that it has a power oppofite to that of the loadftone. Although Pliny, that eminent man and prince of compilers (for it is what others had feen and difcovered, not always or mainly his own obfervations, that he has handed down to pofterity) has copied from others the fable now made familiar by repetition: That in India there are two mountains near the river Indus; the nature of one being to hold faft all that is iron, for it confifts of loadftone; the other's nature being to repel it, for it confifts of the Theamedes. Thus if one had iron nails in one's boots, one could not tear away one's foot on the one mountain, nor ftand ftill on the other. Albertus Magnus writes that a loadftone had been found in his day which with one part drew to itfelf iron, and repelled it with its other end; but Albertus obferved the facts badly; for every loadftone attracts with one end iron that has been touched with a loadftone, and drives it away with the other; and draws iron that has been touched with a loadftone more powerfully than iron that has not been fo touched.

CHAP.

CHAP. VII.

What Iron is, and of what substance,
and its uses.

OR that now we have declared the origin and nature of the loadstone, we think it necessary first to add a history of iron and to indicate the hitherto unknown forces of iron, before this our discourse goes on to the explanation of magnetick difficulties and demonstrations, and to deal with the coitions and harmonies of loadstone with iron. Iron is by all reckoned in the class of metals, and is a metal livid in colour, very hard, glows red-hot before it melts, being most difficult of fusion, is beaten out under the hammer, and is very resonant. Chemists say that if a bed of fixed earthy sulphur be combined with fixed earthy quicksilver, and the two together are neither pure white but of a livid whiteness, if the sulphur prevail, iron is formed. For these stern masters of metals who by many inventions twisting them about, pound, calcine, dissolve, sublime, and precipitate, decide that this metal, both on account of the earthy sulphur and of the earthy mercury, is more truly a son of the earth than any other; they do not even think gold or silver, lead, tin, or copper itself so earthy; for that reason it is not smelted except in the hottest furnaces, with bellows; and when thus fused, on having again grown hard it is not melted again without heavy labour; but its slag with the utmost difficulty. It is the hardest of metals, subduing and breaking all things, by reason of the strong concretion of the more earthy matter. Wherefore we shall better understand what iron is, when we shall declare what are the causes and substance of metals, in a different way from those who before our time have considered them. Aristotle takes the material of the metals to be vapour. The chemists in chorus pronounce their actual elements to be sulphur and quicksilver. Gilgil Mauritanus gives it as ashes moistened with water. Georgius Agricola makes it out to be water and earth mixed; nor, to be sure, is there any difference between his opinion and the position taken by Mauritanus. But ours is that metals arise and efflorefce at the summits of the earth's globe, being distinguished each by its own form, like some of the other substances dug out of it, and all bodies around us. The earth's globe does not consist of ashes or inert dust. Nor is fresh water an element, but a more simple consistency of evaporated fluids of the earth. Unctuous bodies, fresh water devoid of properties, quicksilver and sulphur, none of these are principia of metals: these latter
                                                                    things

things are the refults of a different nature, they are neither conftant nor antecedent in the courfe of the generation of metals. The earth emits various humours, not begotten of water nor of dry earth, nor from mixtures of thefe, but from the fubftance of the earth itfelf: thefe humours are not diftinguifhed by contrary qualities or fubftance, nor is the earth a fimple fubftance, as the Peripateticks dream. The humours proceed from vapours fublimated from great depths; all waters are extracts and, as it were, exudations from the earth. Rightly then in fome meafure does Ariftotle make out the matter of metals to be that exhalation which in continuance thickens in the lodes of certain foils: for the vapours are condenfed in places which are lefs hot than the fpot whence they iffued, and by help of the nature of the foils and mountains, as in a womb, they are at fitting feafons congealed and changed into metals: but it is not they alone which form ores, but they flow into and enter a more folid material, and fo form metals. So when this concreted matter has fettled down in more temperate beds, it begins to take fhape in thofe tepid places, juft as feed in the warm womb, or as the embryo acquires growth: fometimes the vapour conjoins with fuitable matter alone: hence fome metals are occafionally though rarely dug up native, and come into exiftence perfect without fmelting: but other vapours which are mixed with alien foils require fmelting in the way that the ores of all metals are treated, which are rid of all their drofs by the force of fires, and being fufed flow out metallick, and are feparated from earthy impurities but not from the true fubftance of the earth. But in fo far as that it becomes gold, or filver, or copper, or any other of the exifting metals, this does not happen from the quantity or proportion of material, nor from any forces of matter, as the Chemifts fondly imagine; but when the beds and region concur fitly with the material, the metals affume forms from the univerfal nature by which they are perfected; in the fame manner as all the other minerals, plants, and animals whatever: otherwife the fpecies of metals would be vague and undefined, which are even now turned up in fuch fcanty numbers that fcarce ten kinds are known. Why, however, nature has been fo ftingy as regards the number of metals, or why there fhould be as many as are known to man, it is not eafy to explain; though the fimple-minded and raving Aftrologers refer the metals each to its own planet. But there is no agreement of the metals with the planets, nor of the planets with the metals, either in numbers or in properties. For what connexion is there of iron with Mars? unlefs it be that from the former numerous inftruments, particularly fwords and engines of war, are fafhioned. What has copper to do with Venus? or how does tin, or how does fpelter correfpond with Jupiter? They fhould rather be dedicated to Venus. But this is old wives' talk. Vapour is then a remote caufe in the generation of the metals; the fluid condenfed from

vapours

vapours is a more proximate one, like the blood and femen in the generation of animals.   But thofe vapours and juices from vapours pafs for the moft part into bodies and change them into marcafites and are carried into lodes (for we have numerous cafes of wood fo tranfmuted), the fitting matrices of bodies, where they are formed as metals.   They enter moft often into the truer and more homogeneal fubftance of the globe, and in the procefs of time a vein of iron refults; loadftone is alfo produced, which is nought elfe than a noble kind of iron ore : and for this reafon, and on account of its fubftance being fingular, alien from all other metals, nature very rarely, if ever, mixes with iron any other metal, while the other metals are very often minutely mixed, and are produced together. Now when that vapour or thofe juices happen to meet, in fitting matrices, with efflorefcences deformed from the earth's homogenic fubftance, and with divers precipitates (the forms working thereto), the remainder of the metals are generated (a fpecifick nature affecting the properties in that place).   For the hidden primordial elements of metals and ftones lie concealed in the earth, as thofe of herbs and plants do in its outer cruft.   For the foil dug out of a deep well, where would feem to be no fufpicion of a conception of feed, when placed on a very high tower, produces, by the incubation of fun and fky, green herbage and unbidden weeds; and thofe of the kind which grow fpontaneoufly in that region, for each region produces its own herbs and plants, alfo its own metals.

> *Here corn exults, and there the grape is glad,*
> *Here trees and grafs unbidden verdure add.*
> *So mark how Tmolus yields his faffron ftore,*
> *But ivory is the gift of Indian fhore;*
> *With incenfe foft the fofter Shebans deal;*
> *The ftark Chalybeans' element is fteel:*
> *With acrid caftor reek the Pontic wares,*
> *Epirus wins the palm of Elian mares.*

But what the Chemifts (as Geber, and others) call fixed earthy fulphur in iron is nothing elfe than the homogenic earth-fubftance concreted by its own humour, amalgamated with a double fluid : a metallick humour is inferted along with a fmall quantity of the fubftance of the earth not devoid of humour.   Wherefore the common faying that in gold there is pure earth, but in iron moftly impure, is wrong; as though there were indeed fuch a thing as natural earth, and that the globe itfelf were (by fome unknown procefs of refining) depurate.   In iron, efpecially in the beft iron, there is earth in its own nature true and genuine ; in the other metals there is not fo much earth as that in place of earth and precipitates there are confolidated and (fo to fpeak) fixed falts, which are efflorefcences of the globe, and which differ alfo greatly

in

in firmnefs and confiftency : In the mines their force rifes up along with a twofold humour from the exhalations, they folidify in the underground fpaces into metallic veins : fo too they are alfo connate by virtue of their place and of the furrounding bodies, in natural matrices, and take on their fpecific forms. Of the various con-ftitutions of loadftones and their diverfe fubftances, colours, and virtues, mention has been made before : but, now having ftated the caufe and origin of metals, we have to examine ferruginous matter not as it is in the fmelted metal, but as that from which the metal is refined. Quafi-pure iron is found of its proper colour and in its own lodes ; ftill, not as it will prefently be, nor as adapted for its various ufes. It is fometimes dug up covered with white filex or with other ftones. It is often the fame in river fand, as in Noricum. A nearly pure ore of iron is now often dug up in Ireland, which the fmiths, without the labours of furnaces, hammer out in the fmithy into iron implements. In France iron is very commonly fmelted out of a liver-coloured ftone, in which are glittering fcales ; the fame kind without the fcales is found in England, which alfo they ufe for craftfmen's ruddle. In Suffex in England is a rich dufky ore and alfo one of a pale afhen hue, both of which on being dried for a time, or kept in moderate fires, prefently acquire a liver-colour ; here alfo is found a dufky ore fquare-fhaped with a black rind of greater hardnefs. An ore having the appearance of liver is often varioufly intermingled with other ftones : as alfo with the perfect loadftone which yields the beft of iron. There is alfo a rufty ore of iron, one of a leaden hue tending to black, one quite black, or black mixed with true cobalt : there is another fort mixed either with pyrites, or with fterile plumbago. One kind is alfo like jet, another like bloodftone. The emery ufed by armourers, and by glaziers for glafs-cutting, called amongft the Englifh Emerel-ftone, by the Germans Smeargel, is ferruginous ; albeit iron is extracted from it with difficulty, yet it attracts the verforium. It is now and then found in deep iron and filver diggings. Thomas Eraftus fays he had heard from a certain learned man of iron ores, of the colour of iron, but quite foft and fatty, which can be fmoothed with the fingers like butter, out of which excellent iron can be fmelted : fomewhat the fame we have feen found in England, having the afpect of Spanifh foap. Befides the number-lefs kinds of ftony ores, iron is extracted from clay, from clayey earth, from ochre, from a rufty matter depofited from chalybeate waters ; In England iron is copioufly extracted in furnaces often from fandy and clayey ftones which appear to contain iron not more than fand, marl, or any other clay foils contain it. Thus in Ariftotle's book *De Mirabilibus Aufcultationibus*, " There is faid " (he ftates) " to be a peculiar formation of Chalybean and Mifenian " iron, for inftance the fort collected from river gravel ; fome fay that

" that after being fimply wafhed it is fmelted in the furnace; others
" declare that it and the fediment which fubfides after feveral wafhings
" are caft in and purified together by the fire; with the addition of
" the ftone pyrimachus which is found there in abundance." Thus
do numerous forts of things contain in their various fubftances
notably and abundantly this element of iron and earth. However,
there are many ftones, and very common ones, found in every foil,
alfo earths, and various and mixed materials, which do not hold rich
fubftances, but yet have their own iron elements, and yield them to
fkilfully-made fires, yet which are left afide by metallick men
becaufe they are lefs profitable; while other foils give fome fhow
of a ferruginous nature, yet (being very barren) are hardly ever
fmelted down into iron; and being neglected are not generally
known. Manufactured irons differ very greatly amongft themfelves.
For one kind is tenacious in its nature, and this is the beft; one is
of medium quality: another is brittle, and this is the worft. Sometimes the iron, by reafon of the excellency of the ore, is wrought
into fteel, as to-day in Noricum. From the fineft iron, too, well
wrought and purged from all drofs, or by being plunged in water
after heating, there iffues what the Greeks call στόμωμα; the Latins
acies; others *aciarium*, fuch as was at times called Syrian, Parthian,
Noric, Comefe, Spanifh; elfewhere it is named from the water in
which it is fo often plunged, as at Como in Italy, Bambola and
Tarazona in Spain. *Acies* fetches a much larger price than mere
iron. And owing to its fuperiority it better accords with the loadftone, from which more powerful quality it is often fmelted, and it
acquires the virtues from it more quickly, retains them longer at
their full, and in the beft condition for magnetical experiments.
After iron has been fmelted in the firft furnaces, it is afterward
wrought by various arts in large workfteads or mills, the metal
acquiring confiftency when hammered with ponderous blows, and
throwing off the drofs. After the firft fmelting it is rather brittle
and by no means perfect. Wherefore with us (Englifh) when the
larger military guns are caft, they purify the metal from drofs more
fully, fo that they may be ftronger to withftand the force of the
firing; and they do this by making it pafs again (in a fluid ftate)
through a chink, by which procefs it fheds its recremental matter.
Smiths render iron fheets tougher with certain liquids, and by blows
of the hammer, and from them make fhields and breaftplates that
defy the blows of battle-axes. Iron becomes harder through fkill
and proper tempering, but alfo by fkill turns out in a fofter condition
and as pliable as lead. It is made hard by the action of certain
waters into which while glowing it is plunged, as at Bambola and
Tarazona in Spain: It grows foft again, either by the effect of fire
alone, when without hammering and without water, it is left to
cool by itfelf; or by that of greafe into which it is plunged; or

(that

(that it may the better ferve for various trades) it is tempered varioufly by being fkilfully befmeared. Baptifta Porta expounds this art in book 13 of his *Magia Naturalis*. Thus this ferric and telluric nature is included and taken up in various bodies of ftones, ores, and earths; fo too it differs in afpeét, in form, and in efficiency. Art fmelts it by various proceffes, improves it, and turns it, above all material fubftances, to the fervice of man in trades and appliances without end. One kind of iron is adapted for breaftplates, another ferves as a defence againft fhot, another proteéts againft fwords and curved blades (commonly called fcimitars), another is ufed for making fwords, another for horfefhoes. From iron are made nails, hinges, bolts, faws, keys, grids, doors, folding-doors, fpades, rods, pitch-forks, hooks, barbs, tridents, pots, tripods, anvils, hammers, wedges, chains, hand-cuffs, fetters, hoes, mattocks, fickles, bafkets, fhovels, harrows, planes, rakes, ploughfhares, forks, pans, difhes, ladles, fpoons, fpits, knives, daggers, fwords, axes, darts, javelins, lances, fpears, anchors, and much fhip's gear. Befides thefe, balls, darts, pikes, breaftplates, helmets, cuiraffes, horfefhoes, greaves, wire, ftrings of mufical inftruments, chairs, portcullifes, bows, catapults, and (pefts of human kind) cannon, mufkets, and cannon-balls, with endlefs inftruments unknown to the Latins : which things I have rehearfed in order that it may be underftood how great is the ufe of iron, which furpaffes a hundred times that of all the other metals ; and is day by day being wrought by metal-workers whofe ftithies are found in almoft every village. For this is the foremoft of metals, fubferving many and the greateft needs of man, and abounds in the earth above all other metals, and is predominant. Wherefore thofe Chemifts are fools who think that nature's will is to perfeét all metals into gold ; fhe might as well be making ready to change all ftones to diamonds, fince diamond furpaffes all in fplendour and hardnefs, becaufe gold excels in fplendour, gravity, and denfity, being in-vincible againft all deterioration. Iron as dug up is therefore, like iron that has been fmelted, a metal, differing a little indeed from the primary homogenic terreftrial body, owing to the metallick humour it has imbibed ; yet not fo alien as that it will not, after the manner of refined matter, admit largely of the magnetick forces, and
may be affociated with that prepotent form
belonging to the earth, and yield
to it a due fubmiffion.

CHAP.

CHAP. VIII.

In what countries and diftricts iron
originates.

PLENTY of iron mines exift everywhere, both thofe of old time recorded in early ages by the moft ancient writers, and the new and modern ones. The earlieft and moft important feem to me to be thofe of Afia.   For in thofe countries which abound naturally in iron, governments and the arts flourifhed exceedingly, and things needful for the ufe of man were difcovered and fought after.   It is recorded to have been found about Andria, in the region of the Chalybes near the river Thermodon in Pontus; in the mountains of Paleftine which face Arabia; in Carmania: in Africa there was a mine of iron in the Ifle of Meroe; in Europe in the hills of Britain, as Strabo writes; in Hither Spain, in Cantabria.   Among the Petrocorii and Cubi Biturges (peoples of Gaul), there were workfteads in which iron ufed to be wrought.   In greater Germany near Luna, as recorded by Ptolemy; Gothinian iron is mentioned by Cornelius Tacitus; Noric iron is celebrated in the verfes of poets; and Cretan, and that of Eubœa; many other iron mines were paffed over by thefe writers or unknown to them; and yet they were neither poor nor fcanty, but moft extenfive. Pliny fays that Hither Spain and all the diftrict from the Pyrenees is ferruginous, and on the part of maritime Cantabria wafhed by the Ocean (fays the fame writer) there is (incredible to relate) a precipitoufly high mountain wholly compofed of this material.   The moft ancient mines were of iron rather than of gold, filver, copper or lead; fince mainly this was fought becaufe of the demand; and alfo becaufe in every diftrict and foil they were eafy to find, not fo deep-lying, and lefs befet by difficulties.   If, however, I were to enumerate modern iron workings, and thofe of this age and over Europe only, I fhould have to write a large and bulky volume, and fheets of paper would run fhort quicker than the iron, and yet for one fheet they could furnifh a thoufand workfteads.   For amongft minerals, no material is fo ample; all metals, and all ftones diftinct from iron, are outdone by ferric and ferruginous matter.   For you will not readily find any region, and fcarcely any country diftrict over the whole of Europe (if you fearch at all deeply), that does not either produce a rich and abundant vein of iron or fome foil containing or flightly charged with ferruginous ftuff; and that this is

E   true

true any expert in the arts of metals and chemiftry will eafily find. Befide that which has ferruginous nature, and the metallick lode, there is another ferric fubftance which does not yield the metal in this way becaufe its thin humour is burnt out by fierce fires, and it is changed into an iron flag like that which is feparated from the metal in the firft furnaces. And of this kind is all clay and argillaceous earth, fuch as that which apparently forms a large part of the whole of our ifland of Britain : all of which, if fubjected very vehemently to intenfe heat, exhibits a ferric and metallick body, or paffes into ferric vitreous matter, as can be eafily feen in buildings in bricks baked from clay, which, when placed next the fires in the open kilns (which our folk call *clamps*) and burned, prefent an iron vitrification, black at the other end. Moreover all thofe earths as prepared are drawn by the magnet, and like iron are attracted by it. So perpetual and ample is the iron offspring of the terreftrial globe. Georgius Agricola fays that almoft all mountainous regions are full of its ores, while as we know a rich iron lode is frequently dug in the open country and plains over nearly the whole of England and Ireland ; in no other wife than as, fays he, iron is dug out of the meadows at the town of Saga in pits driven to a two-foot depth. Nor are the Weft Indies without their iron lodes, as writers tell us ; but the Spaniards, intent upon gold, neglect the toilfome work of iron-founding, and do not fearch for lodes and mines abounding in iron. It is probable that nature and the globe of the earth are not able to hide, and are evermore bringing to the light of day, a great mafs of inborn matter, and are not invariably obftructed by the fettling of mixtures and efflorefcences at the earth's furface. It is not only in the common mother (the terreftrial globe) that iron is produced, but fometimes alfo in the air from the earth's exhalations, in the higheft clouds. It rained iron in Lucania, the year in which M. Craffus was flain. The tale is told, too, that a mafs of iron, like flag, fell from the air in the Nethorian foreft, near Grina, and they narrate that the mafs was many pounds in weight ; fo that it could neither be conveyed to that place, on account of its weight, nor be brought away by cart, the place being without roads. This happened before the civil war waged between the rival dukes in Saxony. A fimilar ftory, too, comes to us from Avicenna. It once rained iron in the Torinefe, in various places (Julius Scaliger telling us that he had a piece of it in his houfe), about three years before that province was taken over by the king. In the year 1510 in the country bordering on the river Abdua (as Cardan writes in his book *De Rerum Varietate*) there fell from the fky 1200 ftones, one weighing 120 pounds, another 30 or 40 pounds, of a rufty iron colour and remarkably hard. Thefe occurrences being rare are regarded as portents, like the fhowers of earth and ftones mentioned in Roman hiftory. But that it ever rained other metals is not recorded ;

corded ; for it has never been known to rain from the fky gold, filver, lead, tin, or fpelter.   Copper, however, has been at fome time noticed to fall from the fky, and this is not very unlike iron ; and in fact cloud-born iron of this fort, or copper, are feen to be imperfectly metallick, incapable of being caft in any way, or wrought with facility.   For the earth hath of her ftore plenty of iron in her highlands, and the globe contains the ferric and magnetick element in rich abundance.   The exhalations forcibly derived from fuch material may well become concreted in the upper air by the help of more powerful caufes, and hence fome monftrous progeny of iron be begotten.

CHAP. IX.

Iron ore attracts iron ore.

FROM various fubftances iron (like all the reft of the metals) is extracted: fuch fubftances being ftones, earth, and fimilar concretions which miners call veins becaufe it is in veins, as it were, that they are generated.   We have fpoken above of the variety of thefe veins.   If a properly coloured ore of iron and a rich one (as miners call it) is placed, as foon as mined, upon water in a bowl or any fmall veffel (as we have fhown before in the cafe of a loadftone), it is attracted by a fimilar piece of ore brought near by hand, yet not fo powerfully and quickly as one loadftone is drawn by another loadftone, but flowly and feebly.   Ores of iron that are ftony, cindery, dufky, red, and feveral more of other colours, do not attract one another mutually, nor are they attracted by the loadftone itfelf, even by a ftrong one, no more than wood, or lead, filver, or gold.   Take thofe ores and burn, or rather roaft them, in a moderate fire, fo that they are not fuddenly fplit up, or fly afunder, keeping up the fire ten or twelve hours, and gently increafing it, then let them grow cold, fkill being fhown in the direction in which they are placed : Thefe ores thus prepared a loadftone will now draw, and they now fhow a mutual fympathy, and when fkilfully arranged run together by their own forces.

CHAP.

CHAP. X.

✳   ## Iron ore has poles, and acquires them, and settles
itself toward the poles of the univerſe.

DEPLORABLE is man's ignorance in natural ſcience, and modern philoſophers, like thoſe who dream in darkneſs, need to be arouſed, and taught the uſes of things and how to deal with them, and to be induced to leave the learning ſought at leiſure from books alone, and that is ſupported only by un-realities of arguments and by conjectures.   For the knowledge of iron (than which nothing is in more common uſe), and that of many more ſubſtances around us, remains unlearned; iron, a rich ore of which, placed in a veſſel upon water, by an innate property of its own directs itſelf, juſt like the loadſtone, North and South, at which points it reſts, and to which, if it be turned aſide, it reverts by its own inherent vigour.   But many ores, leſs perfect in their nature, which yet contain amid ſtone or earthy ſubſtances plenty of iron, have no ſuch motion; but when prepared by ſkilful treat-ment in the fires, as ſhown in the foregoing chapter, they acquire a polar vigour (which we call verticity); and not only the iron ores in requeſt by miners, but even earth merely charged with ferruginous matter, and many rocks, do in like manner tend and lean toward those portions of the heavens, or more truly of the earth, if they be ſkilfully placed, until they reach the deſired location, in which they eagerly repoſe.

CHAP. XI.

Wrought Iron, not excited by a loadftone, ✳
draws iron.

FROM the ore, which is converted, or feparated, partly into metal, partly into flag, by the intenfe heat of fires, iron is fmelted in the firft furnaces in a fpace of eight, ten, or twelve hours, and the metal flows away from the drofs and ufelefs matter, forming a large and long mafs, which being fub-jected to a fharp hammering is cut into parts, out of which when reheated in the fecond hearth of the forge, and again placed on the anvil, the fmiths fafhion quadrangular lumps, or more fpecially bars which are bought by merchants and blackfmiths, from which in fmithies ufually it is the cuftom to fafhion the various implements. This iron we term *wrought*, and its attraction by the loadftone is manifeft to all. But we, by more carefully trying everything, have found out that iron merely, by itfelf alone, not excited by any loadftone, not charged by any alien forces, attracts other iron; though it does not fo eagerly fnatch and fuddenly pluck at it as would a fairly ftrong loadftone; this you may know thus: A fmall piece of cork, the fize of a hazel-nut, rounded, is traverfed by an iron wire up to the middle of the wire: when fet fwimming on ftill water apply to one end of it, clofe (yet fo as not to touch), the end of another iron wire; and wire draws wire, and one follows the other when flowly drawn back, and this goes on up to the proper boundaries. Let A be the cork with the iron wire, B one end of it raifed a little above the furface of the water, C the end of the

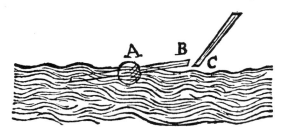

fecond wire, fhowing the way in which B is drawn by C. You may prove it in another way in a larger body. Let a long bright iron rod (fuch as is made for hangings and window curtains) be hung in balance by a flender filken cord: to one end of this as it refts in the air bring a fmall oblong mafs of polifhed iron, with its proper
end

end at the diſtance of half a digit. The balanced iron turns itſelf to the maſs; do you with the ſame quickneſs draw back the maſs in your hand in a circular path about the point of equilibrium of the ſuſpenſion; the end of the balanced iron follows after it, and turns in an orbit.

CHAP. XII.

✻ A long piece of Iron, even though not excited by a
loadſtone, ſettles itſelf toward North and South.

EVERY good and perfect piece of iron, if drawn out in length, points North and South, juſt as the load-ſtone or iron rubbed with a magnetical body does; a thing that our famous philoſophers have little underſtood, who have ſweated in vain to ſet forth the magnetick virtues and the cauſes of the friendſhip of iron for the ſtone. You may experiment with either large or ſmall iron works, and either in air or in water. A ſtraight piece of iron ſix feet long of the thickneſs of your finger is ſuſpended (in the way deſcribed in the foregoing chapter) in exact æquipoiſe by a ſtrong and ſlender ſilken cord. But the cord ſhould be croſs-woven of ſeveral ſilk filaments, not twiſted ſimply in one way; and it ſhould be in a ſmall chamber with all doors and windows cloſed, that the wind may not enter, nor the air of the room be in any way diſturbed; for which reaſon it is not expedient that the trial ſhould be made on windy days, or while a ſtorm is brewing. For thus it freely follows its bent, and ſlowly moves until at length, as it reſts, it points with its ends North and South, juſt as iron touched with a loadſtone does in ſhadow-clocks, and in compaſſes, and in the mariners' com-paſs. You will be able, if curious enough, to balance all at the ſame time by fine threads a number of ſmall rods, or iron wires, or long pins with which women knit ſtockings; you will ſee that all of them at the ſame time are in accord, unleſs there be ſome error in this delicate operation: for unleſs you prepare everything fitly and ſkilfully, the labour will be void. Make trial of this thing in water alſo, which is done both more certainly and more eaſily. Let an iron wire two or three digits long, more or leſs, be paſſed through a round cork, ſo that it may juſt float upon water; and as ſoon as you have committed it to the waves, it turns upon its own centre, and one end tends to the North, the other to the South; the cauſes

of

of which you will afterwards find in the laws of the direction. This too you fhould underftand, and hold firmly in memory, that ✳ as a ftrong loadftone, and iron touched with the fame, do not invariably point exactly to the true pole but to the point of the variation ; fo does a weaker loadftone, and fo does the iron, which directs itfelf by its own forces only, not by thofe impreffed by the ftone ; and fo every ore of iron, and all bodies naturally endowed with fomething of the iron nature, and prepared, turn to the fame point of the horizon, according to the place of the variation in that particular region (if there be any variation therein), and there abide and reft.

CHAP. XIII.

Wrought iron has in itfelf certain parts Boreal and Auftral: ✳
A magnetick vigour, verticity, and determinate
vertices, or poles.

RON fettles itfelf toward the North and South ; not with one and the fame point toward this pole or that : for one end of the piece of ore itfelf and one extremity alfo of a wrought-iron wire have a fure and conftant deftination to the North, the other to the South, whether the iron hang in the air, or float on water, be the iron large rods or thinner wires. Even if it be a little rod, or a wire ten or twenty or more ells in length ; one end as a rule is Boreal, the other Auftral. If you cut off part of that wire, and if the end of that divided part were Boreal, the other end (which was joined to it) will be Auftral. Thus if you divide it into feveral parts, before making an experiment on the furface of water, you can recognize the vertex. In all of them a Boreal end draws an Auftral and repels a Boreal, and contrariwife, according to the laws magnetical. Yet herein wrought iron differs from the loadftone and from its own ore, inafmuch as in an iron ball of any fize, fuch as thofe ufed for artillery or cannon, or bullets ufed for carbines or fowling-pieces, verticity is harder to acquire and is lefs apparent than in a piece of loadftone, or of ore itfelf, or than in a round loadftone. But in long and extended pieces of iron a power is at once difcerned ; the caufes of which fact, and the methods by which it acquires its verticity and its poles without ufe of a loadftone, as well as the reafons for all the other obfcure features of verticity, we fhall fet forth in defcribing the motion of direction.

CHAP.

CHAP. XIIII.

Concerning other powers of loadſtone, and its
medicinal properties.

IOSCORIDES preſcribes loadſtone to be given with ſweetened water, three ſcruples' weight, to expel groſs humours. Galen writes that a like quantity of bloodſtone avails. Others relate that loadſtone perturbs the mind and makes folk melan- cholick, and moſtly kills. Gartias ab Horto thinks it not deleterious or injurious to health. The natives of Eaſt India tell us, he ſays, that loadſtone taken in ſmall doſes preſerves youth. On which account the aged king, Zeilam, is ſaid to have ordered the pans in which his victuals were cooked to be made of loadſtone. The perſon (ſays he) to whom this order was given told me ſo him- ſelf. There are many varieties of loadſtone produced by differences in the mingling of earths, metals, and juices ; hence they are al- together unlike in their virtues and effects, due to propinquities of places and of agnate bodies, and ariſing from the pits themſelves as it were from the matrices being foul. One loadſtone is therefore able to purge the ſtomach, and another to check purging, to cauſe by its fumes a ſerious ſhock to the mind, to produce a gnawing at the vitals, or to bring on a grave relapſe ; in caſe of which ills they exhibit gold and emerald, uſing an abominable impoſture for lucre. Pure loadſtone may, indeed, be not only harmleſs, but even able to correct an over-fluid and putreſcent ſtate of the bowels and bring them back to a better temperament ; of this ſort uſually are the oriental magnets from China, and the denſer ones from Bengal, which are neither miſliking nor unpleaſant to the actual ſenſes. Plutarch and Claudius Ptolemy, and all the copyiſts ſince their time, think that a loadſtone ſmeared with garlick does not allure iron. Hence ſome ſuſpect that garlick is of avail againſt any dele- terious power of the magnet : thus in philoſophy many falſe and idle conjectures ariſe from fables and falſehoods. Some phyſicians have opined that a loadſtone has power to extract the iron of an arrow from the human body. But it is when whole that the loadſtone draws, not when pulverized and formleſs, buried in plaſters ; for it does not attract by reaſon of its material, but is rather adapted for the healing of open wounds, by reaſon of exſiccation, cloſing up and drying the ſore, an effect by which the arrow-heads would rather be retained in the wounds. Thus vainly and prepoſterouſly do the ſcioliſts

look

look for remedies while ignorant of the true caufes of things. The application of a loadftone for all forts of headaches no more cures them (as fome make out) than would an iron helmet or a fteel cap. To give it in a draught to dropfical perfons is an error of the ancients, or an impudent tale of the copyifts, though one kind of ore may be found which, like many more minerals, purges the ftomach; but this is due to fome defect of that ore and not to any magnetick property. Nicolaus puts a large quantity of loadftone into his divine plafter, juft as the Augfburgers do into a black plafter for frefh wounds and ftabs; the virtue of which dries them up without fmart, fo that it proves an efficacious medicament. In like manner alfo Paracelfus to the fame end mingles it in his plafter for ftab wounds.

CHAP. XV.

The Medicinal Virtue of Iron.

OT foreign to our prefent purpofe will it be to treat briefly alfo of the medicinal virtue of iron: for it is a prime remedial for fome difeafes of the human body, and by its virtues, both thofe that are natural and thofe acquired by fuitable preparation, it works marvellous changes in the human body, fo that we may the more furely recognize its nature through its medicinal virtue and through certain manifeft experiments. So that even thofe tyros in medicine who abufe this moft famous medicament may learn to prefcribe it with better judgment for the healing of the fick, and not, as too often they ufe it, to their harm. The beft iron, Stomoma, or Chalybs, Acies, or Aciarium, is reduced to a fine powder by a file; the powder is fteeped in the fharpeft vinegar, and dried in the fun, and again foufed in vinegar, and dried; afterwards it is wafhed in fpring water or other fuitable water, and dried; then for the fecond time it is pulverized and reduced on porphyry, paffed through a very fine fieve, and put back for ufe. It is given chiefly in cafes of laxity and over-humidity of the liver, in enlargement of the fpleen, after due evacuations; for which reafon it reftores young girls when pallid, fickly, and lacking colour, to health and beauty; fince it is very ficcative, and is aftringent without harm. But fome who in every internal malady always talk of obftruction

F   of

of the liver and spleen, think it beneficial in those cases because it removes obstructions, mainly trusting to the opinions of certain Arabians: wherefore they administer it to the dropsical and to those suffering from tumour of the liver or from chronic jaundice, and to persons troubled with hypochondrical melancholia or any stomachic disorder, or add it to electuaries, without doubt to the grievous injury of many of their patients. Fallopius commends it prepared in his own way for tumours of the spleen, but is much mistaken; for loadstone is pre-eminently good for spleens relaxed with humour, and swollen; but it is so far from curing spleens thickened into a tumour that it mightily confirms the malady. For those drugs which are strong siccatives and absorb humour force the viscera when hardened into a tumour more completely into a quasi-stony body. There are some who roast iron in a closed oven with fierce firing, and burn it strongly, until it turns red, and they call this Saffron of Mars; which is a powerful siccative, and more quickly penetrates the intestines. Moreover they order violent exercise, that the drug may enter the viscera while heated and so reach the place affected; wherefore also it is reduced to a very fine flour; otherwise it only sticks in the stomach and in the chyle and does not penetrate to the intestines. As a dry and earthy medicament, then, it is shown by the most certain experiments to be, after proper evacuations, a remedy for diseases arising from humour (when the viscera are charged and overflowing with watery rheum). Prepared steel is a medicament proper for enlarged spleen. Iron waters too are effectual in reducing the spleen, although as a rule iron is of a frigid and astringent efficiency, not a laxative; but it effects this neither by heat nor by cold, but from its own dryness when mixed with a penetrative fluid: it thus disperses the humour, thickens the villi, hardens the tissues, and contracts them when lax; while the inherent heat in the member thus strengthened, being increased in power, dissipates what is left. Whereas if the liver be hardened and weakened by old age or a chronic obstruction, or the spleen be shrivelled and contracted to a schirrus, by which troubles the fleshy parts of the limbs grow flaccid, and water under the skin invades the body, in the case of these conditions the introduction of iron accelerates the fatal end, and considerably increases the malady. Amongst recent writers there are some who in cases of drought of the liver prescribe, as a much lauded and famous remedy, the electuary of iron flag, described by Rhazes in his ninth book *ad Almansorem*, Chap. 63, or prepared filings of steel; an evil and deadly advice: which if they do not some time understand from our philosophy, at least everyday experience, and the decline and death of their patients, will convince them, even the sluggish and lazy. Whether iron be warm or cold is variously contended by many.

many. By Manardus, Curtius, Fallopius and others, many reasons are adduced on both sides; each settles it according to his own sentiment. Some make it to be cold, saying that iron has the property of refrigerating, because Aristotle in his *Meteorologica* would put iron in the class of things which grow concreted in cold by emission of the whole of their Heat: Galen, too, says that iron has its consistency from cold; also that it is an earthy and dense body. Further that iron is astringent, also that Chalybeate water quenches thirst: and they adduce the cooling effect of thermal iron waters. Others, however, maintain that it is Warm, because of Hippocrates making out that waters are warm which burst forth from places where iron exists. Galen says that in all metals there is considerable substance, or essence, of fire. Paolo affirms that iron waters are warm. Rhazes will have it that iron is warm and dry in the third degree. The Arabians think that it opens the spleen and liver; wherefore also that iron is warm. Montagnana recommends it in cold affections of the uterus and stomach. Thus do the smatterers cross swords together, and puzzle inquiring minds by their vague conjectures, and wrangle for trifles as for goats' wool, when they philosophize, wrongly allowing and accepting properties: but these matters will appear more plainly by and by when we begin to discuss the causes of things; the clouds being dispersed that have so darkened all Philosophy. Filings, scales, and slag of iron are, as Avicenna makes out, not wanting in deleterious power (haply when they are not well prepared or are taken in larger quantity than is fit), hence they cause violent pain in the bowels, roughness of the mouth and tongue, marasmus, and shrivelling of the limbs. But Avicenna wrongly and old-womanishly makes out that the proper antidote to this iron poison is loadstone to the weight of a drachm taken as a draught in the juice of mercurialis or of Beet; for loadstone is of a twofold nature, usually malefiant
and pernicious, nor does it resist iron, since it attracts it;
nor when drunk in a draught in the form of
powder does it avail to attract or repel,
but rather inflicts the
same evils.

CHAP.

CHAP. XVI.

That loadftone & iron ore are the fame, but iron an
extract from both, as other metals are from their own
ores ; & that all magnetick virtues, though
weaker, exift in the ore itfelf & in
fmelted iron.

ITHERTO we have declared the nature & powers
of the loadftone, & alfo the properties & effence of
iron ; it now remains to fhow their mutual affinities,
& kinfhip, fo to fpeak, & how very clofely conjoined
thefe fubftances are.   At the higheft part of the
terreftrial globe, or at its perifhable furface & rind,
as it were, thefe two bodies ufually originate & are produced in one
and the fame matrix, as twins in one mine.   Strong loadftones are
dug up by themfelves, weaker ones too have their own proper vein.
Both are found in iron mines.   Iron ore moft often occurs alone,
without ftrong loadftone (for the more perfect are rarely met with).
Strong loadftone is a ftone refembling iron ;   out of it is ufually
fmelted the fineft iron, which the Greeks call *ftomoma*, the Latins
acies, the Barbarians (not amifs) *aciare*, or *aciarium*.   This fame
ftone draws, repels, controls other loadftones, directs itfelf to the
poles of the world, picks up fmelted iron, and works many other
wonders, fome already fet forth by us, but many more which we
muft demonftrate more fully.   A weaker loadftone, however, will
exhibit all thefe powers, but in a leffer degree; while iron ore, &
alfo wrought iron (if they have been prepared) fhow their ftrength
in all magnetick experiments not lefs than do feeble and weak
* loadftones; & an inert piece of ore, & one poffeffed of no magnetick
properties, & juft thrown out of the pit, when roafted in the fire
& prepared with due art (by the elimination of humours & foreign
excretions) awakes, and becomes in power & potency a magnet.
* Occafionally a ftone or iron ore is mined, which attracts forthwith
without being prepared : for native iron of the right colour attracts
and governs iron magnetically.   One form then belongs to the one
mineral, one fpecies, one felf-fame effence.   For to me there feems
to be a greater difference, & unlikenefs, between the ftrongeft loadftone,

stone, & a weak one which scarce can attract a single chip of iron; between one that is stout, strong, metallick, & one that is soft, friable, clayey; amidst such variety of colour, substance, quality, & weight; than there is on the one hand between the best ore, rich in iron, or iron that is metallick from the beginning, and on the other the most excellent loadstone. Usually, too, there are no marks to distinguish them, and even metallurgists cannot decide between them, because they agree together in all respects. Moreover we see that the best loadstone and the ore of iron are both as it were distressed by the same maladies & diseases, both run to old age in the same way & exhibit the same marks of it, are preserved & keep their properties by the same remedies & safeguards; & yet again the one increases the potency of the other, & by artfully devised adjuncts marvellously intensifies, & exalts it. For both are impaired by the more acrid juices as by poisons, & the aqua fortis of the Chemists inflicts on both the same wounds, and when exposed too long to harm from the atmosphere, they both alike pine away, so to speak, & grow old; each is preserved by being kept in the dust & scrapings of the other; & when a fit piece of steel or iron is adjoined above its pole, the loadstone's vigour is augmented through the firm union. The loadstone is laid up in iron filings, not that iron is its food; as though loadstone were alive and needed feeding, as Cardan philosophizes; nor yet that so it is delivered from the inclemency of the weather (for which cause it as well as iron is laid up in bran by Scaliger; mistakenly, however, for they are not preserved well in this way, and keep for years their own fixed forms): nor yet, since they remain perfect by the mutual action of their powders, do their extremities waste away, but are cherished & preserved, like by like. For just as in their own places, in the mines, bodies like to each other endure for many ages entire and uncorrupt, when surrounded by bodies of the same stuff, as the lesser interior parts in a great mass: so loadstone and ore of iron, when inclosed in a mound of the same material, do not exhale their native humour, do not waste away, but retain their soundness. A loadstone lasts longer in filings of smelted iron, & a piece of iron ore excellently also in dust of loadstone.; as also smelted iron in filings of loadstone & even in those of iron. Then both these allied bodies have a true & just form of one & the same species; a form which until this day was considered by all, owing to their outward unlikeness & the inequality of the potency that is the same innate in both, to be different & unlike in kind; the smatterers not understanding that the same powers, though differing in strength, exist in both alike. And in fact they both are true & intimate parts of the earth, & as such retain the prime natural properties of mutually attracting, of moving, & of disposing themselves toward the position of the world,

and

and of the terreftrial globe; which properties they alfo impart to each other, and increafe, confirm, receive, and retain each other's forces. The ftronger fortifies the weaker, not as though aught were taken away from its own fubftance, or its proper vigour, nor becaufe any corporeal fubftance is imparted, but the dormant virtue of the one is aroufed by the other, without lofs. For if with a fingle fmall ftone you touch a thoufand bits of iron for the ufe of mariners, that loadftone attracts iron no lefs ftrongly than before; with the fame ftone weighing one pound, any one will be able to fufpend in the air a thoufand pounds of iron. For if any one were to fix high up on the walls fo many iron nails of fo great a weight, & were to apply to them the fame number of nails touched, according to the art, by a loadftone, they would all be feen to hang in the air through the force of one fmall ftone. So this is not folely the action, labour, or outlay of the loadftone; but the iron, which is in a fenfe an extract from loadftone, and a fufion of loadftone into metal, & conceives vigour from it, & by proximity ftrengthens the magnetick faculties, doth itfelf, from whatever lode it may have come, raife its own inborn forces through the prefence & contact of the ftone, even when folid bodies intervene. Iron that has been touched, acts anew on another piece of iron by contact, & adapts it for magnetick movements, & this again a third. But if you rub with a loadftone any other metal, or wood, or bones, or glafs, as they will not be moved toward any particular and determinate quarter of heaven, nor be attracted by any magnetick body, fo they are able not to impart any magnetick property to other bodies or to iron itfelf by attrition, & by infection. Loadftone differs from iron ore, as alfo from fome weaker magnets, in that when molten in the furnace into a ferric & metallick fufed mafs, it does not fo readily flow & diffolve into metal; but is fometimes burnt to afhes in large furnaces; a refult which it is reafonable to fuppofe arifes from its having fome kind of fulphureous matter mixed with it, or from its own excellence & fimpler nature, or from the likenefs & common form which it has with the common mother, the Great Magnet. For earths, and iron ftones, magnets abounding in metal, are the more imbued & marred with excrementitious metallick humours, and earthy corruptions of fubftance, as numbers of loadftones are weaker from the mine; hence they are a little further remote from the common mother, & are degenerate, & when fmelted in the furnace undergo fufion more eafily, & give out a more certain metallick product, & a metal that is fofter, not a tough fteel. The majority of loadftones (if not unfairly burnt) yield in the furnace a very excellent iron. But iron ore alfo agrees in all thofe primary qualities with loadftone; for both, being nearer and more clofely akin to the earth above all bodies known to us, have in themfelves

a

a magnetick fubftance, & one that is more homogenic, true & cognate with the globe of the earth; lefs infected & fpoiled by foreign blemifh; lefs confufed with the outgrowths of earth's furface, & lefs debafed by corrupt products. And for this reafon Ariftotle in the fourth book of his *Meteora* feems not unfairly to feparate iron from all the reft of the metals. Gold, he fays, filver, copper, tin, lead, belong to water; but iron is of the earth. Galen, in the fourth chapter of *De Facultatibus Simplicium Medicamentorum*, fays that iron is an earthy & denfe body. Accordingly a ftrong loadftone is on our fhowing efpecially of the earth: the next place is occupied by iron ore or weaker loadftone; fo the loadftone is by nature and origin of iron, and it and magnetick iron are both one in kind. Iron ore yields iron in furnaces; loadftone alfo pours forth iron in the furnaces, but of a much more excellent fort, that which is called fteel or blade-edge; and the better fort of iron ore is a weak loadftone, the beft loadftone being a moft excellent ore of iron, in which, as is to be fhown by us, the primary properties are grand and confpicuous. Weaker loadftone or iron ore is that in which thefe properties are more obfcure, feeble, and are fcarce perceptible to the fenfes.

CHAP. XVII.

That the globe of the earth is magnetick, & a magnet; &

how in our hands the magnet ftone has all the primary
forces of the earth, while the earth by the
fame powers remains conftant in a
fixed direction in the
univerfe.

RIOR to bringing forward the caufes of magnetical motions, & laying open the proofs of things hidden for fo many ages, & our experiments (the true foundations of terreftrial philofophy), we have to eftablifh & prefent to the view of the learned our New & unheard of doctrine about the earth; and this, when argued by us on the grounds of its probability, with fubfequent
experiments

experiments & proofs, will be as certainly affured as anything in philofophy ever has been confidered & confirmed by clever arguments or mathematical proofs. The terrene mafs, which together with the vafty ocean produces the fphærick figure & conftitutes our globe, being of a firm & conftant fubftance, is not eafily changed, does not wander about, & fluctuate with uncertain motions, like the feas, & flowing waves: but holds all its volume of moifture in certain beds & bounds, & as it were in oft-met veins, that it may be the lefs diffufed & diffipated at random. Yet the folid magnitude of the earth prevails & reigns fupreme in the nature of our globe. Water, however, is attached to it, & as an appendage only, & a flux emanating from it; whofe force from the beginning is conjoined with the earth through its fmalleft parts, and is innate in its fubftance. This moifture the earth as it grows hot throws off freely when it is of the greateft poffible fervice in the generation of things. But the thews and dominant ftuff of the globe is that terrene body which far exceeds in quantity all the volume of flowing ftreams and open waters (whatever vulgar philofophers may dream of the magnitudes and proportions of their elements), and which takes up moft of the whole globe and almoft fills it internally, and by itfelf almoft fuffices to endow it with fphærick fhape. For the feas only fill certain not very deep or profound hollows, fince they rarely go down to a depth of a mile and generally do not exceed a hundred or 50 fathoms. For fo it is afcertained by the obfervations of feamen when by the plumb-line and finker its abyfms are explored with the nautical founder; which depths relatively to the dimenfions of the globe, do not much deform its globular fhape. Small then appears to be that portion of the real earth that ever emerges to be feen by man, or is turned up; fince we cannot penetrate deeper into its bowels, further than the wreckage of its outer efflorefcence, either by reafon of the waters which gufh up in deep workings, as through veins, or for want of a wholefome air to fupport life in the miners, or on account of the vaft coft that would be incurred in pumping out fuch huge workings, and many other difficulties; fo that to have gone down to a depth of four hundred, or (which is of rareft occurrence) of five hundred fathoms as in a few mines, appears to all a ftupendous undertaking. But it is eafy to underftand how minute, how almoft negligibly fmall a portion that 500 fathoms is of the earth's diameter, which is 6,872 miles. It is then parts only of the earth's circumference and of its prominences that are perceived by us with our fenfes; and thefe in all regions appear to us to be either loamy, or clayey, or fandy, or full of various foils, or marls: or lots of ftones or gravel meet us, or beds of falt, or a metallick lode, and metals in abundance. In the fea and in deep waters, however, either reefs, and huge boulders, or fmaller ftones, or fands, or mud

are

are found by mariners as they found the depths. Nowhere does the Ariftotelian element of *earth* come to light; and the Peripateticks are the fport of their own vain dreams about elements. Yet the lower bulk of the earth and the inward parts of the globe confift of fuch bodies; for they could not have exifted, unlefs they had been related to and expofed to the air and water, and to the light and influences of the heavenly bodies, in like manner as they are generated, and pafs into many diffimilar forms of things, and are changed by a perpetual law of fucceffion. Yet the interior parts imitate them, and betake themfelves to their own fource, on the principle of terrene matter, albeit they have loft the firft qualities and the natural terrene form, and are borne towards the earth's centre, and cohære with the globe of the earth, from which they cannot be wrenched afunder except by force. But the loadftone and all magneticks, not the ftone only, but every magnetick homogenic fubftance, would feem to contain the virtue of the earth's core and of its inmoft bowels, and to hold within itfelf and to have conceived that which is the fecret and inward principle of its fubftance; and it poffeffes the actions peculiar to the globe of attracting, directing, difpofing, rotating, ftationing itfelf in the univerfe, according to the rule of the whole, and it contains and regulates the dominant powers of the globe; which are the chief tokens and proofs of a certain diftinguifhing combination, and of a nature moft thoroughly conjoint. For if among actual bodies one fees fomething move and breathe, and experience fenfations, and be inclined and impelled by reafon, will one not, knowing and feeing this, conclude that it is a man or fomething rather like a man, than that it is a ftone or a ftick? The loadftone far excels all other bodies known to us in virtues and properties pertaining to the common mother: but thofe properties have been far too little underftood or realized by philofophers: for to its body bodies magnetical rufh in from all fides and cleave to it, as we fee them do in the cafe of the earth. It has poles, not mathematical points, but natural termini of force excelling in primary efficiency by the co-operation of the whole: and there are poles in like manner in the earth which our forefathers fought ever in the fky: it has an æquator, a natural dividing line between the two poles, juft as the earth has: for of all lines drawn by the mathematicians on the terreftrial globe, the æquator is the natural boundary, and is not, as will hereafter appear, merely a mathematical circle. It, like the earth, acquires Direction and ftability toward North and South, as the earth does; alfo it has a circular motion toward the pofition of the earth, wherein it adjufts itfelf to its rule: it follows the afcenfions and declinations of the earth's poles, and conforms exactly to the fame, and by itfelf raifes its own poles above the

G

horizon

horizon naturally according to the law of the particular country and region, or finks below it. The loadftone derives temporary properties, and acquires its verticity from the earth, and iron is affected by the verticity of the globe even as iron is by a loadftone: Magneticks are conformable to and are regulated by the earth, and are fubject to the earth in all their motions. All its movements harmonize with, and ftrictly wait upon, the geometry and form of the earth, as we fhall afterwards prove by moft conclufive experiments and diagrams; and the chief part of the vifible earth is alfo magnetical, and has magnetick motions, although it be disfigured by corruptions and mutations without end. Why then do we not recognize this the chief homogenic fubftance of the earth, likeft of fubftances to its inner nature and clofeft allied to its very marrow? For none of the other mixed earths fuitable for agriculture, no other metalliferous veins, nor ftones, nor fand, nor other fragments of the earth which have come to our view poffefs fuch conftant and peculiar powers. And yet we do not affume that the whole interior of this globe of ours is compofed of ftones or iron (although Francifcus Maurolycus, that learned man, deems the whole of the earth's interior to confift of folid ftone). For not every loadftone that we have is a ftone, it being fometimes like a clod, or like clay and iron either firmly compacted together out of various materials, or of a fofter compofition, or by heat reduced to the metallick ftate; and the magnetick fubftance by reafon of its location and of its furroundings, and of the metallick matrix itfelf, is diftinguifhed, at the furface of the terrene mafs, by many qualities and adventitious natures, juft as in clay it is marked by certain ftones and iron lodes. But we maintain that the true earth is a folid fubftance, homogeneous with the globe, clofely coherent, endowed with a primordial and (as in the other globes of the univerfe) with a prepotent form; in which pofition it perfifts with a fixed verticity, and revolves with a neceffary motion and an inherent tendency to turn, and it is this conftitution, when true and native, and not injured or disfigured by outward defects, that the loadftone poffeffes above all bodies apparent to us, as if it were a more truly homogenic part taken from the earth. Accordingly native iron which is *fui generis* (as metallurgifts term it), is formed when homogenic parts of the earth grow together into a metallick lode; Loadftone being formed when they are changed into metallick ftone, or a lode of the fineft iron, or fteel: fo in other iron lodes the homogenic matter that goes together is fomewhat more imperfect; juft as many parts of the earth, even the high ground, is homogenic but fo much more deformate. Smelted iron is fufed and fmelted out of homogenic ftuffs, and cleaves to the earth more tenacioufly than the ores themfelves. Such then is our earth in its
inward

inward parts, poffeffed of a magnetick homogeneal nature, and upon fuch more perfect foundations as thefe refts the whole nature of things terreftrial, manifefting itfelf to us, in our more diligent fcrutiny, everywhere in all magnetick minerals, and iron ores, in all clay, and in numerous earths and ftones; while Ariftotle's fimple element, that moft empty terreftrial phantom of the Peripateticks, a rude, inert, cold, dry, fimple matter, the univerfal fubftratum, is dead, devoid of vigour, and has never prefented itfelf to any one, not even in fleep, and would be of no potency in nature. Our philofophers were only dreaming when they fpoke of a kind of fimple and inert matter. Cardan does not confider the loadftone to be any kind of ftone, " but a fort of perfected portion of fome " kind of earth that is abfolute; a token of which is its abundance, " there being no place where it is not found. And there is " (he fays) " a power of iron in the wedded Earth which is perfect in its " own kind when it has received fertilizing force from the male, " that is to fay, the ftone of Hercules " (in his book *De Proportionibus*). And later: " Becaufe " (he fays) " in the previous propofition I " have taught that iron is true earth." A ftrong loadftone fhows itfelf to be of the inward earth, and upon innumerable tefts claims to rank with the earth in the poffeffion of a primary form, that by which Earth herfelf abides in her own ftation and is directed in her courfes. Thus a weaker loadftone and every ore of iron, and nearly all clay, or clayey earth, and numerous other forts (yet more, or lefs, owing to the different labefaction of fluids and flimes), keep their magnetick and genuine earth-properties open to view, falling fhort of the characteriftic form, and deformate. For it is not iron alone (the fmelted metal) that points to the poles, nor is it the loadftone alone that is attracted by another and made to revolve magnetically; but all iron ores, and other ftones, as Rhenifh flates and the black ones from Avignon (the French call them *Ardoifes*) which they ufe for tiles, and many more of other colours and fubftances, provided they have been prepared; as well as all clay, grit, and fome forts of rocks, and, to fpeak more clearly, all the more folid earth that is everywhere apparent; given that that earth be not fouled with fatty and fluid corruptions; as mud, as mire, as accumulations of putrid matter; nor deformate by the imperfec- tions of fundry admixtures; nor dripping with ooze, as marls: all are attracted by the loadftone, when fimply prepared by fire, and freed from their refufe humour; and as by the loadftone fo alfo by the earth herfelf they are drawn and controlled mag- netically, in a way different from all other bodies; and by that inherent force fettle themfelves according to the orderly arrange- ment and fabric of the univerfe and of the Earth, as will appear
later

later.   Thus every part of the earth which is removed from it
exhibits by fure experiments every impulfe of the magnetick nature ; by its various motions it obferves the globe of the earth and
the   principle   common
to   both.

BOOK

BOOK SECOND.

CHAP. I.

ON MAGNETICK
Motions.

IVERS things concerning opinions about the magnet-ftone, and its variety, concerning its poles and its known faculties, concerning iron, concerning the properties of iron, concerning a magnetick fubftance common to both of thefe and to the earth itſelf, have been ſpoken briefly by us in the former book. There remain the magnetical motions, and their fuller philofophy, fhown and demonſtrated. Thefe motions are incitements of homogeneal parts either among themſelves or toward the primary conformation of the whole earth. Ariſtotle admits only two fimple motions of his elements, from the centre and toward the centre; of light ones upward, heavy ones downward; ſo that in the earth there exiſts one motion only of all its parts towards the centre of the world,—a rude and inert precipitation. But what of it is light, and how wrongly it is inferred by the Peripateticks from the fimple motion of the elements, and alfo what is its heavy part, we will difcufs elfewhere. But now our inquiry muft be into the caufes of other motions, depending on its true form, which we have plainly feen in our magnetick bodies; and thefe we have feen to be prefent in the earth and in all its homogenic parts alfo. We have noticed that they harmonize with the earth, and are bound up with its forces. Five movements or differences of motions are then obſerved by us: Coition (commonly called attraction), the incitement

citement to magnetick union; Direction towards the poles of the earth, and the vertieity and continuance of the earth towards the determinate poles of the world; Variation, a deflexion from the meridian, which we call a perverted movement; Declination, a defcent of the magnetick pole below the horizon; and circular motion, or Revolution. Concerning all thefe we fhall difcufs feparately, and how they all proceed from a nature tending to aggregation, either by verticity or by volubility. Jofrancus Offufius makes out different magnetick motions; a firft toward a centre; a fecond toward a pole at feventy-feven degrees; a third toward iron; a fourth toward loadftone. The first is not always to a centre, but exifts only at the poles in a ftraight courfe toward the centre, if the motion is magnetick; otherwife it is only motion of matter toward its own mafs and toward the globe. The fecond toward a pole at feventy-feven degrees is no motion, but is direction with refpect to the pole of the earth, or variation. The third and fourth are magnetick and are the fame. So he truly recognizes no magnetick motion except the Coition toward iron or loadftone, commonly called attraction. There is another motion in the whole earth, which does not exift towards the terrella or towards its parts; videlicet, a motion of aggregation, and that movement of matter, which is called by philofophers a right motion, of which elfewhere.

CHAP. II.

On the Magnetick Coition, and firft on the
Attraction of Amber, or more truly, on the
Attaching of Bodies to Amber.

CELEBRATED has the fame of the loadftone and of amber ever been in the memoirs of the learned. Loadftone and alfo amber do fome philofophers invoke when in explaining many fecrets their fenfes become dim and reafoning cannot go further. Inquifitive theologians alfo would throw light on the divine myfteries fet beyond the range of human fenfe, by means of loadftone and amber; juft as idle Metaphyficians, when they are fetting up and teaching ufelefs phantafms, have recourfe to the loadftone as if it were a Delphick fword, an illuftration always applicable to everything. But phyficians even (with the authority of Galen),

Galen), defiring to confirm the belief in the attraction of purgative medicines by means of the likenefs of fubftance and the familiarities of the juices—truly a vain and ufelefs error—bring in the loadftone as witnefs as being a nature of great authority and of confpicuous efficacy and a remarkable body. So in very many cafes there are fome who, when they are pleading a caufe and cannot give a reafon for it, bring in loadftone and amber as though they were perfonified witneffes. But thefe men (apart from that common error) being ignorant that the caufes of magnetical motions are widely different from the forces of amber, eafily fall into error, and are themfelves the more deceived by their own cogitations. For in other bodies a confpicuous force of attraction manifefts itfelf otherwife than in load-ftone; like as in amber, concerning which fome things muft firft be faid, that it may appear what is that attaching of bodies, and how it is different from and foreign to the magnetical actions; thofe mortals being ftill ignorant, who think that inclination to be an attraction, and compare it with the magnetick coitions. The Greeks call it ἤλεκτρον, becaufe it attracts ftraws to itfelf, when it is warmed by rubbing; then it is called ἅρπαξ; and χρυσοφόρον, from its golden colour. But the Moors call it Carabe, becaufe they are accuftomed to offer the fame in facrifices and in the worfhip of the Gods. For Carab fignifies to offer in Arabic; fo Carabe, an offering: or feizing chaff, as Scaliger quotes from Abohalis, out of the Arabic or Perfian language. Some alfo call it Amber, efpecially the Indian and Ethiopian amber, called in Latin *Succinum*, as if it were a juice. The Sudavienfes or Sudini call it *geniter*, as though it were generated terreftrially. The errors of the ancients con-cerning its nature and origin having been exploded, it is certain that amber comes for the moft part from the fea, and the ruftics collect it on the coaft after the more violent ftorms, with nets and other tackle; as among the Sudini of Pruffia; and it is alfo found fometimes on the coaft of our own Britain. It feems, however, to be produced alfo in the foil and at fpots of fome depth, like other bitumens; to be wafhed out by the waves of the fea; and to become concreted more firmly from the nature and faltnefs of the fea-water. For it was at firft a foft and vifcous material; wherefore alfo it contains enclofed and entombed in pieces of it, fhining in eternal fepulchres, flies, grubs, gnats, ants; which have all flown or crept or fallen into it when it firft flowed forth in a liquid ftate. The ancients and alfo more recent writers recall (experience proving the fame thing), that amber attracts ftraws and chaff. The fame is alfo done by jet, which is dug out of the earth in Britain, in Germany, and in very many lands, and is a rather hard concretion from black bitumen, and as it were a transformation into ftone. There are many modern authors who have written and copied from others about amber and jet attracting chaff, and about other fub-

ftances

ftances generally unknown; with whofe labours the fhops of book-
fellers are crammed. Our own age has produced many books
about hidden, abftrufe, and occult caufes and wonders, in all of
which amber and jet are fet forth as enticing chaff; but they treat
the fubject in words alone, without finding any reafons or proofs
from experiments, their very ftatements obfcuring the thing in a
greater fog, forfooth in a cryptic, marvellous, abftrufe, fecret, occult,
way. Wherefore alfo fuch philofophy produces no fruit, becaufe
very many philofophers, making no inveftigation themfelves, un-
fupported by any practical experience, idle and inert, make no
progrefs by their records, and do not fee what light they can bring
to their theories; but their philofophy refts fimply on the ufe of
certain Greek words, or uncommon ones; after the manner of our
goffips and barbers nowadays, who make fhow of certain Latin
words to an ignorant populace as the infignia of their craft,
and fnatch at the popular favour. For it is not only amber and
✱ jet (as they fuppofe) which entice fmall bodies; but Diamond,
Sapphire, Carbuncle, Iris gem, Opal, Amethyft, Vincentina, and
Briftolla (an Englifh gem or fpar), Beryl, and Cryftal do the fame.
Similar powers of attraction are feen alfo to be poffeffed by glafs
(efpecially when clear and lucid), as alfo by falfe gems made of glafs
or Cryftal, by glafs of antimony, and by many kinds of fpars from
the mines, and by Belemnites. Sulphur alfo attracts, and maftick,
and hard fealing-wax compounded of lac tinctured of various colours.
Rather hard refin entices, as does orpiment, but lefs ftrongly; with
difficulty alfo and indiftinctly under a fuitable dry fky, Rock falt,
mufcovy ftone, and rock alum. This one may fee when the air is
fharp and clear and rare in mid-winter, when the emanations from
the earth hinder electricks lefs, and the electrick bodies become
✱ more firmly indurated; about which hereafter. Thefe fubftances
draw everything, not ftraws and chaff only, but all metals, woods,
leaves, ftones, earths, even water and oil, and everything which
is fubject to our fenfes, or is folid; although fome write that
amber does not attract anything but chaff and certain twigs;
(wherefore Alexander Aphrodifeus falfely declares the queftion of
amber to be inexplicable, becaufe it attracts dry chaff only, and
not bafil leaves, but thefe are the utterly falfe and difgraceful
tales of the writers. But in order that you may be able clearly to
teft how fuch attraction occurs, and what thofe materials are which
thus entice other bodies (for even if bodies incline towards fome of
thefe, yet on account of weaknefs they feem not to be raifed by
them, but are more eafily turned), make yourfelf a verforium of
any metal you like, three or four digits in length, refting rather
lightly on its point of fupport after the manner of a magnetick
needle, to one end of which bring up a piece of amber or a fmooth
and

and polifhed gem which has been gently rubbed ; for the verforium turns forthwith. Many things are there- by feen to attract, both thofe which are formed by nature alone, and thofe which are by art prepared, fufed, and mixed ; nor is this fo much a fingular property of one or two things (as is commonly fuppofed), but the manifeft nature of very many, both of fimple fubftances, remaining merely in their own form, and of com- pofitions, as of hard fealing-wax, & of certain other mixtures befides, made of unctuous ftuffs. We muft, however, inveftigate more fully whence that tendency arifes, and what thofe forces be, concerning which a few men have brought forward very little, the crowd of philo- fophizers nothing at all. By Galen three kinds of attractives in general were recognized in nature : a Firft clafs of thofe fubftances which attract by their elemental quality, namely, heat ; the Second is the clafs of thofe which attract by the fucceffion of a vacuum ; the Third is the clafs of thofe which attract by a property of their whole fubftance, which are alfo quoted by Avicenna and others. Thefe claffes, however, cannot in any way fatisfy us ; they neither embrace the caufes of amber, jet, and diamond, and of other fimilar fubftances (which derive their forces on account of the fame virtue) ; nor of the loadftone, and of all magnetick fubftances, which obtain their virtue by a very diffimilar and alien influence from them, de- rived from other fources. Wherefore alfo it is fitting that we find other caufes of the motions, or elfe we muft wander (as in darknefs), with thefe men, and in no way reach the goal. Amber truly does ✱ not allure by heat, fince if warmed by fire and brought near ftraws, it does not attract them, whether it be tepid, or hot, or glowing, or even when forced into the flame. Cardan (as alfo Pictorio) reckons that this happens in no different way than with the cupping-glafs, by the force of fire. Yet the attracting force of the cupping-glafs does not really come from the force of fire. But he had previoufly faid that the dry fubftance wifhed to imbibe fatty humour, and therefore it was borne towards it. But thefe ftatements are at variance with one another, and alfo foreign to reafon. For if amber had moved towards its food, or if other bodies had inclined towards amber as to- wards provender, there would have been a diminution of the one which was devoured, juft as there would have been a growth of the other which was fated. Then why fhould an attractive force of fire be looked for in amber ? If the attraction exifted from heat, why fhould not very many other bodies alfo attract, if warmed by fire, by the fun, or by friction ? Neither can the attraction be on ac- count of the diffipating of the air, when it takes place in open air (yet Lucretius the poet adduces this as the reafon for magnetical mo- tions). Nor in the cupping-glafs can heat or fire attract by feeding on air : in the cupping-glafs air, having been exhaufted into flame,

H   when

when it condenfes again and is forced into a narrow fpace, makes
the fkin and flefh rife in avoiding a vacuum.   In the open air
warm things cannot attract, not metals even or ftones, if they fhould
* be ftrongly incandefcent by fire.   For a rod of glowing iron, or a
flame, or a candle, or a blazing torch, or a live coal, when they are
brought near to ftraws, or to a verforium, do not attract ; yet at the
fame time they manifeftly call in the air in fucceffion ; becaufe they
confume it, as lamps do oil.   But concerning heat, how it is
reckoned by the crowd of philofophizers, in natural philofophy
and in *materia medica* to exert an attraction otherwife than nature
allows, to which true attractions are falfely imputed, we will difcufs
more at length elfewhere, when we fhall determine what are the properties of heat and cold.   They are very general qualities or kinfhips
of a fubftance, and yet are not to be affigned as true caufes, and, if I
may fay fo, thofe philofophizers utter fome refounding words ; but
about the thing itfelf prove nothing in particular.   Nor does this
attraction accredited to amber arife from any fingular quality of the
fubftance or kinfhip, fince by more thorough refearch we find the
fame effect in very many other bodies ; and all bodies, moreover, of
whatever quality, are allured by all thofe bodies.   Similarity alfo is
not the caufe ; becaufe all things around us placed on this globe of
the earth, fimilar and diffimilar, are allured by amber and bodies of
this kind ; and on that account no cogent analogy is to be drawn
either from fimilarity or identity of fubftance.   But neither do fimilars mutually attract one another, as ftone ftone, flefh flefh, nor aught
elfe outfide the clafs of magneticks and electricks.   Fracaftorio would
have it that " things which mutually attract one another are fimilars,
" as being of the fame fpecies, either in action or in right fubjection.
" Right fubjection is that from which is emitted the emanation which
" attracts and which in mixtures often lies hidden on account of
" their lack of form, by reafon of which they are often different in
" act from what they are in potency.   Hence it may be that hairs
" and twigs move towards amber and towards diamond, not becaufe
" they are hairs, but becaufe either there is fhut up in them air or
" fome other principle, which is attracted in the firft place, and
" which bears fome relation and analogy to that which attracts of
" itfelf ; in which diamond and amber agree through a principle
" common to each."   Thus far Fracaftorio.   Who if he had obferved
by a large number of experiments that all bodies are drawn to
electricks except thofe which are aglow and aflame, and highly
rarefied, would never have given a thought to fuch things.   It is eafy
for men of acute intellect, apart from experiments and practice, to
flip and err.   In greater error do they remain funk who maintain
thefe fame fubftances to be not fimilar, but to be fubftances near
akin ; and hold that on that account a thing moves towards another,
its like, by which it is brought to more perfection.   But thefe are
                                                    ill-confidered

ill-confidered views; for towards all electricks all things move except fuch as are aflame or are too highly rarefied, as air, which is
the universal effluvium of this globe and of the world.   Vegetable
fubftances draw moifture by which their fhoots are rejoiced and
grow; from analogy with that, however, Hippocrates, in his *De
Natura Hominis*, Book I., wrongly concluded that the purging of
morbid humour took place by the fpecifick force of the drug.   Concerning the action and potency of purgatives we fhall fpeak elfewhere.
Wrongly alfo is attraction inferred in other effects; as in the cafe
of a flagon full of water, when buried in a heap of wheat, although
well ftoppered, the moifture is drawn out; fince this moifture is
rather refolved into vapour by the emanation of the fermenting wheat,
and the wheat imbibes the freed vapour.   Nor do elephants' tufks
attract moifture, but drive it into vapour or abforb it.   Thus then
very many things are faid to attract, the reafons for whofe energy muft
be fought from other caufes.   Amber in a fairly large mafs allures, if   ✱
it is polifhed; in a fmaller mafs or lefs pure it feems not to attract
without friction.   But very many electricks (as precious ftones and
fome other fubftances) do not attract at all unlefs rubbed.   On the
other hand many gems, as well as other bodies, are polifhed, yet do   ✱
not allure, and by no amount of friction are they aroufed; thus the
emerald, agate, carnelian, pearls, jafper, chalcedony, alabafter, por-
phyry, coral, the marbles, touchftone, flint, bloodftone, emery, do not
acquire any power; nor do bones, or ivory, or the hardeft woods,
as ebony, nor do cedar, juniper, or cyprefs; nor do metals, filver, gold,
brafs, iron, nor any loadftone, though many of them are finely polifhed
and fhine.   But on the other hand there are fome other polifhed
fubftances of which we have fpoken before, toward which, when they
have been rubbed, bodies incline.   This we fhall underftand only
when we have more clofely looked into the prime origin of bodies.
It is plain to all, and all admit, that the mafs of the earth, or
rather the ftructure and cruft of the earth, confifts of a twofold
material, namely, of fluid and humid matter, and of material of more
confiftency and dry.   From this twofold nature or the more fimple
compacting of one, various fubftances take their rife among us,
which originate in greater proportion now from the earthy, now
from the aqueous nature.   Thofe fubftances which have received
their chief growth from moifture, whether aqueous or fatty, or have
taken on their form by a fimpler compacting from them, or have
been compacted from thefe fame materials in long ages, if they
have a fufficiently firm hardnefs, if rubbed after they have been
polifhed and when they remain bright with the friction—towards
thofe fubftances everything, if prefented to them in the air, turns,
if its too heavy weight does not prevent it.   For amber has been
compacted of moifture, and jet alfo.   Lucid gems are made of water;
juft as Cryftal, which has been concreted from clear water, not
always

always by a very great cold, as some used to judge, and by very hard frost, but sometimes by a less severe one, the nature of the soil fashioning it, the humour or juices being shut up in definite cavities, in the way in which spars are produced in mines. So clear glass is fused out of sand, and from other substances, which have their origin in humid juices. But the dross of metals, as also metals, stones, rocks, woods, contain earth rather, or are mixed with a good deal of earth;

* and therefore they do not attract. Cryftal, mica, glass, and all electricks do not attract if they are burnt or roasted; for their primordial supplies of moisture perish by heat, and are changed and exhaled. All things therefore which have sprung from a predominant moisture and are firmly concreted, and retain the appearance of spar and its resplendent nature in a firm and compact body, allure all bodies, whether humid or dry. Those, however, which partake of the true earth-substance or are very little different from it, are seen to attract also, but from a far different reason, and (so to say) magnetically; concerning these we intend to speak afterwards. But those substances which are more mixed of water and earth, and are produced by the equal degradation of each element (in which the magnetick force of the earth is deformed and remains buried; while the watery humour, being fouled by joining with a more plentiful supply of earth, has not concreted in itself but is mingled with earthy matter), can in no way of themselves attract or move from its place anything which they do not touch. On this account metals, marbles, flints, woods, herbs, flesh, and very many other things can neither allure nor solicit any body either magnetically or electrically. (For it pleases us to call that an electrick force, which hath

* its origin from the humour.) But substances consisting mostly of humour, and which are not very firmly compacted by nature (whereby do they neither bear rubbing, but either melt down and become soft, or are not levigable, such as pitch, the softer kinds of resin, camphor, galbanum, ammoniack, storax, asafœtida, benzoin, asphaltum, especially in rather warm weather) towards them small bodies are not borne; for without rubbing most electricks do not

* emit their peculiar and native exhalation and effluvium. The resin turpentine when liquid does not attract; for it cannot be rubbed; but if it has hardened into a mastick it does attract. But now at length we must understand why small bodies turn towards those substances which have drawn their origin from water; by what force and with what hands (so to speak) electricks seize upon kindred natures. In all bodies in the world two causes or principles have been laid down, from which the bodies themselves were produced, matter and form. Electrical motions become strong from matter, but magnetick from form chiefly; and they differ widely from one another and turn out unlike, since the one is ennobled by numerous virtues and is prepotent; the other is ignoble and of less potency, and

moftly

moftly reftrained, as it were, within certain barriers; and therefore that force muft at times be aroufed by attrition or friction, until it is at a dull heat and gives off an effluvium and a polifh is induced on the body. For fpent air, either blown out of the mouth or given off from moifter air, chokes the virtue. If indeed either a fheet of paper or a piece of linen be interpofed, there will be no movement. But a loadftone, without friction or heat, whether dry or fuffufed with moifture, as well in air as in water, invites magneticks, even with the moft folid bodies interpofed, even planks of wood or pretty thick flabs of ftone or fheets of metal. A loadftone appeals to magneticks only; towards electricks all things move. A loadftone raifes great weights; fo that if there is a loadftone weighing two ounces and ftrong, it attracts half an ounce or a whole ounce. An electrical fubftance only attracts very fmall weights; as, for inftance, a piece of amber of three ounces weight, when rubbed, fcarce raifes a fourth part of a grain of barley. But this attraction of amber and of electrical fubftances muft be further invefligated; and fince there is this particular affection of matter, it may be afked why is amber rubbed, and what affection is produced by the rubbing, and what caufes arife which make it lay hold on everything? As a refult of friction it grows flightly warm and becomes fmooth; two refults which muft often occur together. A large polifhed fragment of amber or jet attracts indeed, even without friction, but lefs ftrongly; but if it be brought gently near a flame or a live coal, fo that it equally becomes warm, it does not attract fmall bodies becaufe it is enveloped in a cloud from the body of the flaming fubftance, which emits a hot breath, and then impinges upon it vapour from a foreign body which for the moft part is at variance with the nature of amber. Moreover the fpirit of the amber which is called forth is enfeebled by alien heat; wherefore it ought not to have heat excepting that produced by motion only and friction, and, as it were, its own, not fent into it by other bodies. For as the igneous heat emitted from any burning fubftance cannot be fo ufed that electricks may acquire their force from it; fo alfo heat from the folar rays does not fit an electrick by the loofening of its right material, becaufe it diffipates rather and confumes it (albeit a body which has been rubbed retains its virtue longer expofed to the rays of the fun than in the fhade; becaufe in the fhade the effluvia are condenfed to a greater degree and more quickly). Then again the fervour from the light of the Sun aroufed by means of a burning mirror confers no vigour on the heated amber; indeed it diffipates and corrupts all the electrick effluvia. Again, burning fulphur and hard wax, made from fhell-lac, when aflame do not allure; for heat from friction refolves bodies into effluvia, which flame confumes away. For it is impoffible for folid electricks to be refolved into their own true effluvia otherwife than by attrition, fave

in

in the cafe of certain fubftances which by reafon of innate vigour emit effluvia conftantly. They are rubbed with bodies which do not befoul their furface, and which produce a polifh, as pretty ftiff filk or a rough wool rag which is as little foiled as poffible, or the dry palm. Amber alfo is rubbed with amber, with diamond, and with glafs, and numerous other fubftances. Thus are electricks manipulated. Thefe things being fo, what is it which moves? Is it the body itfelf, inclofed within its own circumference? Or is it fomething imperceptible to us, which flows out from the fubftance into the ambient air? Somewhat as Plutarch opines, faying in his *Quæftiones Platonicæ*: That there is in amber fomething flammable or fomething having the nature of breath, and this by the attrition of the furface being emitted from its relaxed pores attracts bodies. And if it be an effufion does it feize upon the air whofe motion the bodies follow, or upon the bodies themfelves? But if amber allured the body itfelf, then what need were there of friction, if it is bare and fmooth? Nor does the force arife from the light which is reflected from a fmooth and polifhed body; for a Gem of Vincent's rock, Diamond, and clear glafs, attract when they are rough; but not fo powerfully and quickly, becaufe they are not fo readily cleanfed from extraneous moifture on the furface, and are not rubbed equally fo as to be copioufly refolved at that part. Nor does the fun by its own beams of light and its rays, which are of capital import-ance in nature, attract bodies in this way; and yet the herd of philo-fophizers confiders that humours are attracted by the fun, when it is only denfer humours that are being turned into thinner, into fpirit and air; and fo by the motion of effufion they afcend into the upper regions, or the attenuated exhalations are raifed up from the denfer air. Nor does it feem to take place from the effluvia attenuating the air, fo that bodies impelled by the denfer air pene-trate towards the fource of the rarefaction; in this cafe both hot and flaming bodies would alfo allure other bodies; but not even the lighteft chaff, or any verforium moves towards a flame. If there is a flow and rufh of air towards the body, how can a fmall diamond of the fize of a pea fummon towards itfelf fo much air, that it feizes hold of a biggifh long body placed in equilibrio (the air about one or other very fmall part of an end being attracted)? It ought alfo to have ftopped or moved more flowly, before it came into contact with the body, efpecially if the piece of amber was rather broad and flat, from the accumulation of air on the furface of the amber and its flowing back again. If it is becaufe the effluvia are thinner, and denfer vapours come in return, as in breathing, then the body would rather have had a motion toward the electrick a little while after the beginning of the application; but when electricks which have been rubbed are applied quickly to a verforium then efpecially at once they act on the verforium, and it is attracted more when near them. But if it is becaufe the rarefied
effluvia

effluvia produce a rarefied medium, and on that account bodies are more prone to flip down from a denfer to a more attenuated medium; they might have been carried from the fide in this way or downwards, but not to bodies above them; or the attraction and apprehenfion of contiguous bodies would have been momentary only. But with a fingle friction jet and amber draw and attract bodies to them ftrongly and for a long time, fometimes for the twelfth part of an hour, efpecially in clear weather. But if the mafs of amber be rather large, and the furface polifhed, it attracts without friction. Flint is rubbed and emits by attrition an inflammable matter that turns into fparks and heat. Therefore the denfer effluvia of flint producing fire are very far different from electrical effluvia, which on account of their extreme attenuation do not take fire, nor are fit material for flame. Thofe effluvia are not of the nature of breath, for when emitted they do not propel anything, but are exhaled without fenfible refiftance and touch bodies. They are highly attenuated humours much more fubtile than the ambient air; and in order that they may occur, bodies are required produced from humour and concreted with a confiderable degree of hardnefs. Non-electrick bodies are not refolved into humid effluvia, and thofe effluvia mix with the common and general effluvia of the earth, and are not peculiar. Alfo befides the attraction of bodies, they retain them longer. It is probable therefore that amber does exhale fomething peculiar to ✳ itfelf, which allures bodies themfelves, not the intermediate air. Indeed it plainly does draw the body itfelf in the cafe of a fpherical drop of water ftanding on a dry furface; for a piece of amber applied to it at a fuitable diftance pulls the neareft parts out of their pofition and draws it up into a cone; otherwife, if it were ✳ drawn by means of the air rufhing along, the whole drop would have moved. That it does not attract the air is thus demonftrated: take a very thin wax candle, which makes a very fmall and clear flame; bring up to this, within two digits or any convenient diftance, a piece of amber or jet, a broad flat piece, well prepared ✳ and fkilfully rubbed, fuch a piece of amber as would attract bodies far and wide, yet it does not difturb the flame; which of neceffity would have occurred, if the air was difturbed, for the flame would have followed the current of air. As far as the effluvia are fent out, fo far it allures; but as a body approaches, its motion is accelerated, ftronger forces drawing it; as alfo in the cafe of magneticks and in all natural motion; not by attenuating or by expelling the air, fo that the body moves down into the place of the air which has gone out; for thus it would have allured only and would not have retained; fince it would at firft alfo have repelled approaching bodies juft as it drives the air itfelf; but indeed a particle, be it ever fo fmall, does not avoid the firft application made very quickly after rubbing. An effluvium exhales from amber and is emitted by rubbing : pearls, carnelian, agate, jafper, chalcedony, coral, metals,

and

and other fubftances of that kind, when they are rubbed, produce
no effect.   Is there not alfo fomething which is exhaled from them
by heat and attrition?   Moft truly; but from groffer bodies more
blended with the earthy nature, that which is exhaled is grofs and
* fpent; for even towards very many electricks, if they are rubbed
too hard, there is produced but a weak attraction of bodies, or none
at all; the attraction is beft when the rubbing has been gentle and
very quick; for fo the fineft effluvia are evoked.   The effluvia arife
from the fubtile diffufion of humour, not from exceffive and tur-
bulent violence; efpecially in the cafe of those fubftances which have
been compacted from unctuous matter, which when the atmofphere
is very thin, when the North winds, and amongft us (Englifh) the
Eaft winds, are blowing, have a furer and firmer effect, but during
* South winds and in damp weather, only a weak one; fo that thofe
fubftances which attract with difficulty in clear weather, in thick
weather produce no motion at all; both becaufe in groffer air
lighter fubftances move with greater difficulty; and efpecially
becaufe the effluvia are ftifled, and the furface of the body that has
been rubbed is affected by the fpent humour of the air, and the
effluvia are ftopped at their very ftarting.   On that account in the
cafe of amber, jet, and fulphur, becaufe they do not fo eafily take
up moift air on their furface and are much more plenteoufly fet free,
that force is not fo quickly fuppreffed as in gems, cryftal, glafs,
and fubftances of that kind which collect on their furface the
moifter breath which has grown heavy.   But it may be afked why
does amber allure water, when water placed on its furface removes
its action?   Evidently becaufe it is one thing to fupprefs it at its
* very ftart, and quite another to extinguifh it when it has been
emitted.   So alfo thin and very fine filk, in common language
* *Sarcenet*, placed quickly on the amber, after it has been rubbed,
hinders the attraction of the body; but if it is interpofed in the
intervening fpace, it does not entirely obftruct it.   Moifture alfo
from fpent air, and any breath blown from the mouth, as well as
water put on the amber, immediately extinguifhes its force.   But
* oil, which is light and pure, does not hinder it; for although amber
* be rubbed with a warm finger dipped in oil, ftill it attracts.   But
if that amber, after the rubbing, is moiftened with *aqua vitæ* or
fpirits of wine, it does not attract; for it is heavier than oil, denfer,
and when added to oil finks beneath it.   For oil is light and rare,
and does not refift the moft delicate effluvia.   A breath therefore,
proceeding from a body which had been compacted from humour
or from a watery liquid, reaches the body to be attracted; the body
that is reached is united with the attracting body, and the one body
lying near the other within the peculiar radius of its effluvia makes
one out of two; united, they come together into the clofeft accord,
and this is commonly called attraction.   This unity, according to
the

the opinion of Pythagoras, is the principle of all things, and through participation in it each feveral thing is faid to be one. For fince no action can take place by means of matter unlefs by contact, thefe electricks are not feen to touch, but, as was neceffary, fomething is fent from the one to the other, fomething which may touch clofely and be the beginning of that incitement. All bodies are united and, as it were, cemented together in fome way by moifture; fo that a wet body, when it touches another body, attracts it, if it is fmall. So wet bodies on the furface of water attract wet bodies. But the peculiar electrical effluvia, which are the moft fubtile material of diffufe humour, entice corpufcles. Air (the common effluvium of the earth) not only unites the disjointed parts, but the earth calls bodies back to itfelf by means of the intervening air; other-wife bodies which are in higher places would not fo eagerly make for the earth. Electrical effluvia differ greatly from air; and as air is the effluvium of the earth, fo electricks have their own effluvia and properties, each of them having by reafon of its peculiar effluvia a fingular tendency toward unity, a motion toward its origin and fount, and toward the body emitting the effluvia. But thofe fub-ftances which by attrition emit a grofs or vapourous or aeriform effluvium produce no effect; for either fuch effluvia are alien to the humour (the uniter of all things), or being very like common air are blended with the air and intermingle with the air, wherefore they produce no effect in the air, and do not caufe motions different from thofe fo univerfal and common in nature. In like manner　＊ bodies ftrive to be united and move on the furface of water, juft as the rod C, which is put a little way under water. It is plain

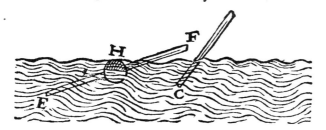

that the rod E F, which floats on the water by reafon of the cork H, and only has its wet end F above the furface of the water, is attracted by the rod C, if the rod C is wet a little above the furface of the water; they are fuddenly united, juft as a drop adjoining a drop is attracted. So a wet thing on the furface of water feeks union with a wet thing, fince the furface of the water is raifed on both; and they immediately flow together, juft like drops or bubbles. But they are in much greater proximity than electricks, and are united by their clammy natures. If, however, the whole rod be dry　＊ above the water, it no longer attracts, but drives away the ftick E F. The fame is feen in thofe bubbles alfo which are made on

water

water. For we fee one drive towards another, and the quicker the nearer they are. Solids are impelled towards folids by the medium of liquid: for example, touch the end of a verforium with the end of a rod on which a drop of water is projecting; as foon as the verforium touches the top of the droplet, immediately it is joined ftrongly by a fwift motion to the body of the rod. So concreted humid things attract when a little refolved into air (the effluvia in the intermediate fpace tending to produce unity); for water has on wet bodies, or on bodies wet with abundant moifture on the top of water, the force of an effluvium. Clear air is a convenient medium for an electrical effluvium excited from concreted humour. Wet bodies projecting above the furface of water (if they are near) run together fo that they may unite; for the furface of the water is raifed around wet fubftances. But a dry thing is not impelled to a wet one, nor a wet to a dry, but feems to run away. For if all is dry above the water, the furface of the water clofe to it does not rife, but fhuns it, the wave finking around a dry thing. So neither does a wet thing move towards the dry rim of a veffel; but it feeks a wet rim. A B is the furface of the water; C D two rods, which

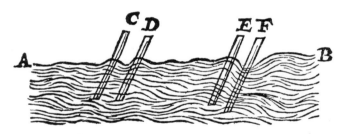

ftand up wet above the water; it is manifeft that the furface of the water is raifed at C and D along with the rods; and therefore the rod C, by reafon of the water ftanding up (which feeks its level and unity), moves with the water to D. On E, on the other hand, a wet rod, the water alfo rifes; but on the dry rod F the furface is depreffed; and as it ftrives to deprefs alfo the wave rifing on E in its neighbourhood, the higher wave at E turns away from F; for it does not fuffer itfelf to be depreffed. All electrical attraction occurs through an intervening humour; fo it is by reafon of humour that all things mutually come together; fluids indeed and aqueous bodies on the furface of water, but concreted things, if they have been refolved into vapour, in air;—in air indeed, the effluvium of electricks being very rare, that it may the better permeate the medium and not impel it by its motion; for if that effluvium had been thick, as that of air, or of the winds, or of faltpetre burnt by fire, as the thick and foul effluvia given out with very great force, from other bodies, or air fet free from humour by heat rufhing out through a pipe (in the inftrument of Hero of Alexandria, defcribed in his book

book *Spiritalia*), then the effluvium would drive everything away, not allure it. But thofe rarer effluvia take hold of bodies and embrace them as if with arms extended, with the electricks to which they are united; and they are drawn to the fource, the effluvia increafing in ftrength with the proximity. But what is that effluvium from cryftal, glafs, and diamond, fince thefe are bodies of confiderable hardnefs and firmly concreted? In order that fuch an effluvium fhould be produced, there is no need of any marked or perceptible flux of the fubftance; nor is it neceffary that the electrick fhould be abraded, or worn away, or deformed. Some odoriferous fubftances are fragrant for many years, exhaling continually, yet are not quickly confumed. Cyprefs wood as long as it is found, and it lafts a very long time indeed, is redolent; as many learned men atteft from experience. Such an electrick only for a moment, when ftimulated by friction, emits powers far more fubtile and more fine beyond all odours; yet fometimes amber, jet, fulphur, when they are fomewhat eafily fet free into vapour, alfo pour out at the fame time an odour; and on this account they allure with the very gentleft rubbing, often even without rubbing; they alfo excite more ftrongly, and retain hold for a longer time, becaufe they have ftronger effluvia and laft longer. But diamond, glafs, rock-cryftal, and numerous others of the harder and firmly concreted gems firft grow warm: therefore at firft they are rubbed longer, and then they alfo attract ftrongly; nor are they otherwife fet free into vapour. Everything rufhes towards electricks excepting flame, and flaming bodies, and the thinneft air. Juft as they do not draw flame, in like manner they do not affect a verforium, if on any fide it is very near to a flame, either the flame of a lamp or of any burning matter. It is manifeft indeed that the effluvia are deftroyed by flame and igneous heat; and therefore they attract neither flame nor bodies very near a flame. For electrical effluvia have the virtue of, and are analogous with, extenuated humour; but they will produce their effect, union and continuity, not by the external impulfe of vapours, not by heat and attenuation of heated bodies, but by their humidity itfelf attenuated into its own peculiar effluvia. Yet they entice fmoke fent out by an extinguifhed light; and the more that fmoke is attenuated in feeking the upper regions, the lefs ftrongly is it turned afide; for things that are too rarefied are not drawn to them; and at length, when it has now almoft vanifhed, it does not incline towards them at all, which is eafily feen againft the light. When in fact the fmoke has paffed into air, it is not moved, as has been demonftrated before. For air itfelf, if fomewhat thin, is not attracted in any way, unlefs on account of fucceeding that which has vacated its place, as in furnaces and fuch-like, where the air is fed in by mechanical devices for drawing it in. Therefore an effluvium refulting from a non-fouling friction, and one which

is

is not changed by heat, but which is its own, caufes union and
cohærency, a prehenfion and a congruence towards its fource, if only
the body to be attracted is not unfitted for motion, either by the
furroundings of the bodies or by its own weight.   To the bodies
therefore of the electricks themfelves fmall bodies are borne.   The
effluvia extend out their virtue—effluvia which are proper and
peculiar to them, and *sui generis,* differing from common air, being
produced from humour, excited by a calorifick motion from attrition
and attenuation.   And as if they were material rays, they hold and
take up chaff, ftraws, and twigs, until they become extinct or vanifh
away : and then they (the corpufcles) being loofed again, attracted
by the earth itself, fall down to the earth.   The difference between
Magneticks and Electricks is that all magneticks run together with
mutual forces ; electricks only allure ; that which is allured is not
changed by an implanted force, but that which has moved up to
 * them voluntarily refts upon them by the law of matter.   Bodies are
borne towards electricks in a ftraight line towards the centre of the
electrick ; a loadftone draws a loadftone directly at the poles only,
in other parts obliquely and tranfverfely, and in this way alfo they
adhere and hang to one another.   Electrical motion is a motion of
aggregation of matter ; magnetical motion is one of difpofition and
conformation.   The globe of the earth is aggregated and cohæres
by itfelf electrically.   The globe of the earth is directed and turned
magnetically ; at the fame time alfo it both cohæres, and in order that
it may be folid, is in its inmoft parts cemented together.

CHAP. III.

Opinions of others on Magnetick Coition,
which they call Attraction.

ISCUSSION having now been made concerning
electricks, the caufes of magnetick coition muft be
fet forth. We fay coition, not attraction. The word
attraction unfortunately crept into magnetick philofophy from the ignorance of the ancients ; for there
feems to be force applied where there is attraction
and an imperious violence dominates. For, if ever there is talk about
magnetick attraction, we underftand thereby magnetick coition,
or a primary running together. Now in truth it will not be ufelefs
here firft briefly to fet forth the views given by others, both the ancient
and

and the more modern writers. Orpheus in his hymns narrates that
iron is attracted by loadſtone as the bride to the arms of her eſpouſed.
Epicurus holds that iron is attracted by a loadſtone juſt as ſtraws by
amber; "and," he adds, " the Atoms and indiviſible particles which
" are given off by the ſtone and by the iron fit one another in ſhape; ſo
" that they eaſily cling to one another; when therefore theſe ſolid
" particles of ſtone or of iron ſtrike againſt one another, then they re-
" bound into ſpace, being brought againſt one another by the way, and
" they draw the iron along with them." But this cannot be the
caſe in the leaſt; ſince ſolid and very denſe ſubſtances interpoſed,
even ſquared blocks of marble, do not obſtruct this power, though
they can ſeparate atoms from atoms; and the ſtone and the iron
would be ſpeedily diſſipated into ſuch profuſe and perpetual ſtreams
of atoms. In the caſe of amber, ſince there is another different
method of attracting, the Epicurean atoms cannot fit one another
in ſhape. Thales, as Ariſtotle writes, *De Anima*, Bk. I., deemed
the loadſtone to be endowed with a ſoul of ſome ſort, becauſe it had
the power of moving and drawing iron towards it. Anaxagoras
alſo held the ſame view. In the *Timæus* of Plato there is an idle
fancy about the efficacy of the ſtone of Hercules. For he ſays that
" all flowings of water, likewiſe the fallings of thunderbolts, and
" the things which are held wonderful in the attraction of Amber,
" and of the Herculean ſtone, are ſuch that in all theſe there is never
" any attraction; but ſince there is no vacuum, the particles drive one
" another mutually around, and when they are diſperſed and con-
" gregated together, they all paſs, each to its proper ſeat, but with
" changed places; and it is, forſooth, on account of theſe inter-
" complicated affections that the effects ſeem to arouſe the wonder in
" him who has rightly inveſtigated them." Galen does not know why
Plato ſhould have ſeen fit to ſelect the theory of circumpulſion
rather than that of attraction (differing almoſt on this point alone
from Hippocrates), though indeed it does not agree in reality with
either reaſon or experiment. Nor indeed is either the air or anything elſe circumpelled; and the bodies themſelves which are
attracted are carried towards the attracting ſubſtance not confuſedly,
or in an orbe. Lucretius, the poet of the Epicurean ſect, ſang his
opinion of it thus :

Firſt, then, know,
Ceaſeleſs effluvia from the magnet flow,—
Effluvia, whoſe ſuperior powers expel
The air that lies between the ſtone and ſteel.
A vacuum formed, the ſteely atoms fly
In a link'd train, and all the void ſupply;
While the whole ring to which the train is join'd
The influence owns, and follows cloſe behind. &c.

Such

Such a reaſon Plutarch alſo alleges in the *Quæſtiones Platonicæ;*
That that ſtone gives off heavy exhalations, whereby the adjacent air,
being impelled along, condenſes that which is in front of it; and
that air, being driven round in an orbe and reverting to the place it
had vacated, drags the iron forcibly along with it.   The following
explanation of the virtues of the loadſtone and of amber is pro-
pounded by Johannes Coſtæus of Lodi.   For he would have it that
" there is mutual work and mutual reſult, and therefore the motion
" is partly due to the attraction of the loadſtone and partly to a
" ſpontaneous movement on the part of the iron :   For as we ſay that
" vapours iſſuing from the loadſtone haſten by their own nature to
" attract the iron, ſo alſo the air repelled by the vapours, whilſt ſeek-
" ing a place for itſelf, is turned back, and when turned back, it
" impels the iron, lifts it up, as it were, and carries it along; the iron
" being of itſelf alſo excited ſomehow.   So by being drawn out and
" by a ſpontaneous motion, and by ſtriking againſt another ſubſtance,
" there is in ſome way produced a compoſite motion, which motion
" would neverthelefs be rightly referred to attraction, becauſe the
" terminus from which this motion invariably begins is the ſame
" terminus at which it ends, which is the characteriſtic proper of an
" attraction."   There is certainly a mutual action, not an operation,
nor does the loadſtone attract in that way; nor is there any impul-
ſion.   But neither is there that origination of the motion by the
vapours, and the turning of them back, which opinion of Epicurus
has ſo often been quoted by others.   Galen errs in his *De Naturalibus Facultatibus*, Book I., chap. 14, when he expreſſes the view
that whatever agents draw out either the venom of ſerpents or darts
alſo exhibit the ſame power as the loadſtone.   Now of what ſort
may be the attraction of ſuch medicaments (if indeed it may be
called attraction) we ſhall conſider elſewhere.   Drugs againſt poiſons
or darts have no relation to, no ſimilitude with, the action of magnetical bodies.   The followers of Galen (who hold that purgative
medicaments attract becauſe of ſimilitude of ſubſtance) ſay that
bodies are attracted on account of ſimilitude, not identity, of ſubſtance; wherefore the loadſtone draws iron, but iron does not draw
iron.   But we declare and prove that this happens in primary
bodies, and in thoſe bodies that are pretty cloſely related to them
and eſpecially like in kind one to another, on account of their
identity; wherefore alſo loadſtone draws loadſtone and likewiſe
iron iron; every really true earth draws earth; and iron fortified
by a loadſtone within the orbe of whoſe virtue it is placed draws
iron more ſtrongly than it does the loadſtone.   Cardan aſks why
no other metal is attracted by any other ſtone; becauſe (he
replies) no metal is ſo cold as iron; as if indeed cold were the
cauſe of the attraction, or as if iron were much colder than
lead, which neither follows nor is deflected towards a loadſtone.
But

But that is a chilly ftory, and worfe than an old woman's tale. So alfo is the notion that the loadftone is alive and that iron is its food. But how does the loadftone feed on the iron, when the filings in which it is kept are neither confumed nor become lighter? Cornelius Gemma, *Cofmographia*, Bk. X., holds that the loadftone draws iron to it by infenfible rays, to which opinion he conjoins a ftory of a fucking fifh and another about an antelope. Guilielmus Puteanus derives it, " not from any property of the whole fubftance " unknown to any one and which cannot be demonftrated in any way " (as Galen, and after him almoft all the phyficians, have afferted), but " from the effential nature of the thing itfelf, as if moving from the " firft by itfelf, and, as it were, by its own moft powerful nature and " from that innate temperament, as it were an inftrument, which its " fubftance, its effective nature ufes in its operations, or a fecondary " caufe and deprived of its intermediary "; fo the loadftone attracts the iron not without a phyfical caufe and for the fake of fome good. But there is no fuch thing in other fubftances fpringing from fome material form ; unlefs it were primary, which he does not recognize. But certes good is fhown to the loadftone by the ftroke of the iron (as it were, affociation with a friend) ; yet it cannot either be difcovered or conceived how that difpofition may be the inftrument of form. For what can temperament do in magnetical motions, which muft be compared with the fixed, definite, conftant motions of the ftars, at great diftances in cafe of the interpofition of very denfe and thick bodies ? To Baptifta Porta the loadftone feems a fort of mixture of ftone and iron, in fuch a way that it is an iron ftone or ftony iron. " But I think " (he fays) " the Loadftone is " a mixture of ftone and iron, as an iron ftone, or a ftone of iron. " Yet do not think the ftone is fo changed into iron, as to lofe its own " Nature, nor that the iron is fo drowned in the ftone, but it preferves " itfelf; and whilft one labours to get the victory of the other, the " attraction is made by the combat between them. In that body " there is more of the ftone than of iron ; and therefore the iron, " that it may not be fubdued by the ftone, defires the force and com- " pany of iron ; that being not able to refift alone, it may be able by " more help to defend itfelf. . . . The Loadftone draws not ftones, " becaufe it wants them not, for there is ftone enough in the body of " it ; and if one Loadftone draw another, it is not for the ftone, but " for the iron that is in it." As if in the loadftone the iron were a diftinct body and not mixed up as the other metals in their ores! And that thefe, being fo mixed up, fhould fight with one another, and fhould extend their quarrel, and that in confequence of the battle auxiliary forces fhould be called in, is indeed abfurd. But iron itfelf, when excited by a loadftone, feizes iron no lefs ftrongly than the loadftone. Therefore thofe fights, feditions, and con- fpiracies in the ftone, as if it were nurfing up perpetual quarrels,

whence

whence it might feek auxiliary forces, are the ravings of a babbling old woman, not the inventions of a diftinguifhed mage.   Others have lit upon fympathy as the caufe.   There may be fellow-feeling, and yet the caufe is not fellow-feeling; for no paffion can rightly be faid to be an efficient caufe.   Others hold likenefs of fubftance, many others infenfible rays as the caufe; men who alfo in very many cafes often wretchedly mifufe rays, which were firft introduced in the natural fciences by the mathematicians.   More eruditely does Scaliger fay that the iron moves toward the loadftone as if toward its parent, by whofe fecret principles it may be perfected, juft as the earth toward its centre.   The Divine Thomas does not differ much from him, when in the 7th book of his *Phyfica* he difcuffes the reafons of motions.   " In another way," he fays, " it may be " faid to attract a thing, becaufe it moves it to itfelf by altering it in " fome way, from which alteration it happens that when altered it " moves according to its pofition, and in this manner the loadftone is " faid to attract iron.   For as the parent moves things whether heavy " or light, in as far as it gives them a form, by means of which they " are moved to their place; fo alfo the loadftone gives a certain " quality to the iron, in accordance with which it moves towards it." This by no means ill-conceived opinion this moft learned man fhortly afterwards endeavoured to confirm by things which had obtained little credence refpecting the loadftone and the adverfe forces of garlick.   Cardinal Cufan alfo is not to be defpifed. " Iron has," he fays, " in the loadftone a certain principle of its " own effluence; and whilft the loadftone by its own prefence excites " the heavy and ponderous iron, the iron is borne by a wonderful " yearning, even above the motion of nature (by which in accordance " with its weight it ought to tend downwards) and moves upwards, " in uniting itfelf with its own principle.   For if there were not in " the iron a certain natural foretafte of the loadftone itfelf, it would " not move to the loadftone any more than to any other ftone; and " unlefs there were in the ftone a greater inclination for iron than for " copper, there would not be that attraction."   Such are the opinions expreffed about the loadftone attracting (or the general fenfe of each), all dubious and untruftworthy.   But thofe caufes of the magnetical motions, which in the fchools of the Philofophers are referred to the four elements and the prime qualities, we relin- quifh to the moths and the worms.

CHAP.

CHAP. IIII.

On Magnetick Force & Form, what it is; and on the
cauſe of the Coition.

RELINQUISHING the opinions of others on the attraction of loadſtone, we ſhall now ſhow the reaſon of that coition and the tranſlatory nature of that motion. Since there are really two kinds of bodies, which ſeem to allure bodies with motions manifeſt to our ſenſes, Electricks and Magneticks, the Electricks produce the tendency by natural effluvia from humour; the Magneticks by agencies due to form, or rather by the prime forces. This form is unique, and particular, not the formal cauſe of the Peripateticks, or the ſpecifick in mixtures, or the ſecondary form; not the propagator of generating bodies, but the form of the primary and chief ſpheres and of thoſe parts of them which are homogeneous and not corrupted, a ſpecial entity and exiſtence, which we may call a primary and radical and aſtral form; not the primary form of Ariſtotle, but that unique form, which preſerves and diſpoſes its own proper ſphere. There is one ſuch in each ſeveral globe, in the Sun, the moon, and the ſtars; one alſo in the earth, which is that true magnetick potency which we call the primary vigour. Wherefore there is a magnetick nature peculiar to the earth and implanted in all its truer parts in a primary and aſtoniſhing manner; this is neither derived nor produced from the whole heaven by ſympathy or influence or more occult qualities, nor from any particular ſtar; for there is in the earth a magnetick vigour of its own, juſt as in the ſun and moon there are forms of their own, and a ſmall portion of the moon ſettles itſelf in moon-manner toward its termini and form; and a piece of the ſun to the ſun, juſt as a loadſtone to the earth and to a ſecond loadſtone by inclining itſelf and alluring in accordance with its nature. We muſt conſider therefore about the earth what magnetical bodies are, and what is a magnet; then alſo about the truer parts of it, which are magnetical, and how they are affected as a reſult of the coition. A body which is attracted by an electrick is not changed by it, but remains unſhaken and unchanged, as it was before, nor does it excel any the more in virtue. A loadſtone draws magnetical ſubſtances, which eagerly acquire power from its ſtrength, not in their extremities only, but in their inward parts and their very marrow. For when a rod of iron is laid hold of, it is magnetically excited in the end by which it is laid hold of, and that

K   force

force penetrates even to the other extremity, not through its furface only, but through the interior and all through the middle. Electrical bodies have material and corporeal effluvia. Is any fuch magnetical effluvium given off, whether corporeal or incorporeal? or is nothing at all given off that fubfifts? If it really has a body, that body muft be thin and fpiritual, fince it is neceffary that it fhould be able to enter into iron. Or what fort of an exhalation is it that comes from lead, when quickfilver which is bright and fluid is bound together by the odour merely and vapour of the lead, and remains, as it were, a firm metal? But even gold, which is exceedingly folid and denfe, is reduced to a powder by the thin vapour of lead. Or, feeing that, as the quickfilver has entrance into gold, fo the magnetical odour has entrance into the fubftance of the iron, how does it change it in its effential property, although no change is perceptible to our fenfes in the bodies themfelves? For without ingreffion into the body, the body is not changed, as the Chemifts not incorrectly teach. But if indeed thefe things refulted from a material ingreffion, then if ftrong and denfe and thick fubftances had been interpofed between the bodies, or if magnetical fubftances had been inclofed in the centres of the moft folid and the denfeft bodies, the iron particles would not have fuffered anything from the load-ftone. But none the lefs they ftrive to come together and are changed. Therefore there is no fuch conception and origin of the magnetick powers; nor do the very minute portions of the ftone exift, which have been wrongly imagined to exift by Baptifta Porta, aggregated, as it were, into hairs, and arifing from the rubbing of the ftone which, fticking to the iron, conftitute its ftrength. Electrick effluvia are not only impeded by any denfe matter, but alfo in like manner by flames, or if a fmall flame is near, they do not allure. But as iron is not hindered by any obftacle from receiving force or motion from a loadftone, fo it will pafs through the midft of flames to the body of the loadftone and adhære to the ftone. Let there be a flame or a candle near the ftone; bring up a fhort piece of iron wire, and when it has come
* near, it will penetrate through the midft of the flames to the ftone; and a verforium turns towards the loadftone nor more flowly nor lefs eagerly through the midft of flames than through open air. So flames interpofed do not hinder the coition. But if the iron itfelf became heated by a great heat, it is demonftrable that it would not be attracted. Bring a ftrongly ignited rod of iron near a magnetized
* verforium; the verforium remains fteady and does not turn towards fuch iron; but it immediately turns towards it, fo foon as it has loft fomewhat of its heat. When a piece of iron has been touched by
* a loadftone, if it be placed in a hot fire until it is perfectly red hot and remain in the fire fome confiderable time, it will lofe that mag-netick ftrength it had acquired. Even a loadftone itfelf through a
longifh

longiſh ſtay in the fire, loſes the powers of attracting implanted and
innate in it, and any other magnetick powers.   And although
certain veins of loadſtone exhale when burnt a dark vapour of a
black colour, or of a ſulphurous foul odour, yet that vapour was
not the ſoul, or the cauſe of its attraction of iron (as Porta thinks),
nor do all loadſtones whilſt they are being baked or burnt ſmell of
or exhale ſulphur.   It is acquired as a ſort of inborn defect from a
rather impure mine or matrix.   Nor does anything analogous penetrate into the iron from that material corporeal cauſe, ſince the iron
conceives the power of attracting and verticity from the loadſtone,
even if glaſs or gold or any other ſtone be interpoſed.   Then alſo
caſt iron acquires the power of attracting iron, and verticity, from
the verticity of the earth, as we ſhall afterwards plainly demonſtrate
in *Direction*.   But fire deſtroys the magnetick virtues in a ſtone, not
becauſe it takes away any parts ſpecially attractive, but becauſe the
conſuming force of the flame mars by the demolition of the material
the form of the whole ; as in the human body the primary faculties
of the ſoul are not burnt, but the charred body remains without
faculties.   The iron indeed may remain after the burning is completed and is not changed into aſh or ſlag ; neverthelefs (as Cardan
not inaptly ſays) burnt iron is not iron, but ſomething placed outſide its nature until it is reduced.   For juſt as by the rigour of the
ſurrounding air water is changed from its nature into ice ; ſo iron,
glowing in fire, is deſtroyed by the violent heat, and has its nature
confuſed and perturbed ; wherefore alſo it is not attracted by a
loadſtone, and even loſes that power of attracting in whatever way
acquired, and acquires another verticity when, being, as it were, born
again, it is impregnated by a loadſtone or the earth, or when its
form is revived, not having been dead but confuſed, concerning
which many things are manifeſt in the change of verticity. Wherefore Fracaſtorio does not confirm his opinion, that the iron is not
altered ; " for if it were altered," he ſays, " by the form of the load-
" ſtone, the form of the iron would have been ſpoiled."   This alteration is not generation, but the reſtitution and reformation of a
confuſed form.   There is not therefore anything corporeal which
comes from the loadſtone or which enters the iron, or which is
ſent back from the iron when it is ſtimulated ; but loadſtone dif-
poſes loadſtone by its primary form ; iron, however, which is
cloſely related to it, loadſtone at the ſame time recalls to its con-
formate ſtrength, and ſettles it ; on account of which it ruſhes to
the loadſtone and eagerly conforms itſelf to it (the forces of each in
harmony bringing them together).   The coition alſo is not vague
or confuſed, not a violent inclination of body to body, no raſh and
mad congruency ; no violence is here applied to the bodies ; there
are no ſtrifes or diſcords ; but there is that concord (without which
the univerſe would go to pieces), that analogy, namely, of the

perfect

perfect and homogeneous parts of the spheres of the universe to the whole, and a mutual concurrency of the principal forces in them, tending to soundness, continuity, position, direction, and to unity. Wherefore in the case of such wonderful action and such a stupendous implanted vigour (diverse from other natures) the opinion of Thales of Miletus was not very absurd, nor was it downright madness, in the judgment of Scaliger, for him to grant the loadstone a soul; for the loadstone is incited, directed, and orbitally moved by this force, which is all in all, and, as will be made clear afterwards, all in every part ; and it seems to be very like a soul. For the power of moving itself seems to point to a soul; and the supernal bodies, which are also celestial, divine, as it were, are thought by some to be animated, because they move with admirable order. If two loadstones be set one over against the other, each in a boat, on the surface of water, they do not immediately run together, but first they turn towards one another, or the lesser conforms to the greater, by moving itself in a somewhat circular manner, and at length, when they are disposed according to their nature, they run together. In smelted iron which has not been excited by a magnet there is no need for such an apparatus ; since it has no verticity, excepting what is adventitious and acquired, and that not stable and confirmed (as is the case with loadstone, even if the iron has been smelted from the best loadstone), on account of the confusion of the parts by fire when it flowed as a liquid ; it suddenly acquires polarity and natural aptitude by the presence of the loadstone, by a powerful mutation, and by a conversion into a perfect magnet, and by an absolute metamorphosis ; and it flies to the body of the magnet as if it were a real piece of loadstone. For a loadstone has no power, nor can a perfect loadstone do anything which iron when excited by loadstone cannot perform, even when it has not been touched but only placed in its vicinity. For when first it is within the orbe of virtue of the loadstone, though it may be some distance away, yet it is immediately changed, and has a renovated form, formerly indeed dormant and inert in body, now lively and strong, which will be clearly apparent in the demonstrations of *Direction*. So the magnetick coition is a motion of the loadstone and of the iron, not an action of one ; an ἐντελέχεια of each, not ἔργον ; a συνεντελέχεια or conjoint action, rather than a sympathy. There is properly no such thing as magnetick antipathy. For the flight and declination of the ends, or an entire turning about, is an action of each towards unity by the conjoint action and συνεντελέχεια of both. It has therefore newly put on the form, and on account of this being roused, it then, in order that it may more surely acquire it, rushes headlong on the loadstone, not with curves and turnings, as a loadstone to a loadstone. For since in a loadstone both verticity and the power disponent have existed through many ages, or from the very beginnings,

have

have been inborn and confirmed, and alfo the fpecial form of the terreftrial globe cannot eafily be changed by another loadftone, as iron is changed ; it happens from the conftant nature of each, that one has not the fudden power over another of changing its verticity, but that they can only mutually come to agreement with each other.   Again, iron which has been excited by a load-   ✱ ftone, if that iron on account of obftacles fhould not be able to turn round immediately in accordance with its nature, as happens with a verforium, is laid hold of, when a loadftone approaches, on either fide or at either end.   Becaufe, juft as it can implant, fo it can fuddenly change the polarity and turn about the formal energies to any part whatever.   So varioufly can iron be transformed when its form is adventitious and has not yet been long refident in the metal.   In the cafe of iron, on account of the fufion of the fubftance when magnetick ore or iron is fmelted, the virtue of its primary form, diftinct before, is now confufed ; but an entire loadftone placed near it again fets up its primal activity ; its adjufted and arranged form joins its allied ftrength with the loadftone ; and both mutually agree and are leagued together magnetically in all their motions towards unity, and whether joined by bodily contact or adjufted within the orbe, they are one and the fame.   For when iron is fmelted out of its own ore, or fteel (the more noble kind of iron) out of its ore, that is, out of loadftone, the material is loofed by the force of the fire, and flows away, and iron as well as fteel flow out from their drofs and are feparated from it ; and the drofs is either fpoiled by the force of the fire and rendered ufelefs, or is a kind of dregs of a certain imperfection and of mixture in the prominent parts of the earth.   The material therefore is a purified one, in which the metallick parts, which are now mixed up by the melting, fince thofe fpecial forces of its form are confufed and uncertain, by the approach of a loadftone are called back to life, as if to a kind of difponent form and integrity.   The material is thus awakened and moves together into unity, the bond of the univerfe and the effential for its confervation.   On this account and by the purging of the material into a cleaner body, the loadftone gives to the iron a greater force of attracting than there is in itfelf.   For if iron duft   ✱ or an iron nail be placed over a large loadftone, a piece of iron joined to it takes away the filings and nail from the loadftone and retains them fo long as it is near the loadftone ; wherefore iron attracts iron more than loadftone does, if it have been conformed by a loadftone and remains within the orbe of its communicated form.   A piece of iron even, fkilfully placed near the pole of a load-ftone, lifts up more than the loadftone.   Therefore the material of its own ore is better, and by the force of fire fteel and iron are re-purged ; and they are again impregnated by the loadftone with its own forms ; therefore they move towards it by a fpontaneous

approach

approach as foon as they have entered within the orbe of the magnetick forces, becaufe they were poffeffed by it before, connected and
united with it in a perfect union; & they have immediately an abfolute continuity within that orbe, & have been joined on account of
their harmony, though their bodies may have been disjoined.   For
the iron is not taken poffeffion of and allured by material effluvia,
after the manner of electricks, but only by the immaterial action of
its form or an incorporeal progreffion, which in a piece of iron as its
fubject acts and is conceived, as it were, in a continuous homogeneous body, and does not need more open ways.   Therefore
(though the moft folid fubftances be interpofed) the iron is ftill
moved and attracted, and by the prefence of loadftone the iron
moves and attracts the loadftone itfelf, and by mutual forces a concurrency is made towards unity, which is commonly called attraction of the iron.   But thofe formal forces pafs out and are united to
one another by meeting together; a force alfo, when conceived in
the iron, begins to flow out without delay.   But Julius Scaliger,
who by other examples contends that this theory is abfurd, makes
in his 344th Exercife a great miftake.   For the virtues of primary
bodies are not to be compared with bodies formed from and mixed
with them.   He would now have been able (had he been ftill alive)
to difcern the nature of effufed forms in the chapter on forms
effufed by fpherical magneticks.   But if iron is injured fomewhat
by ruft, it is affected either only flightly or not at all by the ftone.
For the metal is fpoiled when eaten away and deformed by external
injuries or by lapfe of time (juft as has been faid about the loadftone), and it lofes its prime qualities which are conjoined to its form;
or, being worn out by age, retains them in a languid and weak condition; indeed it cannot be properly re-formed, when it has been
corrupted.   But a powerful and frefh loadftone attracts found and
clean pieces of iron, and thofe pieces of iron (when they have conceived ftrength) have a powerful attraction for other iron wires and
iron nails, not only one at a time, but even fucceffively one behind
another, three, four or five, end to end, fticking and hanging in
order like a chain.   The loadftone, however, would not attract
the laft one following in fuch a row, if there were no nails between.
A loadftone placed as at A draws a nail or a bar B; fimilarly behind B it draws C; and after C, D.   But the nails B and C being

removed, the loadftone A, if it remain at the fame diftance, does not
raife the nail D into the air.   This occurs for this reafon : becaufe
in the cafe of a continuous row of nails the prefence of the loadftone
A, befides its own powers, raifes the magnetick natures of the iron
works B and C, and makes them, as it were, forces auxiliary to itfelf.
But B and C, like a continuous magnetical body, extend as far as

D

D the forces by which D is taken and conformed, though they are weaker than thofe which C receives from B. And thofe iron nails indeed from that contaĉt only, and from the prefence of the load-ftone even without contaĉt, acquire powers which they retain in their own bodies, as will be demonftrated moft clearly in the paffage *on Direĉtion*. For not only whilft the ftone is prefent does the iron affume thefe powers, and take them, as it were, vicarioufly from the ftone, as Themiftius lays down in his 8th book on Phyficks. The beft iron, when it has been melted down (fuch is fteel), is allured by a loadftone from a greater diftance, is raifed though of greater weight, is held more firmly, affumes ftronger powers than the common and lefs expenfive, becaufe it is caft from a better ore or loadftone, imbued with better powers. But what is made from more impure ore turns out weaker and is moved more feebly. As to Fracaftorio's ftatement that he faw a piece of loadftone draw a loadftone by one of its faces, but not iron ; by another face iron, but not loadftone ; by another both ; which he fays is an indication that in one part there is more of the loadftone, in another more of the iron, in another both equally, whence arifes that diverfity of attraĉtion ; it is moft incorreĉt and badly obferved on the part of Fracaftorio, who did not know how to apply fkilfully loadftone to loadftone. A loadftone draws iron and alfo a loadftone, if both are fuitably arranged and free and unreftrained. That is removed more quickly from its pofition and place which is lighter ; for the heavier bodies are in weight, the more they refift ; but the lighter both moves itfelf to meet the heavier and is allured by the other.

CHAP. V.

How the Power dwells in the *Loadftone*.

THAT a loadftone attraĉts loadftone, iron and other magnetical bodies, has been fhown above in the previous book, and alfo with what ftrength the mag-netick coition is ordered ; but now we muft inquire how that vigour is difpofed in a magnetick fubftance. And indeed an analogy muft be inferred from a large loadftone. Any magnetick fubftance joins itfelf with a load-ftone ftrongly, if the loadftone itfelf is ftrong ; but more weakly, when it is fomewhat imperfeĉt or has been weakened by fome flaw. A loadftone does not draw iron equally well with every part; or a magnetick fubftance does not approach every part of a loadftone alike ; becaufe a loadftone has its points, that is its true poles, in which an exceptional virtue excels. Parts nearer the pole are

ftronger

ftronger, thofe far away more weak, and yet in all the power is in a certain way equal. The poles of a terrella are A, B; the æquinoctial is C, D. At A and B the alluring force feems greateft.

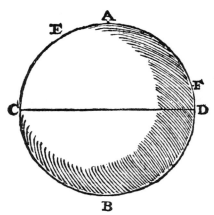

At C and D there is no force alluring magnetick ends to the body, for the forces tend toward both poles. But direction is powerful on the æquator. At C, D, the diftances are equal from both poles; therefore iron which is at C, D, when it is allured in contrary ways, does not adhære with conftancy; but it remains and is joined to the ftone, if only it incline to the one or other fide. At E there is a greater power of alluring than at F, becaufe E is nearer the pole. This is not fo becaufe there is really greater virtue refiding at the pole, but fince all the parts are united in the whole, they direct their forces towards the pole. From the forces flowing from the plane of the æquinoctial towards the pole, the power increafes. A fixed verticity exifts at the pole, fo long as the loadftone remains

★ whole; if it is divided or broken, the verticity obtains other pofitions in the parts into which it is divided. For the verticity always changes in confequence of any change in the mafs, and for this caufe, if the terrella be divided from A to B, fo that there are two ftones, the poles will not be A, B, in the divided parts, but F, G, and H, I.

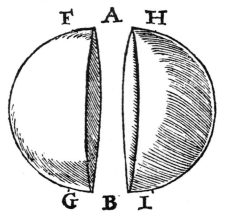
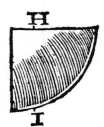

Thefe

Although thefe ftones now are in agreement with one another, fo that F would not feek H, yet if A was previoufly the boreal pole, F is now boreal, and H alfo boreal; for the verticity is not changed (as Baptifta Porta incorrectly affirms in the fourth chapter of his feventh book); fince, though F and H do not agree, fo that the one would incline to the other, yet both turn to the fame point of the horizon. If the hemifphere H I be divided into two quadrants, the one pole takes up its pofition in H, the other in I. The whole mafs of the ftone, as I have faid, retains the fite of its vertex conftant; and any part of the ftone, before it was cut out from the block, might have been the pole or vertex. But concerning this more under *Direction*. It is important now to comprehend and to keep firmly in mind that the vertices are ftrong on account of the force of the whole, fo that (the command being, as it were, divided by the æquinoctial) all the forces on one fide tend towards the north; but thofe of an oppofite way towards the fouth, fo long as the parts are united, as in the following demonftration.

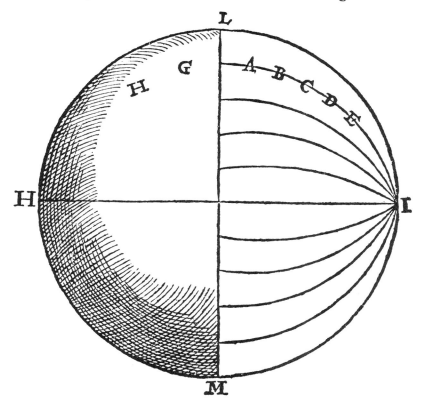

For fo, by an infinite number of curves from every point of the æquator dividing the fphere into two equal parts, and from every point of the furface from the æquator towards the North, and from the æquator towards the Southern pole, the whole force tends afunder toward the poles. So the verticity is from the æquinoctial

L   circle

circle towards the pole in each direction. Such is the power repofed in the undivided ftone. From A vigour is fent to B, from A, B, to C, from A, B, C, to D, and from them likewife to E. In like manner from G to H, and fo forth, as long as the whole is united. But if a piece A B be cut out (although it is near the æquator), yet it will be as ftrong in its magnetical actions as C D or D E, if torn away from the whole in equal quantity. For no part excels in fpecial worth in the whole mafs except by what is owing to the other adjoining parts by which an abfolute and perfect whole is attained.

Diagram of Magnetick Vigour,
tranfmitted from the plane of the Æquator
to the periphery of the terrella,
or of the earth.

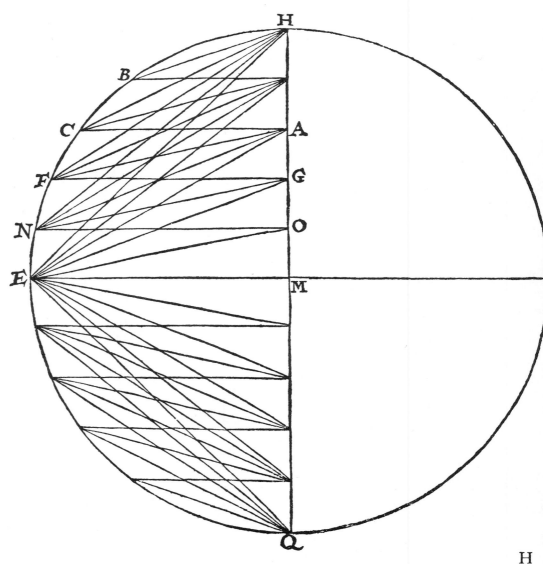

H E Q is a terrella, E a pole, M the centre, H M Q the æquinoctial plane. From every point of the æquinoctial plane vigour extends to the periphery, but by various methods; for from A the formal force is tranfmitted towards C, F, N, E, and to every point from C up to E, the pole; but not towards B; fo neither from G towards C. The power of alluring is not ftrengthened in the part F H G from that which is in G M F E, but F G H increafes the force in the eminence F E. So no force rifes from the internal parts, from the lines parallel to the Axis above thofe parallels, but always inwards from the parallels to the pole. From every point of the plane of the equator force proceeds to the pole E, but the point F has its powers only from G H, and N from O H; but the pole E is ftrengthened from the whole plane H Q. Wherefore in it the mighty power excels (juft as in a palace); but in the intermediate intervals (as in F) only fo much force of alluring is exerted as the portion H G of the plane can contribute.

CHAP. VI.

How magnetick pieces of Iron and fmaller
loadftones conform themfelves to a terrella & to
the earth itfelf, and by them are
difpofed.

COITION of thofe bodies which are divided, and do not naturally cohære, if they are free, occurs through another kind of motion. A terrella fends out in an orbe its powers in proportion to its vigour and quality. But when iron or any other magnetick of convenient magnitude comes within its orbe of virtue, it is allured; but the nearer it comes to the body, the more quickly it runs up to it. They move towards the magnet, not as to a centre, nor towards its centre. For they only do this in the cafe of the poles themfelves, when namely that which is being allured, and the pole of the loadftone, and its centre, are in the fame ftraight line. But in the intervening fpaces they tend obliquely, juft as is evident in the following figure, in which it is fhown how the influence is extended to the adjoining magneticks within the orbe; in the cafe of the poles ftraight out.

The

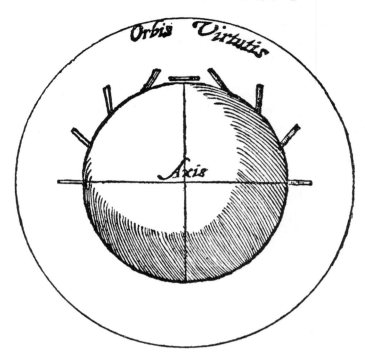

The nearer the parts are to the æquinoctial, the more obliquely are magneticals allured; but the parts nearer the poles appeal more directly, at the poles quite straight. The principle of the turning of all loadstones, of those which are round and those which are long, is the same, but in the case of the long ones the experiment is easier. For in whatever form they are the verticity exists, and there are poles; but on account of bad and unequal form, they are often hindered by certain evils. If the stone were long, the vertex is at the ends, not on the sides; it allures more strongly at the vertex. For the parts bring together stronger forces to the pole in right lines than oblique. So the stone and the earth conform their magnetick motions by their nature.

CHAP. VII.

On the Potency of the Magnetick Virtue, and on
its nature capable of spreading out into an orbe.

ROM about a magnetical body the virtue magnetical is poured out on every side around in an orbe; around a terrella; in the case of other shapes of stones, more confusedly and unevenly. But yet there exists in nature no orbe or permanent or essential virtue spread through the air, but a magnet
only

only excites magneticks at a convenient diftance from it. And as light comes in an inftant (as the opticians teach), fo much more quickly is the magnetick vigour prefent within the limits of its ftrength; and becaufe its activity is much more fubtile than light, and does not confent with a non-magnetick fubftance, it has no intercourfe with air, water, or any non-magnetick; nor does it move a magnetick with any motion by forces rufhing upon it, but being prefent in an inftant, it invites friendly bodies. And as light ftrikes an object, fo a loadftone ftrikes a magnetick body and excites it. And juft as light does not remain in the air above vapours and effluvia, and is not reflected from thofe fpaces, fo neither is the magnetick ray held in air or water. The appearances of things are apprehended in an inftant in mirrors and in the eye by means of light; fo the magnetick virtue feizes upon magneticks. Without the more intangible and fhining bodies, the appearances of things are not feized or reflected; fo without magnetical objects the magnetick power is not perceived, nor are the forces thus conceived fent back again to the magnetick fubftance. In this, however, the magnetick power excels light, in that it is not hindered by any opaque or folid fubftance, but proceeds freely, and extends its forces on every fide. In a terrella and globe-fhaped loadftone the magnetick power is extended outfide the body in an orbe; in a longer one, however, not in an orbe, but it is extended in an ambit conformably to the fhape of the ftone. As in the fomewhat long ftone A, the vigour is

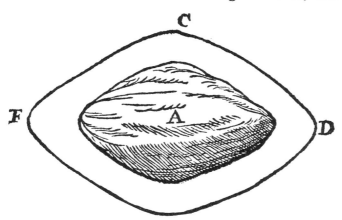

extended to the ambient limit F C D, equidiftant on every fide from the ftone A.

CHAP. VIII.

On the geography of the Earth,
and of the Terrella.

DESIRING that what follows may be better understood, we muft now fay fomething alfo about magnetick circles and limits.   Aftronomers, in order to
underftand and obferve methodically the motion
of the planets and the revolution of the heavens,
and to defcribe with more accuracy the celeftial
attire of the fixed ftars, fettled upon certain circles and definite
limits in the fky (which geographers alfo imitate), fo that the
varied face of the earth and the beauty of its diftricts might be
delineated.   But we, in a way differing from them, recognize thofe
limits and circles, and have found very many fixed by nature, not
merely conceived by the imagination, both in the earth and in our
terrella.   The earth they mark out chiefly by means of the æquator
and the poles; and thofe limits indeed have been arranged and
marked out by nature.   The meridians alfo indicate ftraight paths
from pole to pole through diftinct points on the æquator; by which
way the magnetick virtue directs its courfe and moves.   But the
tropics and arctic circles, as alfo the parallels, are not natural limits
placed on the earth; but all parallel circles indicate a certain agreement of the lands fituated in the fame latitude, or diametrically
oppofite.   All thefe the Mathematicians ufe for convenience, painting them on globes and maps.   In like manner alfo in a terrella all
thefe are required; not, however, in order that its exterior appearance may be geographically delineated, fince the loadftone may be
perfect, even, and uniform on all fides.   And there are no upper
and lower parts in the earth, nor are there in a terrella; unlefs
perchance fome one confiders thofe parts fuperior
which are in the periphery, and thofe inferior which are fituated more towards the centre.

CHAP. IX.

On the Æquinoctial Circle of the Earth
and of a Terrella.

S conceived by aftronomers the æquinoctial circle is equidiftant from both poles, cutting the world in the middle, meafures the motions of their *primum mobile* or tenth fphere, and is named the zone of the *primum mobile.* It is called æquinoctial, becaufe when the fun ftands in it (which muft happen twice in the year) the days are equal to the nights. That circle is alfo fpoken of as *æquidialis*, wherefore it is called by the Greeks ἰσημερινός. In like manner it is alfo properly called Æquator, becaufe it divides the whole frame of the earth between the poles into equal parts. So alfo an æquator may be rightly affigned to a terrella, by which its power is naturally divided, and by the plane of which permeating through its centre, the whole globe is divided into equal parts both in quantity and ftrength (as if by a tranfverfe feptum) between verticities on both fides imbued with equal vigour.

CHAP. X.

Magnetick Meridians of the Earth.

ERIDIANS have been thought out by the geographer, by means of which he might both diftinguifh the longitude and meafure the latitude of each region. But the magnetick meridians are infinite, running in the fame direction alfo, through fixed and oppofite limits on the æquator, and through the poles themfelves. On them alfo the magnetick latitude is meafured, and declinations are reckoned from them; and the fixed direction in them tends to the poles, unlefs it varies from fome defect and the magnetick is difturbed from the right way. What is commonly called a magnetick meridian is not really magnetick, nor is it really a meridian, but it is underftood to pafs through the termini of the variation on the horizon. The variation is a depraved deviation from a meridian, nor is it fixed and conftant in various places on any meridian.

CHAP.

CHAP. XI.

Parallels.

N parallel circles the fame ftrength and equal power are perceived everywhere, when various magneticks are placed on one and the fame parallel either on the earth or on a terrella. For they are diftant from the poles by equal intervals and have equal tendencies of declination, and they are attracted and held, and they come together with like forces; juft as thofe regions which are fituated under the fame parallel, even if they differ in longitude, yet we fay poffefs the fame quantity of daylight and a climate equally tempered.

CHAP. XII.

The Magnetick Horizon.

ORIZON is the name given to the great circle, feparating the things which are feen from thofe which are not feen; fo that a half part of the heaven always is open and eafily feen by us, half is always hidden. This feems fo to us on account of the great diftance of the ftar-bearing orbe : yet the difference is as great as may arife from the ratio of the femi-diameter of the earth compared with the femi-diameter of the ftarry heaven, which difference is in fact not perceived by our fenfes. We maintain, however, that the magnetick horizon is a plane level throughout touching the earth or a terrella in the place of fome one region, with which plane the femi-diameter, whether of the earth or of the terrella, produced to the place of the region, makes right angles on every fide. Such a plane is to be confidered in the earth itfelf and alfo in the terrella, for magnetick proofs and demonftrations. For we confider the bodies themfelves only, not the general appearances of the world. Therefore not with the idea of outlook (which varies with the elevations of the lands), but taking it as a plane which makes equal angles with the perpendicular, we accept in magnetick demonftrations a fenfible horizon or boundary, not that which is called by Aftronomers the rational horizon.

CHAP. XIII.

On the Axis and Magnetick Poles.

ET the line be called the axis which is drawn in the earth (as in a terrella) through the centre to the poles. They are called πόλοι by the Greeks from πολεῖν, to turn, and by the Latins they are alſo called *Cardines* or *Vertices*; becauſe the world rotates and is perpetually carried around them. We are about to ſhow, indeed, that the earth and a terrella are turned about them by a magnetick influence. One of them in the earth, which looks towards the Cynoſure, is called Boreal and Arctic; the other one, oppoſite to this, is called Auſtral and Antarctic. Nor do theſe alſo exiſt on the earth or on a terrella for the ſake of the turning merely; but they are alſo limits of direction and poſition, both as reſpects deſtined diſtricts of the world, and alſo for correct turnings among themſelves.

CHAP. XIIII.

Why at the Pole itſelf the Coition is ſtronger than in
the other parts intermediate between the æquator and the pole;
and on the proportion of forces of the coition in
various parts of the earth and of the terrella.

BSERVATION has already been made that the higheſt power of alluring exiſts in the pole, and that it is weaker and more languid in the parts adjacent to the æquator. And as this is apparent in the declination, becauſe that diſponent and rotational virtue has an augmentation as one proceeds from the Æquator towards the poles: ſo alſo the coition of magneticks grows increaſingly freſh by the ſame ſteps, and in the ſame proportion. For in the parts more remote from the poles the loadſtone does not draw magneticks ſtraight down towards its own viſcera; but they tend obliquely and they allure obliquely. For as the ſmalleſt chords in a circle differ from the diameter, ſo much do the forces of attracting differ between themſelves in different parts of the terrella.

M   For

For fince attraction is coition towards a body, but magneticks run together by their verfatory tendency, it comes about that in the diameter drawn from pole to pole the body appeals directly, but in other places lefs directly. So the lefs the magnetick is turned toward the body, the lefs, and the more feebly, does it approach and adhære.

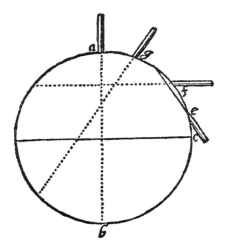

Juft as if A B were the poles and a bar of iron or a magnetick fragment C is allured at the part E; yet the end laid hold of does not tend towards the centre of the loadftone, but verges obliquely towards the pole; and a chord drawn from that end obliquely as the attracted body tends is fhort; therefore it has lefs vigour and likewife lefs inclination. But as a greater chord proceeds from a body at F, fo its action is ftronger; at G ftill longer; longeft at A, the pole (for the diameter is the longeft way) to which all the parts from all fides bring affiftance, in which is conftituted, as it were, the citadel and tribunal of the whole province, not from any worth of its own, but becaufe a force refides in it contributed from all the other parts, juft as all the foldiers bring help to their own commander. Wherefore alfo a flightly longer ftone attracts more than a fpherical one, fince the length from pole to pole is extended, even if the ftones are both from the fame mine and of the fame weight and fize. The way from pole to pole is longer in a longer ftone, and the forces brought together from other parts are not fo fcattered as in a round magnet and terrella, and in a narrow one they agree more and are better united, and a united ftronger force excels and is preeminent. A much weaker office, however, does a plane or oblong ftone perform, when the length is extended according to the leading of the parallels, and the pole ftops neither on the apex nor in the circle and orbe, but is fpread over the flat. Wherefore alfo it invites a friend wretchedly, and feebly retains him, fo that it is efteemed as one of an abject and contemptible clafs, according to its lefs apt and lefs fuitable figure.

CHAP.

CHAP. XV.

The Magnetick Virtue which is conceived in Iron is ∗
more apparent in an iron rod than in a piece of iron that
is round, fquare, or of other figure.

DULY was it faid before that the longer magnet attracts the greater weight of iron; fo alfo in a longifh piece of iron which has been touched the magnetick force conceived is ftronger when the poles exift at the ends. For the magnetick forces which are driven from the whole in every part into the poles are not fcattered but united in the narrow ends. In fquare and other angular figures the influence is diffipated, and does not proceed in ftraight lines or in convenient arcs. Suppofe alfo an iron globe have the fhape of the earth, yet for the fame reafons it drags magnetick fubftances lefs; wherefore a fmall iron fphere, when excited, draws another piece of iron more fluggifhly than an excited rod of equal weight.

CHAP. XVI.

Showing that Movements take place by the Magnetical
Vigour though folid bodies lie between; and on
the interpofition of iron plates.

FLOAT a piece of iron wire on the furface of water by transfixing it through a fuitable cork; or fet a verfatory piece of iron on a pin or in a feaman's compafs (a magnet being brought near or moved about underneath), it is put into a ftate of motion; neither the water, nor the veffel, nor the compafs-box offering refiftance in any way. Thick boards do not obftruct, nor earthen veffels nor marble vafes, nor the metals themfelves; nothing is fo folid as to carry away or impede the forces excepting an iron plate. Everything which is interpofed (even though it is very denfe) does not carry away its influence or obftruct its path, or indeed in any way hinder, diminifh, or retard it. But all the force is not fuppreffed by an iron plate, but it is in fome meafure diverted afide. For when the vigour paffes into the middle of an iron plate within the orbe of the magnetick virtue or placed juft
oppofite

oppofite the pole of the ftone, that virtue is fcattered in very large
* meafure towards its extremities; fo that the edges of a fmall round
plate of fuitable fize allure iron wires on every fide. This is alfo
apparent in the cafe of a long iron wand, which, when it has been
* touched by a magnet in the middle, has a like verticity at either end.

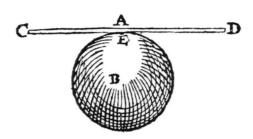

B is a loadftone, C D a long rod magnetized in the middle
A; E being the Boreal pole; C is an Auftral end or pole; in like
manner alfo the end D is another Auftral pole.   But obferve here
the exactnefs with which a verforium touched by a pole, when a
* round plate is interpofed, turns towards the fame pole in the fame
way as before the interpofition, only weaker; the plate not ftanding in the way, becaufe the vigour is diverted through the edges
of the fmall plate, and paffes out of its ftraight courfe, but yet the
plate retains in the middle the fame verticity, when it is in the
neighbourhood of that pole, and clofe to it; wherefore the verforium
tends towards the plate, having been touched by the fame pole.
If a loadftone is rather weak, a verforium hardly turns when a plate
is put in between; for the vigour of the rather weak loadftone,
* being diffufed through the extremities, paffes lefs through the
middle.   But if the plate has been touched in this way by a pole
in the middle and has been removed from the ftone outfide its orbe
of virtue, then you will fee the point of the fame verforium tend
in the contrary direction and defert the centre of the fmall plate,
which formerly it defired; for outfide the orbe of virtue it has an
oppofite verticity, in the vicinity the fame; for in the vicinity it
is, as it were, a part of the loadftone, and has the fame pole.

A is an iron plate near the pole, B a verforium which tends with its
point towards the centre of the fmall plate, which has been touched
by the pole of the loadftone C.   But if the fame fmall plate be
placed

placed outfide the orbe of magnetick virtue, the point will not turn towards its centre, but the crofs E of the fame verforium does. But an iron globe interpofed (if it is not too large) attracts the ✱ point of the iron on the other fide of the ftone.   For the verticity of that fide is the fame as that of the adjoining pole of the ftone. And this turning of the cufp (that is, of the end touched by that pole) as well as of the crofs-end, at a greater diftance, takes place with an iron globe interpofed, which would not happen at all if ✱ the fpace were empty, becaufe the magnetick virtue is paffed on and continued through magnetick bodies.

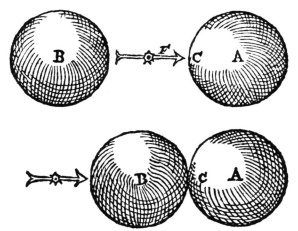

A is a terrella, B an iron globe ; between the two bodies is F, a ver- forium whofe point has been excited by the pole C.   In the other figure A is a terrella, C its pole, B an iron globe; where the verforium tends towards C, the pole of the terrella, through the iron globe.   So a verforium placed between a terrella and an iron globe vibrates more forcibly towards the pole of the terrella; becaufe the loadftone fends an inftantaneous verticity into the oppofite globe.   There is the fame efficiency in the earth, produced from the fame caufe.   For if a revolvable needle is fhut up in a rather thick gold box (this metal indeed excels all others in denfity) or a glafs or ftone box, neverthelefs that magnetick needle has its forces connected and united with the influences of the earth, and the iron will turn freely and readily (unhindered by its prifon) to its defired points, North and South.   ✱ It even does this when fhut up in iron caverns, if they are fufficiently fpacious.   Whatever bodies are produced among us, or are artificially forged from things which are produced, confift of matter of the terreftrial globe ; nor do thofe bodies hinder the prime forces of nature which are derived from their primary form, nor can they refift them except by contrary forms.   But no forms of mixed bodies are inimical to the primary implanted earth-nature, although fome often do not agree with one another.   But in the cafe of all thofe fubftances which have a material caufe for their inclining (as amber,

jet,

jet, fulphur), their action is impeded by the interpofition of a body (as paper, leaves, glafs, or the like) when that way is impeded and obftructed, fo that that which exhales cannot reach the corpufcle to be allured.   Terreftrial and magnetick coition and motion, when corporeal impediments are interpofed, is demonftrated alfo by the efficiencies of other chief bodies due to their primary form.   The moon (more than all the ftars) agrees with internal parts of the earth on account of its nearnefs and fimilarity in form.   The moon produces the movements of the waters and the tides of the fea; twice it fills up the fhores and empties them whilft it moves from a certain definite point in the fky back to the fame point in a daily revolution.   This motion of the waters is incited and the feas rife and fall no lefs when the moon is below the horizon and in the loweft part of the heavens, than if it had been raifed at a height above the horizon.   So the whole mafs of the earth interpofed does not refift the action of the moon, when it is below the earth ; but the feas bordering on our fhores, in certain pofitions of the fky when it is below the horizon, are kept in motion, and likewife ftirred by its power (though they are not ftruck by its rays nor illuminated by its light), rife, come up with great force, and recede.   But about the reafon of the tides anon; here let it fuffice to have merely touched the threfhold of the queftion.   In like manner nothing on the earth can be hidden from the magnetick difpofition of the earth or of the ftone, and all magnetical bodies are reduced to order by the dominant form of the earth, and loadftone and iron fhow fympathy with a loadftone though folid bodies be interpofed.

CHAP. XVII.

On the Iron Cap of a Loadftone, with which
it is armed at the pole (for the fake of the
virtue) and on the efficacy of the fame.

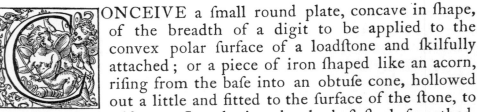

CONCEIVE a fmall round plate, concave in fhape, of the breadth of a digit to be applied to the convex polar furface of a loadftone and fkilfully attached ; or a piece of iron fhaped like an acorn, rifing from the bafe into an obtufe cone, hollowed out a little and fitted to the furface of the ftone, to be tied to the loadftone.   Let the iron be the beft fteel, fmoothed, fhining, and even.   A loadftone with fuch an appliance, which before only bore four ounces of iron, will now raife twelve.   But the greateft force of a combining or rather united nature is feen
when

when two loadftones, armed with iron caps, are fo joined by their concurrent (commonly called contrary) ends, that they mutually ✳ attract and raife one another. In this way a weight of twenty ounces is raifed, when either ftone unarmed would only allure four ounces of iron. Iron unites to an armed loadftone more firmly than to a loadftone; and on that account raifes greater weights, becaufe the pieces of iron ftick more pertinacioufly to one that is armed. For by the near prefence of the magnet they are cemented together, and fince the armature conceives a magnetick vigour from its prefence and the other conjoined piece of iron is at the fame time endued with vigour from the prefence of the loadftone, they are firmly bound together. Therefore by the mutual contact of ftrong pieces of iron, the cohefion is ftrong. Which thing is alfo made clear and is exhibited by means of rods fticking together, Bk. 3, chap 4; and alfo when the queftion of the concretion of iron duft into a united body was difcuffed. For this reafon a piece of iron fet near a loadftone draws away any fuitable piece of iron from the loadftone, if only it touch the iron; otherwife it does not fnatch it away, though in clofeft proximity. For magnetick pieces of iron within the orbe of virtue, or near a loadftone, do not rufh together with a greater endeavour than the iron and the magnet; but joined they are united more ftrongly and, as it were, cemented together, though the fubftance remain the fame with the fame forces acting.

CHAP. XVIII.

An armed Loadftone does not endow an
excited piece of Iron with greater vigour
than an unarmed.

UPPOSE there are two pieces of iron, one of ✳ which has been excited by an armed loadftone, the other by one unarmed; and let there be applied to one of them another piece of iron of a weight juft proportional to its ftrength, it is manifeft that the remaining one in like manner raifes the fame and no more. Magnetick verforia alfo touched by an armed loadftone turn with the fame velocity and conftancy towards the poles of the earth as thofe magnetized by the fame loadftone unarmed.

CHAP.

CHAP. XIX.

Union with an armed Loadſtone is ſtronger;
hence greater weights are raiſed; but the
coition is not ſtronger, but gener-
ally weaker.

AN armed magnet raiſes a greater weight, as is manifeſt to all; but a piece of iron moves towards a
ſtone at an equal, or rather greater, diſtance when it
is bare, without an iron cap.   This muſt be tried
with two pieces of iron of the ſame weight and
figure at an equal diſtance, or with one and the
ſame verſorium, the teſt being made firſt with an armed, then with
an unarmed loadſtone, at equal diſtances.

CHAP. XX.

An armed Loadſtone raiſes an armed Load-
ſtone, which alſo attracts a third; which likewiſe
happens, though the virtue in the firſt
be ſomewhat ſmall.

MAGNETS armed cohære firmly
when duly joined, and accord into
one; and though the firſt be rather weak, yet the ſecond one
adhæres to it not only by the
ſtrength of the firſt, but of the
ſecond, which mutually give helping hands;
alſo to the ſecond a third often adhæres and in
the caſe of robuſt ſtones, a fourth to the third.

CHAP.

CHAP. XXI.

If Paper or any other Medium be interpofed,
an armed loadftone raifes no more than an
unarmed one.

BSERVATION has fhown above that an armed loadftone does not attraft at a greater diftance than an unarmed one; yet raifes iron in greater quantity, if it is joined to and made continuous with the iron. But if Paper be placed between, that intimate cohæfion of the metal is hindered, nor are the metals cemented together at the fame time by the operation of the magnet.

CHAP. XXII.

That an armed Loadftone draws Iron no more than an
unarmed one: And that an armed one is more ftrongly united
to iron is fhown by means of an armed loadftone
and a polifhed cylinder of iron.

F a cylinder be lying on a level furface, of too great a weight for an unarmed loadftone to lift, and (a piece of paper being interpofed) if the pole of an armed loadftone be joined to the middle of it; if the cylinder were drawn from there by the load-ftone, it would follow rolling; but if no medium were interpofed, the cylinder would be drawn along firmly united with the armed loadftone, and in no wife rolling. But if the fame loadftone be unarmed, it will draw the cylinder rolling with the fame fpeed as the armed loadftone with the paper between or when it was wrapped in paper.

Armed loadftones of diverfe weights, of the fame ore, vigour and form, cling and hang to pieces of iron of a convenient fize and proportionate figure with an equal proportion of ftrength. The fame is apparent in the cafe of unarmed ftones. A fuitable piece of iron being applied to the lower part of a loadftone, which is hanging from a magnetick body, excites its vigour, fo that the loadftone hangs on more firmly. For a pendent loadftone clings

more firmly to a magnetick body joined to it above with a hanging piece of iron added to it, than when lead or any other non-magnetick body is hung on.

A loadſtone, whether armed or unarmed, joined by its proper pole to the pole of another loadſtone, armed or unarmed, makes the loadſtone raiſe a greater weight by the oppoſite end. A piece of iron alſo applied to the pole of a magnet produces the ſame reſult, namely, that the other pole will carry a greater weight of iron; juſt as a loadſtone with a piece of iron ſuperpoſed on it (as in this figure) holds up a piece of iron below, which it cannot hold, if the upper one be removed. Magneticks in conjunction make one magnetick. Wherefore as the maſs increaſes, the magnetick vigour is alſo augmented.

An armed loadſtone, as well as an unarmed one, runs more readily to a larger piece of iron and combines more firmly with a larger piece than with a leſſer one.

CHAP. XXIII.

Magnetick Force cauſes motion towards unity,
and binds firmly together bodies which are united.

MAGNETICK fragments cohære within their ſtrength well and harmoniouſly together. Pieces of iron in the preſence of a loadſtone (even if they are not touching the loadſtone) run together, ſeek one another anxiouſly and embrace one another, and when joined are as if they were cemented. Iron filings or the ſame reduced to powder inſerted in paper tubes, placed upon a ſtone meridionally or merely brought rather cloſe to it, coaleſce into one body, and ſo many parts ſuddenly are concreted and combine; and the whole company of corpuſcles thus conſpiring together affects another piece of iron and attracts it, as if it conſtituted one integral rod of iron; and above the ſtone it is directed toward the North and South. But when they are removed a long
way

way from the ftone, the particles (as if loofed again) are feparated and move apart fingly. In this way alfo the foundations of the world are connected and joined and cemented together magnetic-ally. So let Ptolemy of Alexandria, and his followers, and thofe philofophers of ours, be the lefs terrified if the earth do move round in a circle, nor threaten its diffolution.

Iron filings, after being heated for a long time, are attracted by ✳ a loadftone, yet not fo ftrongly or from fo great a diftance as when not heated. A loadftone lofes fome of its virtue by too great a ✳ heat; for its humour is fet free, whence its peculiar nature is marred. Likewife alfo, if iron filings are well burnt in a reverbera- ✳ tory furnace and converted into faffron of Mars, they are not attracted by a loadftone; but if they are heated, but not thoroughly burnt, they do ftick to a magnet, but lefs ftrongly than the filings themfelves not acted upon by fire. For the faffron has become totally deformate, but the heated metal acquires a defect from the fire, and the forces in the enfeebled body are lefs excited by a loadftone; and, the nature of the iron being now ruined, it is not attracted by a loadftone.

CHAP. XXIIII.

A piece of Iron placed within the Orbe of a
Loadftone hangs fufpended in the air, if on account
of fome impediment it cannot approach it.

ITHIN the magnetick orbe a piece of iron ✳ moves towards the more powerful points of the ftone, if it be not hindered by force or by the material of a body placed between them; either it falls down from above, or tends fide-ways or obliquely, or flies up above. But if the iron cannot reach the ftone on account of fome obftacle, it cleaves to it and remains there, but with a lefs firm and conftant connection, fince at greater intervals or diftances the alliance is lefs amicable. Fracaftorio, in the eighth chapter of his *De Sympathia*, fays that a piece of iron is fufpended in the air, fo that it can be moved neither up nor down, if a loadftone be placed above which is able to draw the iron up juft as much as the iron itfelf inclines downwards with equal force; for thus the iron would be fupported in the air: which thing is abfurd; becaufe the force of a magnet is
always

always the ftronger the nearer it is. So that when a piece of iron is raifed a very little from the earth by the force of the magnet, it needs muft be drawn fteadily on towards the magnet (if nothing elfe come in the way) and cleave to it. Baptifta Porta fufpends a piece of iron in the air (a magnet being fixed above), and, by no very fubtile procefs, the iron is detained by a flender thread from its lower part, fo that it cannot rife up to the ftone. The iron ✳ is raifed upright by the magnet, although the magnet does not touch the iron, but becaufe it is in its vicinity; but when the whole iron on account of its greater nearnefs is moved by that which erected it, immediately it hurries with a fwift motion to the magnet and cleaves to it. For by approaching the iron is more and more excited, and the coition grows ftronger.

CHAP. XXV.

Exaltation of the power of the Magnet.

NE loadftone far furpaffes another in power, fince one draws iron of almoft its own weight, another can hardly ftir fome fhreds. Whatever things, whether animals or plants, are endowed with life need fome fort of nourifhment, by which their ftrength not only perfifts but grows firmer and more vigorous. But iron is not, as it feemed to Cardan and to Alexander Aphrodifeus, attracted by the loadftone in order that it may feed on fhreds of it, nor does the loadftone take up vigour from iron filings as if by a repaft on victuals. Since Porta had doubts on this and refolved to teft it, he took a loadftone of afcertained weight, and buried it in iron filings of not unknown weight; and when he had left it there for many months, he found the ftone of greater weight, the filings of lefs. But the difference was fo flender that he was even then doubtful as to the truth. What was done by him does not convict the ftone of voracity, nor does it fhow any nutrition; for minute portions of the filings are eafily fcattered in handling. So alfo a very fine duft is infenfibly born on a loadftone in fome very flight quantity, by which fomething might have been added to the weight of the loadftone, but which is only a furface accretion and might even be wiped off with no great difficulty. Some think that a weak and fluggifh ftone can bring itfelf back into better condition, and that a very powerful one alfo might prefent it with the higheft powers. Do they acquire ftrength like animals when
they

they eat and are fated? Is the medicine prepared by addition or subtraction? Is there anything which can re-create this primary form or bestow it anew? And, certes, nothing can do this which is not magnetical. Magneticks can restore a certain soundness to magneticks (when not incurable); some can even exalt them beyond their proper strength; but when a body is at the height of perfection in its own nature, it is not capable of being strengthened further. So that that imposture of Paracelfus, who affirms that the force and virtue can be increased and transmuted tenfold, turns out to be the more infamous. The method of effecting this is as follows, viz., you make it femi-incandefcent in a fire of charcoal (that is, you heat it very hot), so that it does not become red-hot, however, and immediately flake it, as much indeed as it can imbibe, in oil of faffron of Mars, made from the best Carynthian steel. " In this way you will be able fo to strengthen a loadftone " that it can draw a nail out of a wall and accomplish many other " like wonderful things, which are not poffible for a common load- " ftone." But a loadftone thus flaked in oil not only does not gain power, but fuffers alfo a certain lofs of its inborn strength. A loadftone is improved if polifhed and rubbed with fteel. Buried in filings of the best iron or of pure fteel, not rufty, it preferves its strength. Sometimes alfo a fomewhat good and ftrong one gains some strength when it is rubbed on the pole of another, on the oppofite part, and receives virtue. In all thefe experiments it is an advantage to obferve the pole of the earth, and to adjuft according to magnetick laws the ftone which we wifh to ftrengthen; which we fhall fet forth below. A fomewhat powerful and fairly large loadftone increafes the ftrength of a loadftone as it does of iron. A loadftone being placed over the boreal pole of a loadftone, ✱

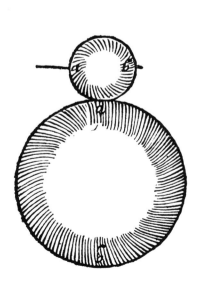 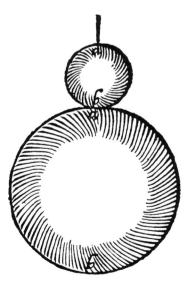

the

the boreal pole becomes ftronger, and an iron rod (like an arrow) fticks to the boreal pole A, but not at all to the pole B. The pole A alfo, when it is at the top in a right line with the axis of both loadftones joined in accordance with magnetick laws, raifes the rod to the perpendicular, which it cannot do if the large loadftone be removed, on account of its own weaker ftrength. But as a fmall iron ✱ globe, when placed above the pole of a terrella, raifes the rod to the perpendicular, fo, when placed at the fide, the rod is not directed towards the centre of the globe, but is raifed obliquely and cleaves anywhere, becaufe the pole in a round piece of iron is always the point which is joined moft clofely to the pole of the terrella and is not conftant as in a fmaller terrella. The parts of the earth, as of all magneticks, are in agreement and take delight in their mutual proximity; if placed in the higheft power, they do not harm their inferiors, nor flight them; there is a mutual love among them all, a perennial good feeling. The weaker loadftones are re-created by the more powerful, and the lefs powerful caufe no harm to the ftronger. But a powerful one attracts and turns a fomewhat ftrong one more than it does an impotent one. Becaufe a ftrenuous one confers a ftronger activity, and itfelf haftens, flies up to the other, and folicits it more keenly; therefore there is a more certain and a ftronger co-action and cohærency.

CHAP. XXVI.

Why there fhould appear to be a greater love between
iron and loadftone, than between loadftone and loadftone, or
between iron and iron, when clofe to the load-
ftone, within its orbe of virtue.

MAGNET attracts magnet, not in every part and on every fide with equal conditions, as iron, but at one and a fixed point; therefore the poles of both muft be exactly difpofed, otherwife they do not cleave together duly and ftrongly. But this difpofition is not eafy and expeditious; wherefore a loadftone feems not to conform to a loadftone, when neverthelefs they agree very well together. A piece of iron by the fudden impreffion of a loadftone is not only allured by the ftone, but is renewed, its forces being drawn forth; by which it follows and folicits the loadftone with no lefs impulfe, and even leads another piece of iron captive. Let there be a fmall iron fpike above a loadftone clinging firmly to it; if you apply an unmagnetized rod of iron to the fpike, not, however,

fo

fo that it touches the ftone, you will fee the fpike when it has touched the iron, leaving the loadftone, follow the rod, try to grafp it by leaning toward it, and (if it fhould touch it) cleave firmly to it: for a piece of iron, when united and joined to another piece of iron placed within the orbe of virtue of the loadftone, draws it more ftrongly than does the loadftone itfelf. The natural magnetick virtue, confufed and dormant in the iron, is aroufed by the loadftone, is linked to the loadftone, and rejoices with it in its primary form; then fmelted iron becomes a perfect magnetick, as robuft as the loadftone itfelf. For as the one imparts and ftirs, fo the other conceives, and being ftirred remains in virtue, and pours back the forces alfo by its own activity. But fince iron is more like iron than loadftone, and the virtue in both pieces of iron is exalted by the proximity of the loadftone, fo in the loadftone itfelf, in cafe of equal ftrength, likenefs of fubftance prevails, and iron gives itfelf up rather to iron, and they are united by their very fimilar homogenic powers. Which thing happens not fo much from a coition, as from a firmer unition; and a knob or fnout of fteel, fixed fkilfully on the pole of the ftone, raifes greater weights of iron than the ftone of itfelf could. When fteel or iron is fmelted from loadftone or iron ore, the flag and corrupt fubftances are feparated from the better by the fufion of the material; whence (in very large meafure) that iron contains the nature of the earth, purified from alien flaw and blemifh, and more homogenic and perfect, though deformed by the fufion. And when that material indeed is provoked by a loadftone, it conceives the magnetick virtues, and within their orbe is raifed in ftrength more than the weaker loadftone, which with us is often not free from fome admixture of impurities.

CHAP. XXVII.

The Centre of the Magnetick Virtues in the earth

is the centre of the earth; and in a terrella
is the centre of the ftone.

RAYS of magnetick virtue fpread out in every direction in an orbe; the centre of this orbe is not at the pole (as Baptifta Porta reckons, Chap. 22), but in the centre of the ftone and of the terrella. So alfo the centre of the earth is the centre of the magnetick motions of the earth; though magneticks are not borne directly toward the centre by magnetical motion, except when they are attracted by the true pole. For fince the formal

power

power of the ftone and of the earth does not promote anything but the unity and conformity of disjoined bodies, it comes about that everywhere at an equal diftance from the centre or from the circumference, juft as it feems to attract perpendicularly at one place, fo at another it is able even to difpofe and to turn, provided the ftone is not uneven in virtue.   For if at the diftance C from the pole D the ftone is able to allure a verforium,

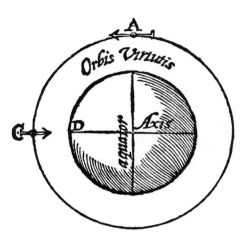

at an equally long interval above the æquator at A that ftone can alfo direct and turn the verforium.   So the very centre and middle of the terrella is the centre of its virtue, and from this to the circumference of the orbe (at equal intervals on every fide) its magnetick virtues are emitted.

CHAP. XXVIII.

A Loadftone attracts magneticks not only to a
fixed point or pole, but to every part of a
terrella fave the æquinoctial zone.

COITIONS are always more powerful when poles are near poles, fince in them by the concordancy of the whole there exifts a ftronger force ; wherefore the one embraces the other more ftrongly.   Places declining from the poles have attractive forces, but a little weaker and languid in the ratio of their diftance; fo that at length on the æquinoctial circle they are utterly enervated and evanefcent.   Neither do even the poles attract as mathematical points ; nor do magneticks come into conjunction by their own poles, only on the poles of a loadftone.   But coition
is

is made on every part of the periphery, both Northern and Southern, by virtue emanating from the whole body; magneticks neverthelefs incline languidly towards magneticks in the parts bordering on the æquator, but quickly in places nearer the pole. Wherefore not the poles, not the parts alone neareft to the pole allure and invite magneticks, but magneticks are difpofed and turned round and combine with magneticks in proportion as the parts facing and adjoined unite their forces together, which are always of the fame potency in the fame parallel, unlefs they are diftributed otherwife from caufes of variation.

CHAP. XXIX.

On Variety of Strength due to Quantity
or Mafs.

QUITE fimilar in potency are thofe ftones which are of the fame mine, and not corrupted by adjacent ores or veins. Neverthelefs that which excels in fize fhows greater powers, fince it feizes greater weights and has a wider orbe of virtue. For a loadftone weighing one ounce does not lift a large nail as does one weighing a pound, nor does it rule fo widely, nor extend its forces; and if from a loadftone of a pound weight a portion is taken away, fomething of its power will be feen to go alfo; for when a portion is abftracted the virtue is leffened. But if that part is properly applied and united to it, though it is not faftened ✳ to nor grown into it, yet by the application it obtains its priftine power and its vigour returns. Sometimes, however, when a part is taken away, the virtue turns out to be ftronger on account of the ✳ bad fhape of the ftone, namely, when the vigour is fcattered through inconvenient angles. In various fpecies the ratio is various, for one ftone of a drachm weight draws more than another of twenty pounds. Since in very many the influence is fo effete that it can hardly be perceived, thofe weak ftones are furpaffed by prepared pieces of clay. But, it may be afked, if a ftone of the fame fpecies and goodnefs weighing a drachm would feize upon a drachm of iron, would a ftone of an ounce weight feize on an ounce, a pound on a pound, and fo on? And this is indeed true; for it both ✳ ftrains and remits its ftrength proportionately, fo that if a loadftone, one drachm of which would attract one drachm of iron, were in equal proportion applied either to a fuitably large obelifk or to an immenfe pyramid of iron, it would lift it directly in fuch propor-

tion

tion and would draw it towards itfelf with no greater effort of its nature or trouble than a loadftone of a drachm weight embraces a drachm. But in all fuch experiments as this let the vigour of the magnets be equal; let there be alfo a juft proportion in all of the fhapes of the ftones, and let the fhape of the iron to be attracted be the fame, and the goodnefs of the metal, and let the pofition of the poles of the loadftones be moft exact. This is alfo no lefs true in the cafe of an armed loadftone than of an unarmed one. For the fake of experiment, let there be given a loadftone of eight ounces weight, which when armed lifts twelve ounces of iron; if you cut

✻ off from that loadftone a certain portion, which when it has been reduced to the fhape of the former whole one is then only of two ounces, fuch a loadftone armed lifts a piece of iron applied to it of three ounces, in proportion to the mafs. In this experiment alfo the piece of iron of three ounces ought to have the fame fhape as the former one of twelve ounces; if that rofe up into a cone, it is neceffary that this alfo in the ratio of its mafs fhould be given a pyramidal fhape proportioned to the former.

CHAP. XXX.

The Shape and Mafs of the Iron are of moft
importance in coition.

BSERVATION has fhown above that the fhape and mafs of the loadftone have great influence in magnetick coitions; likewife alfo the fhape and mafs of the iron bodies give back more powerful and fteady forces. Oblong iron rods are both drawn more quickly to a loadftone and cleave to it with greater obftinacy than round or fquare pieces, for the fame reafons which we have proven in the cafe of the loadftone. But, moreover, this is alfo worthy of obfervation, that a fmaller piece of iron, to which is hung a weight of another material, fo that it is altogether in

✻ weight equal to another large whole piece of iron of a right weight (as regards the ftrength of the loadftone), is not lifted by the loadftone as the larger piece of iron would be. For a fmaller piece of iron does not join with a loadftone fo firmly, becaufe it fends back lefs ftrength, and only that which is magnetick conceives ftrength; the foreign material hung on cannot acquire magnetick forces.

CHAP.

CHAP. XXXI.

On Long and Round Stones.

IECES of iron join more firmly with a long ftone than with a round one, provided that the pole of the ftone is at the extremity and end of its length; becaufe, forfooth, in the cafe of a long ftone, a magnetick is directed at the end ftraight towards the body in which the virtue proceeds in ftraighter lines and through the longer diameter. But a fomewhat long ftone has but little power on the fide, much lefs indeed than a round one. It is demonftrable, indeed, that at A and B the coition is ✱ ftronger in a round ftone than at C and D, at like diftances from the pole.

 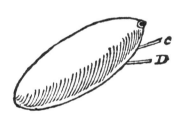

CHAP. XXXII.

Certain Problems and Magnetick Experiments about
the Coition, and Separation, and regular Motion
of bodies magnetical.

QUAL loadftones come together with equal incitation. ✱
Alfo magnetick bodies of iron, if alike in all re- ✱
fpects, come together when excited with fimilar incitation.
Furthermore, bodies of iron not excited by a ✱
loadftone, if they are alike and not weighed down
by their bulk, move towards one another with equal motion.
Two loadftones, difpofed on the furface of fome water in fuitable

able fkiffs, if they are drawn up fuitably within their orbes of virtue,
* incite one another mutually to an embrace.   So a proportionate
piece of iron in one fkiff hurries with the fame fpeed towards the
loadftone as the loadftone itfelf in its boat ftrives towards the iron.
From their own pofitions, indeed, they are fo borne together, that
they are joined and come to reft at length in the middle of the fpace.
* Two iron wires magnetically excited, floating in water by means of
fuitable pieces of cork, ftrive to touch and mutually ftrike one
another with their correfponding ends, and are conjoined.

* Coition is firmer and fwifter than repulfion and feparation in
equal magnetick fubftances.   That magnetick fubftances are more
fluggifhly repelled than they are attracted is manifeft in all magnetical experiments in the cafe of ftones floating on water in fuitable fkiffs; alfo in the cafe of iron wires or rods fwimming (tranf-
fixed through corks) and well excited by a loadftone, and in the cafe
of verforia.   This comes about becaufe, though there is one faculty
of coition, another of conformation or difpofition, repulfion and
averfion is caufed merely by fomething difpofing; on the other
hand, the coming together is by a mutual alluring to contact and
a difpofing, that is, by a double vigour.

A difponent vigour is often only the precurfor of coition, in
order that the bodies may ftand conveniently for one another before
conjunction; wherefore alfo they are turned round to the correfponding ends, if they can [not] reach them through the hindrances.

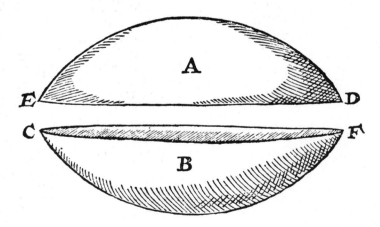

If a loadftone be divided through a meridian into two equal
* parts, the feparate parts mutually repel one another, the poles being
placed directly oppofite one another at a convenient and equal diftance.   They repel one another alfo with a greater velocity than
when pole is put oppofite pole incongruoufly.   Juft as the part B
of the loadftone, placed almoft oppofite the part A, repels it floating
in its fkiff, becaufe D turns away from F, and E from C; but if B
is exactly joined with A again, they agree and become one body
                                                                              mag-

magnetical; but in proximity they raife enmities. But if one part of the ftone is turned round, fo that C faces D and F faces E, then A purfues B within its orbe until they are united.

The Southern parts of the ftone avoid the Southern parts, and the Northern parts the Northern. Neverthelefs, if by force you move up the Southern cufp of a piece of iron too near the Southern part of the ftone, the cufp is feized and both are linked together in friendly embraces: becaufe it immediately reverfes the implanted verticity of the iron, and it is changed by the prefence of the more powerful ftone, which is more conftant in its forces than the iron. For they come together according to their nature, if by reverfal and mutation true conformity is produced, and juft coition, as alfo regular direction. Loadftones of the fame fhape, fize, and vigour, attract one another mutually with like efficacy, and in the oppofite pofition repel one another mutually with a like vigour.

Iron rods not touched, though alike and equal, do yet often act ✳ upon one another with different forces; becaufe as the reafons of their acquired verticity, alfo of their ftability and vigour, are different, fo the more ftrongly they are excited, the more vigoroufly do they incite.

Pieces of iron excited by one and the fame pole mutually repel ✳ one another by thofe ends at which they were excited; then alfo the oppofite ends to thofe in thefe iron pieces raife enmities one to another.

In verforia whofe cufps have been rubbed, but not their crofs- ✳ ends, the croffes mutually repel one another, but weakly and in proportion to their length.

In like verforia the cufps, having been touched by the fame ✳ pole of the loadftone, attract the crofs-ends with equal ftrength.

In a fomewhat long verforium the crofs-end is attracted rather ✳ weakly by the cufp of a fhorter iron verforium; the crofs of the fhorter more ftrongly by the cufp of the longer, becaufe the crofs of the longer verforium has a weak verticity, but the cufp has a ftronger.

The cufp of a longer verforium drives away the cufp of a ✳ fhorter one more vehemently than the cufp of the fhorter the cufp of the longer, if the one is free upon a pin, and the other is held in the hand; for though both were equally excited by the fame loadftone, yet the longer one is ftronger at its cufp on account of its greater mafs.

The Southern end of an iron rod which is not excited attracts ✳ the Northern, and the Northern the Southern; moreover, alfo the Southern parts repel the Southern, and the Northern the Northern.

If magnetick fubftances are divided or in any way broken in pieces, each part has a Northern and a Southern end.

A

* A verforium is moved as far off by a loadftone when an obftacle is put in the way, as through air and an open medium.

* Rods rubbed upon the pole of a ftone ftrive after the fame pole and follow it. Therefore Baptifta Porta errs when he fays, chapter 40, " If you put that part to it from which it received its force, it " will not endure it, but drives it from it, and draws to it the con- " trary and oppofite part."

The principles of turning round and inclining are the fame in the cafe of loadftone to loadftone, of loadftone to iron, of iron alfo to iron.

When magnetick fubftances which have been feparated by force and diffected into parts flow together into a true union and are fuit- ably connected, the body becomes one, and one united virtue, nor have they diverfe ends.

* The feparate parts affume two oppofite poles, if the divifion has not been made along a parallel: if the divifion has been made along a parallel, they are able to retain one pole in the fame fite as before.

Pieces of iron which have been rubbed and excited by a load- ftone are more furely and fwiftly feized by a loadftone at fitting ends than fuch as have not been rubbed.

* If a fpike is fet up on the pole of a loadftone, a fpike or ftyle of iron placed on the upper end is ftrongly cemented to it, and draws away the erect fpike from the terrella when motion is made.

* If to the lower end of the erect fpike the end of another fpike is applied, it does not cohære with it, nor do they unite together.

As a rod of iron draws away a piece of iron from a terrella, fo is it alfo with a minute loadftone and a leffer terrella, though weaker in ftrength.

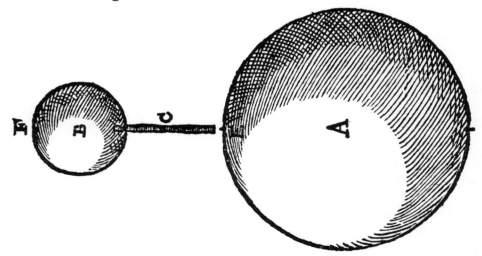

The piece of iron C comes into conjunction with the terrella A, and the vigour in it is magnetically exalted and excited, both in the adjoining end and in the other alfo which is turned away through
its

its conjunction with the terrella.   The end that is turned away alfo
conceives vigour from the loadftone B; likewife the pole D of that
loadftone is powerful on account of its fuitable afpect and the nearnefs of the pole E of the terrella.   Several caufes therefore concur
why the piece of iron C fhould cleave to the terrella B, to which it
is joined more firmly than to the terrella A ; the vigour excited in
the rod, the vigour alfo excited in the ftone B, and the ftrength implanted in B concur; therefore D is more firmly cemented magnetically with C than E with C.

But if you were to turn the vertex F round to the iron C, C
would not adhære to F as formerly to D ; for ftones fo arranged
being within the orbe of virtue are placed contrary to natural
order ; wherefore F does not receive power from E.

Two loadftones or excited pieces of iron, duly cohæring, fly *
afunder on the approach of another more powerful loadftone or
magnetized piece of iron.   Becaufe the new-comer repels the other
with its oppofing face, and dominates it, and ends the relationfhip
of the two which were formerly joined.   So the forces of the other
are leffened and fuccumb; but if it conveniently could, being di-
vefted of its affociation with the weaker, and rolling round, it
would turn about to the ftronger.   Wherefore alfo magnetick bodies
fufpended in the air fall when a loadftone is brought near them
with an oppofing face, not (as Baptifta Porta teaches) becaufe the
faculty of both thofe which were joined before grows faint and
torpid, for no face can be hoftile to both the ends which cohære,
but to one only ; and when the ftronger loadftone, coming frefh
with oppofing face, impels this further from it, it is put to flight
by the friendly reception of the former.

CHAP. XXXIII.

On the Varying Ratio of Strength, and of the Motion
of coition, within the orbe of virtue.

HOULD a very large weight, which at a very
fmall diftance is drawn towards a loadftone, be
divided into ever fo many equal parts, and fhould
the radius of the orbe of magnetick attraction be
divided into the fame number of parts, the like
named parts of the weight will correfpond to the
intermediate parts of the radius.

The orbe of virtue extends more widely than the orbe of motion
of any magnetick ; for the magnetick is affected at its extremity,
even if it is not moved with local motion, which effect is produced

by

by the loadftone being brought nearer.   A fmall verforium alfo is
turned when a good diftance off, even if at the fame diftance it
would not flow towards the loadftone, though free and difengaged
from impediment.

The fwiftnefs of the motion of a magnetick body to a loadftone
is dependent on either the power of the loadftone, on its mafs, on its
fhape, on the medium, or on its diftance within the magnetick orbe.

* A magnetick moves more quickly towards a more powerful
ftone than towards a fluggifh one in proportion to the ftrength,
and [as appears] by a comparifon of the loadftones together.   A
leffer mafs of iron alfo is carried more quickly towards a loadftone,
juft as alfo one that is a little longer in fhape.   The fwiftnefs of
magnetick motion towards a loadftone is changed by reafon of the
medium ; for bodies are moved more quickly in air than in water,
and in clear air than in air that is thick and cloudy.

By reafon of the diftance, the motion is quicker in the cafe of
bodies near together than when they are far off.   At the limits of
the orbe of virtue of a terrella a magnetick is moved feebly and
flowly.   At very fhort diftances clofe to the terrella the moving
impetus is greateft.

* A loadftone which in the outmoft part of its orbe of virtue
hardly moves a verforium when one foot removed from it, doth, if
a long piece of iron is joined to it, attraét and repel the verforium
more ftrongly with its oppofite poles when even three feet diftant.
The refult is the fame whether the loadftone is armed or unarmed.
Let the iron be a fuitable piece of the thicknefs of the little finger.

For the vigour of the loadftone excites verticity in the iron and
proceeds in the iron and through the iron much further than it
extends through the air.

* The vigour proceeds even through feveral pieces of iron (joined
to one another end to end), not fo regularly, however, as through
one continuous folid.

Duft of fteel placed upon paper rifes up when a loadftone is
moved near above it in a fort of fteely hairinefs ; but if the loadftone is placed below, fuch a hairinefs is likewife raifed.

* Steel duft (when the pole of a loadftone is placed near) is cemented into one body ; but when it defires coition with the loadftone, the mafs is fplit and it rifes in conglomerated parts.

But if there is a loadftone beneath the paper, the mafs is fplit
in the fame way and many portions refult, each of which confifts
of very many parts, and remains cemented together, as individual
bodies.   Whilft the lower parts of thefe purfue greedily the pole
of the loadftone placed direétly beneath, even they alfo are raifed
up as magnetick wholes, juft as a fmall iron wire of the length of a
grain or two grains of barley is raifed up, both when the loadftone
is moved near both beneath and above.

CHAP.

CHAP. XXXIIII.

Why a Loadftone fhould be ftronger in its poles
in a different ratio; as well in the Northern
regions as in the Southern.

HE extraordinary magnetick virtue of the earth is ✳
remarkably demonftrated by the fubtility of the
following magnetical experiment. Let there be
given a terrella of no contemptible power, or a
long loadftone with equal cones as polar extremities; but in any other fhape which is not exactly
round error is eafy, and the experiment difficult. In the Northern regions, raife the true North pole of the terrella above the
horizon ftraight toward the zenith; it is demonftrable that it
raifes up a larger iron fpike on its North pole, than the South pole
of the fame terrella is able to raife, when turned in the fame way
toward the higheft point of the fky. The fame thing is fhown
by a fmall terrella placed in the fame way above a larger.

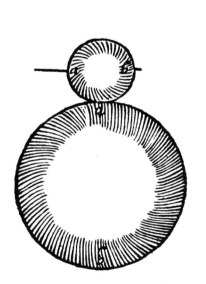
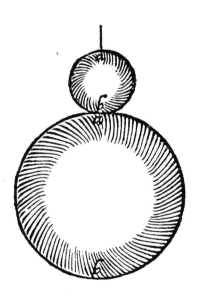

Let *a b* be the earth or a fomewhat large terrella, alfo *a b* a fmaller
terrella. There is fet up above the Northern pole of the fmaller
terrella a fpike larger than the pole *b* of the fmaller terrella can raife,
if it is turned round to the higher parts. And the pole *a* of the

P

fmaller

ſmaller terrella has its ſtrength from the larger, declining from the
Zenith to the plane of the horizon or to the level. But now, if,
leaving the terrella diſpoſed in the ſame way, you bring a piece of
iron to the lower and Southern pole, it will attract and retain a
greater weight than the Boreal pole could, if it were turned round to
the lower parts. Which thing is demonſtrated thus : let A be the
earth or a terrella ; E the Boreal pole or ſome place in ſome great
latitude ; B a rather large terrella above the earth or a ſmaller terrella on the top of a larger ; D its Southern pole. It is manifeſt
that D (the Southern pole) attracts a larger piece of iron, C, than
F (the Boreal pole) will be able to, if it is turned round downward to the poſition D, toward the earth or the terrella in the
Northern regions.

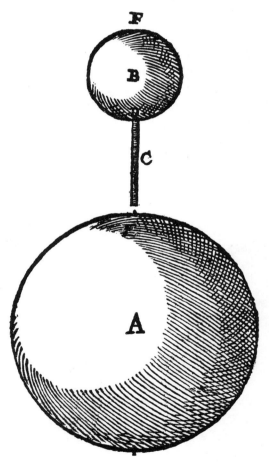

Magneticks acquire ſtrength through magneticks, if they are
properly placed according to their nature, in near neighbourhood
and within the orbe of virtue. Wherefore when a terrella is
placed on the earth or on a terrella, ſo that its Southern pole is
turned round toward the Northern pole, its Northern pole, however,
turned away from the Northern pole, the influence and ſtrength of
its

its poles are increafed.   And fo the Northern pole of a terrella in fuch a pofition lifts up a larger fpike than the Southern pole, if the Southern pole is turned away.   Similarly the Southern pole in a proper and natural arrangement, acquiring ftrength from the earth or from a larger terrella, attracts and retains larger rods of iron.   In ✳ the other part of the terreftrial globe toward the South, as alfo in the Auftral portion of a terrella, the reafoning is converfe ; for the Southern pole of the terrella being turned away is more robuft, as alfo the Northern pole when turned round.   The more a region on the earth is diftant from the æquinoctial (as alfo in a larger terrella), the larger is the acceffion of ftrength perceived ; near the æquator, indeed, the difference is fmall, but on the æquator itfelf null; at the poles finally it is greateft.

CHAP. XXXV.

On a Perpetual Motion Machine, mentioned
by authors, by means of the attraction
of a loadftone.

CARDAN writes that out of iron and the Herculean ftone can be made a perpetual motion machine ; not that he himfelf had ever feen one, but only conceived the idea from an account by Antonius de Fantis, of Treves.   Such a machine he defcribes, Book 9, *De Rerum Varietate*.   But they have been little practifed in magnetick experiments who forge fuch things as that.   For no magnetick attraction can be greater (by any fkill or by any kind of inftrument) than the retention.   Things which are joined and thofe which are approaching near are retained with a greater force than thofe which are enticed and fet in motion, and are moved ; and that coition is, as we have fhown above, a motion of both, not an attraction of one.   Such a machine Peter Peregrinus feigned many centuries before or elfe depicted one which he had received from others, and one which was much better fitted for the purpofe.   Johannes Tayfnier publifhed it alfo, fpoiled by wretched figures, and copied out the whole theory of it word for word.   O that the gods would at length bring to a miferable end fuch fictitious, crazy, deformed labours, with which the minds of the ftudious are blinded!

CHAP.

CHAP. XXXVI.

How a more robuſt Loadſtone may be
recognized.

ERY powerful loadſtones ſometimes lift into the air a weight of iron equal to their own; a weak one barely attracts a ſlender wire. Thoſe therefore are more robuſt which appeal to and retain larger bodies, if there is no defect in their form, or the pole of the ſtone is not ſuitably moved up. Moreover, when placed in a boat a keener influence turns its own poles round more quickly to the poles of the earth or the limits of variation on the horizon. One which performs its function more feebly indicates a defect and an effete nature. There muſt always be a ſimilar preparation, a ſimilar figure, and a like ſize; for in ſuch as are very diſſimilar and unlike, the experiment is doubtful. The method of teſting the ſtrength is the ſame alſo with a verſorium in a place ſomewhat remote from a loadſtone; for the one which is able to turn the verſorium round at the greater diſtance, that one conquers and is held the more potent. Rightly alſo is the force of a loadſtone weighed in a balance by B. Porta; a piece of loadſtone is placed in one ſcale-pan, in the other juſt as much weight of ſomething elſe, ſo that the ſcale-pans hang level. Soon a piece of iron lying on the table is adjuſted ſo that it ſticks to the loadſtone placed in the ſcale, and they cling together moſt perfectly, according to their friendly points; into the other ſcale-pan ſand is gradually thrown, and that until the ſcale in which the loadſtone is placed is ſeparated from the iron. Thus by weighing the weight of ſand, the magnetick force becomes known. Similarly alſo it will be pleaſing to try with another ſtone, in æquilibrium, the weight of the ſand being obſerved, and to find out the ſtronger by means of the weights of ſand. Such is the experiment of Cardinal Cuſan in his *De Staticis*, from whom it would ſeem that B. Porta learnt the experiment. The better loadſtones turn themſelves round more quickly toward the poles or points of variation; then they alſo lead along and turn round more quickly, according to the greater quantity and maſs of wood, a boat and other ſtuff. In a declination inſtrument, the more powerful force of a loadſtone is looked for and required. Thoſe therefore are more lively when they get through their work readily, and paſs through and come back again with ſpeed, and ſwiftly at length ſettle at their own point. Languid and effete ones move more ſluggiſhly, ſettle more tardily, adhære more uncertainly, and are eaſily diſturbed from their poſſeſſion.

CHAP.

CHAP. XXXVII.

Ufe of a Loadftone as it affects
iron.

Y magnetick coition we teft iron ore in a black-fmith's forge.   It is burnt, broken in pieces, wafhed and dried, in which way it lays down its alien humours; in the bits collected from the wafhing is placed a loadftone, which attracts the iron duft to itfelf; this, being brufhed off with feathers, is received in a crucible, and the loadftone is again placed in the bits collected from the wafhing, and the duft wiped off, as long as any remains which it will attract to itfelf.   This is then heated in the crucible along with *fal nitri* until it is liquid, and from this a fmall mafs of iron is caft.   But if the loadftone draws the duft to itfelf quickly and readily, we conjecture that the iron ore is rich; if flowly, poor; if it feems altogether to reject it, there is very little iron in it or none at all.   In like manner iron duft can be feparated from another metal.   Many tricks there are alfo, when iron is fecretly applied to lighter bodies, and, being attracted by the motion of a loadftone which is kept out of fight, caufes movements which are amazing to thofe who do not know the caufe. Very many fuch indeed every ingenious mechanician will perform by fleight of hand, as if by incantations and jugglery.

CHAP. XXXVIII.

On Cafes of Attraction in other Bodies.

ERY often the herd of philofophizers and plagiarifts repeat from the records of others in natural philo-fophy opinions and errors about the attractions of various bodies; as that Diamond attracts iron, and fnatches it away from a magnet; that there are various kinds of magnets, fome which attract gold, others filver, brafs, lead; even fome which attract flefh, water, fifhes.   The flame of fulphur is faid to feek iron and ftones; fo white naphtha is faid to attract fire.   I have faid above that inani-
mate

mate natural bodies do not attract, and are not attracted by, others on the earth, excepting magnetically or electrically. Wherefore it is not true that there are magnets which attract gold or other metals; becaufe a magnetick fubftance draws nothing but magnetick fubftances. Though Fracaftorio fays that he has fhown a magnet drawing filver; if this were true, it muft have happened on account of iron fkilfully mixed with that filver or concealed in it, or elfe becaufe nature (as fhe does fometimes, but rarely) had mixed iron with the filver; iron indeed is rarely mixed with filver by nature; filver with iron very rarely or never. Iron is mixed with filver by forgers of falfe coin or from the avarice of princes in the coining of money, as was the cafe with the denarius of Antony, provided that Pliny is recording a true incident. So Cardan (perhaps deceived by others) fays that there is a certain kind of loadftone which draws filver; he adds a moft foolifh teft of this: "If there-" fore" (he fays) "a flender rod of filver be fteeped in that in which "a verfatory needle has ftood, it will turn toward filver (efpecially "toward a large quantity) although it be buried; by this means any-" one will be able eafily to dig up concealed treafures." He adds that "it fhould be very good ftone, fuch as he has not yet feen." Nor indeed will either he or anyone elfe ever fee fuch a ftone or fuch an experiment. Cardan brings forward an attraction of flefh, wrongly fo named and very diffimilar from that of the loadftone; for his *magnes creagus* or flefh-magnet, from the experiment that it fticks to the lips, muft be hooted out from the affembly of load-ftones, or by all means from the family of things attractive. Lemnian earth, ruddle, and very many minerals do this, and yet they are fatuoufly faid to attract. He will have it that there is another loadftone, as it were, a third fpecies, into which, if a needle is driven and afterwards ftuck into the body, it is not felt. But what has attraction to do with ftupefaction, or ftupor with a Philofopher's intellect, when he is difcourfing about attraction? There are many ftones, both found in nature and made by art, which have the power of ftupefying. Sulphur flame is faid by fome to attract, becaufe it confumes certain metals by its power of penetration. So white naphtha attracts flame, becaufe it gives off and exhales an inflammable vapour, on which account it is kindled at fome diftance, juft as the fmoke of a recently extinguifhed candle takes fire again from another flame; for fire creeps to fire through an inflammable medium. Why the fucking fifh Echineis or the Remora fhould ftay fhips has been varioufly treated by Philofophers, who are often accuftomed to fit this fable (as many others) to their theories, before they find out whether the thing is fo in nature. Therefore, in order that they may fupport and agree with the fatuities of the ancients, they put forward even the moft fatuous ratiocinations and ridiculous problems, cliffs that attract, where the

fucking

fucking fifh tarry, and the neceffity of fome vacuum, I know not what, or how produced.   Pliny and Julius Solinus make mention of a ftone Chatochitis.   They fay that it attracts flefh, and keeps hold of the hands, juft as a loadftone does iron, and amber chaff.   But that happens only from a ftickinefs and from glue contained in it, fince it fticks more eafily to the hands when they are warm.   Sagda or Sagdo, of the colour of a fard, is a precious ftone mentioned by Pliny, Solinus, Albertus, and Evax; they defcribe its nature and relate, on the authority of others, that it fpecially attracts wood to itfelf.   Some even babble that woods cannot be wrenched away except they are cut off.   Some alfo narrate that a ftone is found which grows pertinacioufly into fhips, in the fame way as certain teftacea on long voyages.   But a ftone does not draw becaufe it fticks; and if it drew, it would certainly draw fhreds electrically.   Encelius faw in the hands of a failor fuch a ftone of feeble virtue, which would hardly attract even the fmalleft twigs; and in truth, not of the colour of the fard. So Diamond, Carbuncle, Cryftal, and others do attract.   I pafs over other fabulous ftones; Pantarbe, about which Philoftratus writes that it draws other ftones to itfelf; Amphitane alfo, which attracts gold.   Pliny in his origin of glafs will have it that a load-ftone is an attractor of glafs, as well as of iron.   For in his method of preparing glafs, when he has indicated its nature, he fubjoins this about loadftone.   " Soon (fuch is the aftute and refourceful " craft) it was not content to have mixed natron; loadftone alfo began " to be added, fince it was thought to attract to itfelf the liquor of " glafs (as it does iron)."   Georgius Agricola writes that to the material of glafs (fand and natron) one part alfo of loadftone is added. " Becaufe that force is believed, in our times juft as in former times, " to attract the liquor of glafs to itfelf, as it attracts iron to itfelf, " purges it when drawn, and makes clear glafs from green or muddy; " but the fire afterwards burns up the loadftone."   It is true indeed that fome fort of *magnes* (as the magnefia of the glafs-makers im-bued with no magnetick virtues) is fometimes put in and mixed with the material of the glafs; not, however, becaufe it attracts glafs. But when a loadftone is burnt, it does not lay hold of iron at all, nor is iron when red-hot allured by any loadftone; and loadftone alfo is burntup by more powerful fires and lofes its attractive potency. Nor is this a function of loadftone alone in the glafs furnaces; but alfo of certain pyrites and of fome eafily combuftible iron ores, which are the only ones ufed by our glafs-makers, who make clear, bright glafs.   They are mixed with the fand, afhes, and natron (juft as they are accuftomed to make additions in the cafe of metallick ores whilft they are fmelted), fo that when the material flows down into glafs, the green and muddy colour of the glafs may be purged by the penetrating heat.   For no other material becomes fo hot,

or

or bears the fire for fuch a convenient time, until the material of the glafs is perfectly fluid, and is at the fame time burnt up by that ardent fire. It happens, however, fometimes, that on account of the magnetick ftone, the magnefia, or the ore, or the pyrites, the glafs has a dufky colour, when they refift the fire too much and are not burnt up, or are put in in too great quantity. Wherefore manufacturers are feeking for a ftone fuitable for them, and are obferving alfo more diligently the proportion of the mixture. Badly therefore did the unfkilful philofophy of Pliny impofe upon Georgius Agricola and the more recent writers, fo that they thought the loadftone was wanted by glafs-makers on account of its magnetick ftrength and attraction. But Scaliger in *De Subtilitate ad Cardanum*, in making diamond attract iron, when he is difcuffing magneticks, wanders far from the truth, unlefs it be that diamond attracts iron electrically, as it attracts wood, ftraws, and all other minute bodies when it is rubbed. Fallopius reckons that quick-filver draws metals by reafon of an occult property, juft as a load-ftone iron, amber chaff. But when quickfilver enters metals, it is wrongly called attraction. For metals imbibe quickfilver, juft as clay water; nor do they do this unlefs they are touching, for quickfilver does not allure gold or lead to itfelf from afar, but they remain motionlefs in their places.

CHAP. XXXIX.

On Bodies which mutually repel one another.

WRITERS who have difcourfed on the forces of bodies which attract others have alfo fpoken about the powers of bodies which repel, but efpecially thofe who have inftituted claffes for natural objects on the bafis of fympathy and antipathy. Wherefore it would feem necef-fary for us to fpeak alfo about the mutual ftrife of bodies, fo that publifhed errors fhould not creep further, and be received by all to the ruin of true philofophy. They fay that, juft as like things attract for the fake of prefervation, fo unlike and contrary things for the fame purpofe mutually repel and put one another to flight. This is evident in the reaction of many things, but it is moft manifeft in the cafe of plants and animals, which attract kindred and familiar things, and in like manner reject foreign and unfuitable things. But in other bodies there is not the fame reafon, fo that when they are feparated, they fhould come together by mutually
attracting

attracting one another. Animals take food (as everything which
grows), and draw it into their interior; they abforb the nourifhment by certain parts and inftruments (through the action and
operation of the *anima*). They enjoy by natural inftinct only the
things fet in front of them and near them, not things placed afar
off; and this without any alien force or motion. Wherefore animals
neither attract any bodies nor drive them away. Water does not
repel oil (as fome think) becaufe the oil floats on water; nor does
water repel mud, becaufe the mud, if mixed in water, fettles down
in time. This is a feparation of unlike bodies or fuch as are not
perfectly mixed as refpects the material; the feparated bodies neverthelefs remain joined without any natural ftrife. Wherefore a
muddy fediment fettles quietly on the bottom of veffels, and oil
remains on the top of the water and is not fent further away.
A drop of water remains intact on a dry furface, and is not expelled
from the dry fubftance. Wrongly therefore do thofe who difcourfe
on thefe matters infer an antipathy (that is, the force of repelling
by contrary paffions); for there is no repelling force in them; and
repulfion comes from action, not from paffion. But their greek
vocables pleafe them too much. We, however, muft inquire
whether there is any body which drives anything elfe further off
without material impetus, as a loadftone attracts. But a loadftone
feems even to repel loadftone. For the pole of one loadftone repels
the pole of another, which does not agree with it according to
nature; by repelling, it turns it round in an orbit fo that they may
exactly agree according to their nature. But if a fomewhat weak
loadftone, floating freely on water, cannot readily be turned round
on account of impediments, the whole loadftone is repelled and
fent further away from the other. All electricks attract all things:
they never repel or propel anything at all. As to what is related
about certain plants (as about the cucumber, which turns afide
when oil is applied to it), there is a material change from the
vicinity, not a hidden antipathy. But when they fhow a candle
flame put againft a cold folid fubftance (as iron) turn away to the
fide, and allege antipathy as the caufe, they fay nothing. The
reafon of this they will fee clearer than the day, when
we difcourfe on what heat is. But Fracaftorio's
opinion that a loadftone can be found, which
would drive iron away, on account of
fome oppofing principle lurking
in the iron, is foolifh.

BOOK

Q

BOOK THIRD.

Chap. I.

ON DIRECTION.

N referring to the earlier books it will be found
fhown that a loadftone has its poles, and that a
piece of iron has alfo poles, and rotation, and a
certain verticity; finally, that the loadftone and
the iron direct their poles toward the poles of the
earth. Now, however, we muft make clear the
caufes of thefe things and their admirable workings, pointed out
indeed before, but not proven. All thofe who have written before
us about thefe rotations have left us their opinions fo briefly, fo
meagrely, and with fuch hefitating judgment that they feem hardly
likely ever to perfuade anyone, or even to be able to fatisfy themfelves; and all their petty reafons are rejected by the more prudent
as ufelefs, uncertain, and abfurd, being fupported by no proofs or
arguments; whence alfo magnetick fcience, being all the more
neglected and not underftood, has been in exile. The true auftral
pole of a loadftone, not the boreal (as all before us ufed to think), *
if the loadftone is placed in its boat on the furface of water,
turns to the North; in the cafe of a piece of iron alfo, whether it
has been excited by a loadftone or not, the fouthern end moves
toward the North. An oblong piece of iron of three or four
digits' length, when fkilfully rubbed with a loadftone, quickly turns
north and fouth. Wherefore mechanicians, taking a piece of iron
prepared in this way, balance it on a pin in a box, and fit it
up with the requifites of a fun-dial; or they prepare the verforium
out of two curved pieces of iron with their ends touching one
another, fo that the motion may be more conftant. In this way
the mariners' verforium is arranged, which is an inftrument beneficial, ufeful, and aufpicious to failors for indicating, like a good
genius, fafety and the right way. But it muft be underftood on
the threfhold of this argument (before we proceed further) that
thefe pointings of the loadftone or of iron are not perpetually made

toward

toward the true poles of the world, do not always feek thofe fixed and definite points, or remain on the line of the true meridian; but ufually diverge fome diftance to the Eaft or to the Weft. Sometimes alfo at certain places on land or fea they do indicate exactly the true poles. This difcrepancy is called the *Variation* of the iron or of the loadftone; and fince this is brought about by other caufes, and is merely a certain difturbance and perverfion of the true direction, we are directing our attention in this place to the true direction of the compafs and of the magnetick iron (which would be equally toward the true poles and on the true meridian everywhere on the earth, unlefs other obftacles and an untoward pervertency hindered it). Of its variation and the caufe of the perverfion we fhall treat in the next book. Thofe who wrote about the world and about natural philofophy a century ago, efpecially thofe remarkable elementary philofophers, and all thofe who trace their knowledge and training to them down to our own times, thofe men, I fay, who reprefented the earth as always at reft and, as it were, a ufelefs weight, placed in the centre of the univerfe at an equal diftance from the fky on every fide, and its nature to be fimple, imbued only with the qualities of drynefs and cold, fought diligently for the caufes of all things and of all effects in the heavens, the ftars, the planets, in fire, air, waters and fubftances of mixed natures. Never indeed did they recognize that the terreftrial globe had, befides drynefs and cold, fome fpecial, effective, and predominant properties, ftrengthening, directing, and moving the globe itfelf through its whole mafs and its very deepeft vitals; nor did they ever inquire whether there were any fuch. For this reafon the crowd of philofophizers, in order to difcover the reafons of the magnetical motions, called up caufes lying remote and far away. And one man feems to me beyond all others worthy of cenfure, Martin Cortes, who, fince there was no caufe which could fatisfy him in the whole of nature, dreamed that there was a point of magnetical attraction beyond the heavens, which attracted iron. Peter Peregrinus thinks that the direction arifes from the poles of the fky. Cardan thought that the turning of iron was caufed by a ftar in the tail of the Great Bear; Beffard, the Frenchman, opines that a magnetick turns toward the pole of the zodiack. Marfilius Ficinus will have it that the loadftone follows its own Arctick pole; but that iron follows the loadftone, ftraws amber; whilft this perhaps follows the Antarctick pole—a moft foolifh dream. Others have recourfe to I know not what magnetick rocks and mountains. Thus it is always cuftomary with mortals, that they defpife things near home, whilft foreign and diftant things are dear and prized. But we ftudy the earth itfelf and obferve in it the caufe 'of fo great an effect. The earth, as the common mother, has thefe caufes inclofed in her innermoft parts; in accordance with her rule,

pofition,

pofition, condition, verticity, poles, æquator, horizons, meridians, centre, circumference, diameter, and the nature of the whole interior of her fubftance, muft all magnetical motions be difcuffed. The earth has been ordered by the higheft Artificer and by nature in fuch a way that it fhould have parts diffimilar in pofition, bounds of the whole and complete body, ennobled by certain functions, by which it might itfelf remain in a definite direction.   For juft as a loadftone, when it is floated on water in a fuitable veffel, or is hung by flender threads in the air, by its implanted verticity conforms its poles to the poles of the common mother in accordance with magnetick laws; fo if the earth were to deviate from its natural direction and its true pofition in the univerfe, or if its poles were to be drawn afide (if this were poffible) toward the fun-rifing or the fun-fetting or toward any other points whatfoever in the vifible firmament, they would return again to the north and fouth by magnetical motion, and would fettle at the fame points at which they are now fixed.   The reafon why the terreftrial globe feems to remain more fteadily with the one pole toward thofe parts and directed toward the Cynofure, and why its pole diverges by 23 degrees 29 minutes, with a certain variation not fufficiently inveftigated as yet by Aftronomers, from the poles of the ecliptick, depends on its virtue magnetical.   The caufes of the preceffion of the æquinoxes and the progreffion of the fixed ftars, and of the change, moreover, in the declinations of the fun and of the tropicks, muft be fought from magnetick influences; fo that neither that abfurd motion of trepidation of Thebit Bencora, which is at great variance with obfervations, nor the monftrous fuperftructures of other heavens, are any longer needed.   A verfatory iron turns to the pofition of the earth, and if difturbed ever fo often returns always to the fame points.   For in the far regions of the north, in a latitude of 70 or 80 degrees (to which at the milder feafons of the year our failors are accuftomed to penetrate without injury from the cold) ; in the regions halfway between the poles ; on the æquator in the torrid zone; and again in all the maritime places and lands of the fouth, in the higheft latitude which has thus far been reached, always the iron magnetick finds its way, and points to the poles in the fame manner (excepting for the difference of variation) ; on this fide of the æquator (where we live), and on the other fide to the fouth, lefs well known, but yet in fome meafure explored by failors : and always the lily of the compafs points toward the North.   This we have had confirmed by the moft eminent captains, and alfo by very many of the more intelligent failors.   Thefe facts have been pointed out to me and confirmed by our moft illuftrious Sea-god, Francis Drake, and by another circumnavigator of the globe, Thomas Candifh ; our terrella alfo indicates the fame thing.   This is demonftrated in the cafe of the

orbicular

orbicular ftone, whofe poles are A and B ; an iron wire C D, which
is placed upon the ftone, always points directly along the meridian
toward the poles A B, whether the centre of the wire is on the
central line or æquator of the ftone, or on any other part fituated

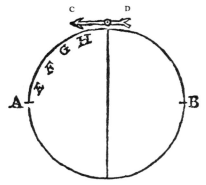

between the æquator and the poles, as at H, G, F, E.   So the cufp
of a verforium on this fide of the æquator points toward the north ;
on the other fide the crofs is always directed toward the fouth ;
but the cufp or lily does not, as fome one has thought, turn toward
the fouth beyond the æquator.   Some inexperienced people indeed,
who in diftant parts beyond the æquator have feen the verforium
fometimes become more fluggifh and lefs prompt, thought that the
diftance from the arctick pole or from the magnetick rocks was the
caufe of this.   But they are very much miftaken ; for it is as
powerful, and adjufts itfelf as quickly to the meridian or to the
point of variation in the fouthern as in the northern parts of the
earth.   Yet fometimes the motion appears flower, namely, when
the fupporting pin by lapfe of time and long voyaging has become
fomewhat blunt, or the magnetick iron parts have loft, by age or
ruft, fome of their acquired vigour.   This may alfo be fhown ex-
perimentally by the verfatory iron of a fmall fun-dial placed on a
very fhort pin fet perpendicular to the furface of the ftone, for the
iron when touched by a loadftone points toward the poles of the
ftone and leaves the poles of the earth ; for the general and remoter
caufe is overcome by the particular and powerful caufe which is fo
near at hand.   Magnetick bodies have of themfelves an inclination
toward the pofition of the earth and are influenced by a terrella.
Two equal ftones of equal ftrength adjuft themfelves to a terrella
in accordance with magnetick laws.   The iron conceives vigour
from the loadftone and is influenced by the magnetical motions.
Wherefore true direction is the motion of a magnetick body in
regard to the verticity of the earth, the natures of both agreeing
and working together toward a natural pofition and unity.   For
indeed we have found out at length, by many experiments and in
many ways, that there is a difpofing nature, moving them together
by reafon of their various pofitions by one form that is common
                                                                    to

to both, and that in all magnetick fubftances there is attraction and repulfion.   For both the ftone and the magnetick iron arrange themfelves by inclination and declination, according to the common pofition of their nature and the earth.   And the force of the earth by the virtue of the whole, by attracting toward the poles, and repelling, arranges all magneticks which are unfixed and loofe. For in all cafes all magneticks conform themfelves to the globe of the earth in the fame ways and by the fame laws by which another loadftone or any magneticks do to a terrella.

CHAP. II.

The Directive or Verforial Virtue (which we call

verticity) : what it is, how it exifts in the loadftone;
and in what way it is acquired when innate.

DIRECTIVE force, which is alfo called by us ver-ticity, is a virtue which fpreads by an innate vigour from the æquator in both directions toward the poles.   That power, inclining in both directions towards the termini, caufes the motion of direction, and produces a conftant and permanent pofition in Nature, not only in the earth itfelf but alfo in all magneticks. Loadftone is found either in veins of its own or in iron mines, when the homogeneous fubftance of the earth, either having or affuming a primary form, is changed or concreted into a ftony fub-ftance, which befides the primary qualities of its nature has various diffimilitudes and differences in different quarries and mines, as if from different matrices, and very many fecondary qualities and varieties in its fubftance.   A loadftone which is dug out in this breaking up of the earth's furface and of protuberances upon it, whether formed complete in itfelf (as fometimes in China) or in a larger vein, is fafhioned by the earth and follows the nature of the whole.   All the interior parts of the earth mutually confpire together in combination and produce direction toward north and fouth.   But thofe magnetical bodies which come together in the uppermoft parts of the earth are not true united parts of the whole, but appendages and parts joined on, imitating the nature of the whole ; wherefore when floating free on water, they difpofe them-felves juft in the fame way as they are placed in the terreftrial fyftem of nature.   We had a large loadftone of twenty pounds ✱ weight, dug up and cut out of its vein, after we had firft obferved and marked its ends ; then after it was dug out, we placed it in a boat on water, fo that it could turn freely ; then immediately the face which had looked toward the north in the quarry began to

turn

turn to the north on the waves and at length settled toward that point.   For that face which looked toward the north in the quarry is the southern, and is attracted by the northern parts of the earth, in the same way as pieces of iron which acquire their verticity from the earth.   About this point we intend to speak afterwards under change of verticity.   But there is a different rotation of the internal parts of the earth, which are perfectly united to the earth and which are not separated from the true substance of the earth by the interposition of bodies as are loadstones in the upper portion of the earth, which is maimed, corrupt, and variable.   Let A B be a

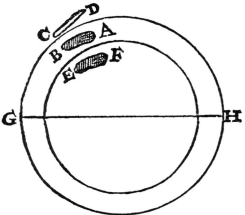

piece of magnetick ore; between which and the uniform globe of the earth lie various soils or mixtures which separate the ore to a certain extent from the globe of the true earth.   It is therefore influenced by the forces of the earth just in the same way as C D, a piece of iron, in the air.   So the face B of some ore or of that piece of it is moved toward the Boreal pole G, just as the extremity C of the iron, not A or D.   But the condition of the piece E F is different, which piece is produced in one connected mass with the whole, and is not separated from it by any earthy mixture.   For if the part E F were taken out and floated freely in a boat by itself, it is not E that would be directed toward the Boreal pole, but F. So in those substances which acquire their verticity in the air, C is the southern part and is seen to be attracted by the Boreal pole G. In the case of others which are found in the upper unstable portion of the earth, B is the south, and in like manner inclines toward the Boreal pole.   But if those pieces deep down which are produced along with the earth are dug up, they turn about on a different plan.   For F turns toward the Boreal parts of the earth, because it is the southern   part; E toward the south, because it is the northern.   So of a magnetick body, C D, placed close to the earth, the end C turns toward the Boreal pole; of one that is adnate to it, B A, B inclines to the North; of one that is innate in it, E F, E turns toward the southern pole; which is confirmed by the

following

following demonſtration, and comes about of neceſſity according to all magnetick laws.   Let there be a terrella with poles A B; from its

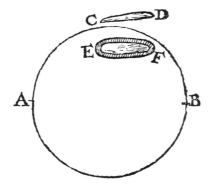

maſs cut out a ſmall part E F; if this be ſuſpended by a fine thread above the hole or over ſome other place, E does not ſeek the pole A but the pole B, and F turns to A; very differently from a rod of iron C D; becauſe C, touching ſome northern part of the terrella, being magnetically carried away makes a turn round to A, not to B.   And yet here it ſhould be obſerved, that if the pole A of the terrella were moved toward the earth's ſouth, the end E of the piece cut out by itſelf, if not brought too near to the ſtone, would alſo move of itſelf toward the ſouth.   But the end C of the piece of iron, placed beyond its orbe of virtue, will turn toward the north.   The part E F of the terrella, whilſt in the maſs, produced the ſame direction as the whole; but when it is ſeparated and ſuſpended by a thread, E turns to B, and F to A.

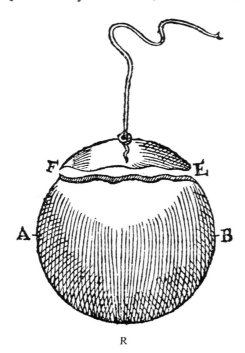

R

So

So parts having the fame verticity with the whole, when feparated, are impelled in the contrary direction; for contrary parts folicit contrary parts. Nor yet is this a true contrariety, but the higheft concordancy, and the true and genuine conformation of bodies mag-netical in the fyftem of nature, if they fhall have been divided and feparated: for the parts thus divided fhould be raifed fome diftance from the whole, as will be made clear afterwards. Magnetick fub-ftances feek a unity as regards form; they do not fo much refpect their own mafs. Wherefore the part F E is not attracted into its
* former bed; but when once it is unfettled and at a diftance, it is folicited by the oppofite pole. But if the fmall piece F E is placed back again in its bed or brought clofe to, without any fubftances intervening, it acquires its former combination, and, as a part of the whole once more united, accords with the whole and fticks readily in its former pofition; and E remains toward A, and F toward B, and they fettle fteadily in their mother's lap. The reafoning is the fame when the ftone is divided into equal parts through the poles.
* A fpherical ftone is divided into two equal parts along the axis A B; whether therefore the furface A B is in the one part facing upward

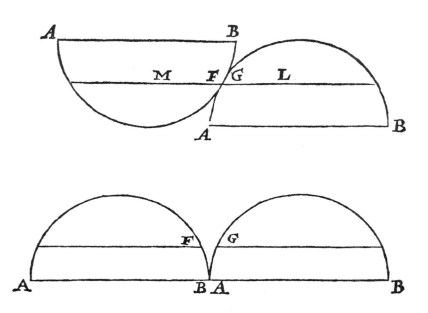

* (as in the former diagram) or lying on its face in both parts (as in the latter), the end A tends toward B. But it muft alfo be under-ftood that the point A is not carried with a definite aim always toward the point B, becaufe in confequence of the divifion the verticity proceeds to other points, as to F G, as appears in the four-teenth chapter of this book. And L M are now the axes in each, and A B is no longer the axis; for magnetick bodies, as foon as they are divided, become fingle magnetick wholes; and they have
vertices

vertices in accordance with their mafs, new poles arifing at each end in confequence of the divifion. Yet the axis and the poles always follow the leading of a meridian; becaufe that force paffes along the meridians of the ftone from the æquator to the poles, by an everlafting rule, the inborn virtue of the fubftance agreeing thereto from the long and lafting pofition and the facing of a fuitable fubftance toward the poles of the earth; by whofe ftrength continued through many centuries it has been fafhioned; toward fixed and determined parts of which it has remained fince its origin firmly and conftantly turned.

CHAP. III.

How Iron acquires Verticity through
a Loadftone, and how that verticity
is loft and changed.

FRICTION between an oblong piece of iron and a loadftone imparts to the former magnetick virtues, which are not corporeal nor inhærent and perfiftent in any body, as we fhowed in the difcuffion on coition. It is plain that the iron, when it has been rubbed hard with one end and applied to the ftone for a pretty long time, receives no ftony nature, acquires no weight; for if, before the iron is touched by the ftone, you weigh *

it in a fmall and very exa& goldfmith's balance, you will fee after the rubbing that it has exactly the fame weight, neither diminifhed nor increafed. But if you wipe the iron with cloths after it has been touched, or wafh it in water, or fcour it with fand or on a grindftone, ftill it in nowife lays afide its acquired ftrength. For the force is fpread through the whole body and conceived in the inmoft parts, and cannot in any way be wafhed or wiped away. Let an experiment then be made in fire, that untamed tyrant of nature. Take a piece of iron of the length of a palm and the thicknefs of a goofequill pen; let this iron be paffed through a fuitable round cork and placed on the furface of water, and obferve the end which turns to the north; rub this particular end with the true fouthern end of a loadftone; the iron fo rubbed turns toward the fouth. Remove the cork, and place the end *

which was excited in the fire until the iron is juft red-hot; when it is cooled, it will retain the ftrength of the loadftone and the verticity, though it will not be fo prompt, whether becaufe the force of the fire had not yet continued long enough to overcome all its

ftrength

strength, or because the whole iron was not heated to redness, for the virtue is diffused through the whole. Remove the cork a second time, and putting the whole iron in the fire, blow the fire with the bellows, so that it may be all aglow, and let it remain a little longer time red-hot; when cooled (so, however, that, whilst it is cooling, it does not rest in one position), place it again on the water with the cork, and you will see that it has lost the verticity which it had acquired from the stone. From these experiments it is clear how difficult it is for the property of polarity implanted by the loadstone to be destroyed. But if a small loadstone had remained as long in the same fire, it would have lost its strength. Iron, because it does not so easily perish, and is not so easily burnt up as very many loadstones, retains its strength more stably, and when it is lost can recover it again from a loadstone; but a loadstone when burnt does not revive. But now that iron, which has been deprived of its magnetick form, moves in a different way from any other piece of iron, for it has lost its polar nature; and whereas before the touch of the loadstone it may have had a motion toward the north, and after contact toward the south; now it turns to no definite and particular point; but afterwards, very slowly and after a long time, it begins to turn in a doubtful fashion toward the poles of the earth (having acquired some power from the earth). I have said that the cause of direction was twofold, one implanted in the stone and iron, but the other in the earth, implanted by the disponent virtue; and for that reason (the distinction of poles and the verticity in the iron having now been destroyed) a slow and weak directive power is acquired anew from the verticity of the earth. We may see, therefore, with what difficulty and only by the application of hot fires and by long ignition of the iron heated to softness, the imparted magnetick virtue is eradicated. When this ignition has overcome the acquired polarity, and it has been now completely subdued and not awakened again, that iron is left unsettled and utterly incapable of direction. But we must further inquire how iron remains affected by verticity. It is manifest that it strongly affects and changes the nature of the iron, because the presence of a loadstone attracts the iron to itself with an altogether wonderful readiness. Nor is it only the part that is rubbed, but on account of the rubbing (on one end only) the whole iron is affected together, and gains by it a permanent though an unequal power. This is demonstrated as follows. Rub an iron wire on the end so that it is excited, and it will turn towards the north; afterward cut off some portion of it; you will see that it still turns toward the north (as before), but more feebly. For it must be understood that the loadstone excites a steady verticity in the whole iron (if the rod be not too long), more vigorous throughout the whole mass in a shorter bar, and as long as the iron remains touching the loadstone a little

stronger

ftronger.   But when the iron is feparated from contact with it,
then it becomes much weaker, efpecially in the end that was not
touched.   Juft as a long rod, one end of which is placed in the fire
and heated, grows exceedingly hot at that end, lefs fo in the parts
adjoining and in the middle, whilft at the other end it can be held
in the hand, and that end is only warm; fo the magnetical vigour
diminifhes from the excited end to the other end; but it is prefent
there inftantly, and does not enter after an interval of time nor
fucceffively, as the heat in the iron; for as foon as a piece of iron
has been touched by a loadftone it is excited throughout its whole
length.   For the fake of experiment, let there be a rod of iron 4 or   ✻
5 digits long, untouched by a loadftone; as foon as you touch one
end only with a loadftone, the oppofite end immediately, or in the
twinkling of an eye, by the power that it has conceived, repels or
attracts a verforium, if it be applied to it ever fo quickly.

CHAP. IIII.

Why Iron touched by a Loadftone acquires an oppofite
verticity, and why iron touched by the true Northern fide of a ftone
turns to the North of the earth, by the true Southern fide
to the South; and does not turn to the South when rubbed
by the Northern point of the ftone, and when by
the Southern to the North, as all who have
written on the loadftone have
falfely fuppofed.

DEMONSTRATION has already been given that the
northern part of a loadftone does not attract the
northern part of another ftone, but the fouthern,
and repels the northern part of another ftone from
its northern fide when it is applied to it.   That
general magnet, the terreftrial globe, difpofes iron
touched by a loadftone in the fame way, and likewife magnetick
iron ftirs this fame iron by its implanted ftrength, and excites motion
and controls it.   For whether the comparifon and experiment has
been made between loadftone and loadftone, or loadftone and iron, or
iron and iron, or the earth and loadftone, or the earth and iron con-   ✻
formed by the earth or ftrengthened by the power of a loadftone,
the ftrength and inclinations of each muft mutually harmonize and
accord in the fame way.   But the reafon muft be fought, why a
piece of iron when touched by a loadftone acquires a difpofition to
motion toward the oppofite pole of the earth, and not toward that

pole

pole of the earth to which that pole of that loadftone turned by which it was excited. It has been pointed out that iron and load-ftone are of one primary nature; when the iron is joined to the loadftone, they become, as it were, one body, and not only is the end of the iron changed, but the remaining parts alfo are affected along with it. A, the north pole of a loadftone, is placed againft the cufp of a piece of iron; the cufp of the iron has now become the fouthern part of the iron,

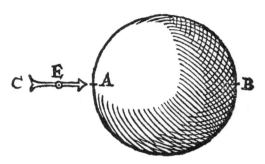

becaufe it is touching the northern part ot the ftone; the crofs-end of the iron has become the northern. For if that contiguous mag-netick fubftance be feparated from the pole of the terrella, or from the parts near the pole, the one end (or the end which, whilft the connection was kept up, was touching the northern part of the ftone) is the fouthern, whilft the other is the northern. So alfo if a ver-forium excited by a loadftone be divided into ever fo many parts (however fmall), thofe parts when feparated will, it is clear, arrange themfelves in the fame difpofition as that in which they were difpofed before, when they were undivided. Wherefore whilft the cufp remains over the northern pole A, it is not the fouthern end, but is, as it were, part of a whole; but when it is taken away from the ftone, it is the fouthern end, becaufe when rubbed it tended toward the northern parts of the ftone, and the crofs (the other end of the verforium) is the northern end. The loadftone and the iron make one body; B is the fouth pole of the whole; C (that is, the crofs) is the northern end of the whole; divide the iron alfo at E, and E will be the fouthern end with refpect to the crofs; and E will likewife be the northern end in refpect to B. A is the true northern pole of the ftone and is attracted by the fouthern pole of the earth. The end of the iron which is touched by the true boreal part of the ftone becomes the fouthern end, and turns to A, the north [pole] of the ftone, if it be near; or if it be fome diftance from the ftone, it turns to the north [pole] of the earth. So always iron which is touched (if it is free and unreftrained) tends to the oppofite part of the earth from that part to which the loadftone that touched it tends. Nor does it make any difference how it is rubbed, whether ftraight up or flanting in fome way. For in any cafe the verticity flows into the iron, pro-vided

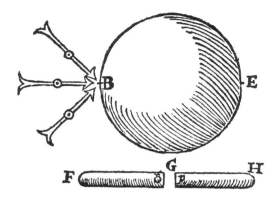

vided it is touched by either end.   Wherefore all the cufps at B
acquire the fame verticity, after they are feparated, but oppofite to that
pole of the ftone; wherefore alfo they are united to the loadftone at
the pole B; and all the croffes in the prefent figure have the oppofite
verticity to the pole E, and are moved and laid hold of by E when
they are in a convenient pofition.   It is exactly the fame in the
cafe of the long ftone F H divided at G; F and H always move,
both in the whole and in the divided ftone, to oppofite poles of
the earth, and O and P mutually attract one another, the one of
them being the northern, the other the fouthern.   For, fuppofing H
to have been the fouthern in the whole ftone and F the northern,
P will be the northern with refpect to H in the divided ftone, and
O the fouthern with refpect to F.   So alfo F and H mutually
incline to a connection, if they are turned a very little toward one
another, and run together at length and join.   But fuppofing the
divifion of the ftone to have been meridional (that is, according to
the line of a meridian, not of any parallel circle), then they turn
round, and A attracts B, and the end B is attracted to A and attracts

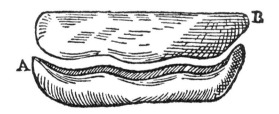

A, until, being turned round, they are connected and cemented
together; becaufe magnetick attraction is not made along the
parallels, but meridionally.   For this reafon pieces of iron placed
on a terrella whofe poles are A B, near the æquator along parallels, ✳
do not combine or ftick together firmly:

But

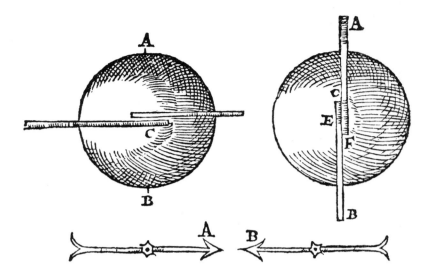

* But if applied to one another along a meridian they are immediately joined firmly together, not only on and near the ftone, but even at fome diftance within the force of the controlling orbe. Thus they are joined and cemented together at E, but not at C in the other figure. For the oppofite ends C and F meet and adhære together in the cafe of the iron juft in the fame way as A and B before in the cafe of the ftone. But they are oppofite ends, becaufe the pieces of iron proceed from the oppofite fides and poles of the terrella; and C in reference to
* the northern pole A is fouthern, and F is boreal in reference to the fouthern pole B. In like manner alfo they are cemented together, if the rod C (being not too long) be moved further toward A, and F toward B, and they be joined together over the terrella, like
* A and B of the divided ftone above. But now if the cufp A, which has been touched by a loadftone, be the fouthern end, and you were to touch and rub with this the cufp of another iron needle B, which has not been touched, B will be northern, and will point to the fouth. But if you were to touch with the northern point B any other iron needle, ftill new, on its cufp, this again will be fouthern, and will turn to the north. The iron not only receives the neceffary ftrength from the loadftone, if it be a good load-ftone, but alfo imparts its acquired ftrength to another piece of iron, and the fecond to a third (always in ftrict accordance with magnetick laws). In all thefe demonftrations of ours it fhould always be borne in mind that the poles of a ftone, as well as thofe of iron, whether touched or untouched, are always in fact and by nature oppofite to the pole toward which they point and are fo defignated by us, as
* we have laid down above. For in them all it is always the northern which tends to the fouth, either of the earth or of the ftone, and the fouthern which tends to the north of the ftone. Northern parts are attracted by the fouthern of the earth; fo in the boat they

tend

tend toward the fouth. A piece of iron touched by the northern parts of a loadftone becomes fouth at the one end and tends always (if it is near and within the orbe of the loadstone) to the north of the ftone, and if it be free and left to itfelf at fome diftance from the ftone, it tends to the northern part of the earth. The northern

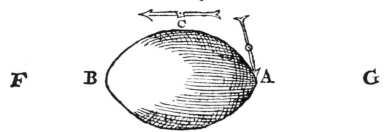

pole A of a loadftone turns to G, the fouth of the earth; a verforium touched at its cufp by the part A follows A, becaufe it has become fouthern. But the verforium C, placed farther away from the loadftone, turns its cufp to F, the north of the earth, becaufe the cufp has become fouthern by contact with the boreal part of the ftone. So the ends touched by the northern part of the ftone are made fouthern, or are excited with a fouthern polarity, and tend toward the north of the earth; thofe touched by the fouthern pole are made northern, or are excited with a northern force, and turn to the fouth of the earth.

CHAP. V.

On the Touching of pieces of Iron
of divers fhapes.

ARS of iron, when touched by a loadftone, have one end north, the other fouth, and in the middle is the limit of verticity, like the æquinoctial circle on the globe of a terrella or on an iron globe. But when an iron ring is rubbed on one fide on a loadftone, then the one pole is on the place that was in contact, whilft the other is at the oppofite point; and the magnetick power divides the ring into two parts by a natural diftinction which, though not in fhape, yet in power and effect is like an æquator. But if a thin ftraight rod be bent into a ring without any welding or union of the ends, and be touched in the middle by a loadftone, both ends will be of the fame verticity. Let a ring be taken which is whole and continuous, and which has been touched by a loadftone at one place, and let it be divided afterward

* at the oppofite point and ftraightened out, both ends will alfo be
of the fame verticity, no otherwife than a thin rod touched in the
middle or a ring not cohærent at the joint.

CHAP. VI.

What feems an Oppofing Motion in Magneticks
is a proper motion toward unity.

IN things magnetical nature always tends to unity,
not merely to confluence and agglomeration, but
to harmony; in fuch a way that the rotational and
difponent faculty fhould not be difturbed, as is
varioufly fhown in the following example.   Let
C D be an entire body of fome magnetick fubftance,

in which C tends to B, the north of the earth, and D to the fouth,
A.   Then divide it in the middle in its æquator, and it will be E
that is tending toward A, and F tending toward B.   For juft as
in the undivided body, fo in the divided, nature aims at thefe bodies
* being united; the end E again joins with F harmonioufly and
eagerly, and they ftick together, but E is never joined to D, nor F
to C; for then C muft be turned contrary to nature toward A, the
fouth, or D toward B, the north, which is foreign to them and
incongruous.   Separate the ftone in the place where it is cut and
turn D round to C; they harmonize and combine excellently.   For
D is tending to the fouth, as before, and C to the north; E and F,
parts which were cognate in the ore, are now widely feparated, for
they do not move together on account of material affinity, but they
take their motion and inclination from their form.   So the ends,
whether joined or divided, tend magnetically in the fame way to the
earth's poles in the firft figure where there is one whole, or divided
as in the fecond figure; and F E in the fecond figure is a perfect
magnetick joined together into one body; and C D, juft as it
was primarily produced in its ore, and F E in its boat, turn in
this

this way to the poles of the earth and are conformed to them.　✳
This harmony of the magnetick form is fhown alfo in the forms
of vegetables.　Let A B be a twig from a branch of ofier or other　✳
tree which fprouts eafily.　Let A be the upper part, B the lower

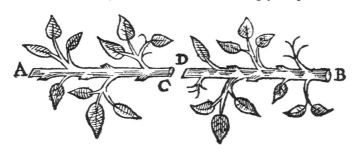

part toward the root; divide it at C D; I fay that the end D, if
grafted again to C by the pruner's art, grows to it; juft as alfo if B
is grafted to A, they grow together and germinate.　But D being
grafted on A, or C on B, they are at variance, and never grow into
one another, but one of them dies on account of the inverted and
inharmonious arrangement, fince the vegetative force, which moves
in one way, is now impelled in oppofite directions.

CHAP. VII.

A determined Verticity and a difponent Faculty are what
arrange magneticks, not a force, attracting or pulling them
together, nor merely a ftrongifh coition or unition.

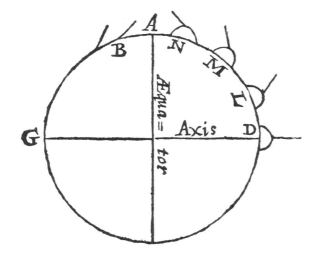

In

N the neighbourhood of the æquinoctial A there is no coition of the ends of a piece of iron with the terrella ; at the poles there is the ftrongeft. The greater the diftance from the æquinoctial, the ftronger is the coition with the ftone itfelf, and with any part of it, not with its pole alone. Yet pieces of iron are not raifed up on account of fome peculiar attracting force or a ftronger combined force, but on account of that common directing or conforming and rotating force ; nor indeed is a fpike in the part about B, even one that is very small and of no weight, raifed up to the perpendicular by the ftrongeft terrella, but cleaves to it obliquely. Alfo juft as a terrella attracts magnetick bodies varioufly with diffimilar forces, fo alfo an iron fnout placed on the ftone obtains a different potency in proportion to the latitude, juft as a fnout at L by its firmer connection refifts a greater weight more ftoutly than one at M, and at M than at N. But neither does the fnout raife the fpike to the perpendicular except at the poles, as is fhown in the figure. A fnout at L may hold and lift from the earth two ounces of iron in one piece ; yet it is not ftrong enough to raife an iron wire of two grains weight to the perpendicular, which would happen if the verticity arofe on account of a ftronger attraction, or rather coition or unition.

CHAP. VIII.

Of Difcords between pieces of Iron upon the fame pole
of a loadftone, and how they can agree and
ftand joined together.

UPPOSE two iron wires or a pair of needles ftuck on the pole of a terrella ; though they ought to ftand perpendicularly, they mutually repel one another at the upper end, and produce the appearance of a fork ; and if one end be forcibly impelled toward the other, the other declines and bends away from affociation with it, as in the following figure.

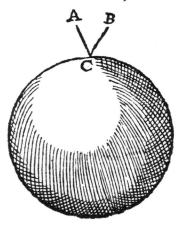

A and B

A and B, iron ſpikes, adhære obliquely upon the pole on account of their nearneſs to one another; either alone would otherwiſe ſtand erect and perpendicular.   For the extremities A B, being of the ſame verticity, mutually abhor and fly one another.   For if C be the northern pole of the terrella, A and B are alſo northern ends; but the ends which are joined to and held at the pole C are both * ſouthern.   But if thoſe ſpikes be a little longer (as, for example, of two digits length) and be joined by force, they adhære together and unite in a friendly ſtyle, and are not ſeparated without force. For they are magnetically welded, and there are now no longer two diſtinct ends, but one end and one body; no leſs than a wire which is doubled and ſet up perpendicularly.   But here is ſeen alſo another ſubtile point, that if thoſe ſpikes were ſhorter, not as much as the * breadth of one digit, or even the length of a barleycorn, they are in no way willing to harmonize or to ſtand ſtraight up at the ſame time, becauſe naturally in ſhorter wires the verticity is ſtronger in the ends which are diſtant from the terrella and the magnetick diſcord more vehement than in long ones.   Wherefore they in no way admit of an intimate aſſociation and connection.

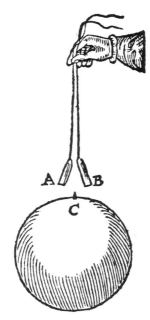

Likewiſe if thoſe lighter pieces of iron or iron wires be ſuf- pended, hanging, as A and B, from a very fine ſilk thread, not twiſted * but braided, diſtant from the ſtone the length of a ſingle barleycorn, then the oppoſing ends, A and B, being ſituated within the orbe of virtue above the pole, keep a little away from one another for the ſame reaſon; except when they are very near the pole of the ſtone C, the ſtone then attracting them more ſtrongly toward one end.

CHAP.

CHAP. IX.

Figures illuſtrating direction and ſhowing varieties
of rotations.

ASSING from the probable cauſe of motion toward fixed points (according to magnetick laws and principles), it remains for us to indicate thoſe motions. Above a round loadſtone (whoſe poles are A, B) let a verſatory needle be placed whoſe cuſp has been excited by the pole A; that cuſp is cer-

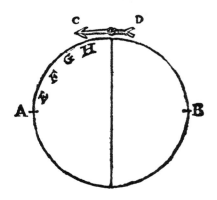

tainly directed toward A, and is ſtrongly attracted by A; becauſe, having been touched by A, it is in true harmony with A, and combines with it; and yet it is called contrary, becauſe when the verſorium is ſeparated from the ſtone, it is ſeen to be moved toward the oppoſite part of the earth to that toward which the pole A of the loadſtone is moved. For if A be the northern pole of the terrella, the cuſp is the ſouthern end of the needle, of which the other end (namely, the croſs) is pointed to B; ſo B is the ſouthern pole of the loadſtone, but the croſs is the northern end of the verſorium. So alſo the cuſp is attracted by E, F, G, H, and by every part of a meridian, from the æquator toward the pole, by the faculty diſponent; and when the verſorium is on the ſame parts of the meridian, the cuſp is directed toward A. For it is not the point A that turns the verſorium toward it, but the whole loadſtone; as alſo the whole earth does, in the turning of loadſtones to the earth.

Figures illuſtrating magnetick directions in a right ſphere of ſtone, and in the right ſphere of the earth, as well as the polar directions to the perpendicular of the poles. All theſe cuſps have been touched by the pole A; all the cuſps are turned toward A, excepting that one which is repelled by B.

Figures

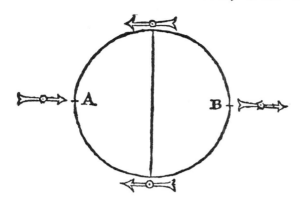

Figures illustrating horizontal directions above the body of a load-stone. All the cusps that have been made southern by rubbing on the boreal pole, or some place round the northern pole A, turn toward the pole A, and turn away from the southern pole B, toward

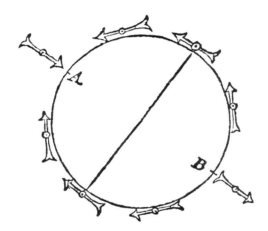

which all the crosses look. I call the direction horizontal, because it is arranged along the plane of the horizon; for nautical and horological instruments are so constructed that the iron hangs or is supported in æquilibrium on the point of a sharp pin, which prevents the dipping of the versorium, about which we intend to speak later. And in this way it is of the greatest use to man, indicating and distinguishing all the points of the horizon and the winds. Otherwise on every oblique sphere (whether of stone or the earth) versoria and all magnetick substances would have a dip by their own nature below the horizon; and at the poles the directions would be perpendicular, which appears in our discussion *On Declination.*

A round stone (or terrella) cut in two at the æquator; and all the cusps have been touched by the pole A. The points at the centre of the earth, and between the two parts of the terrella which has been cut in two through the plane of the æquator,

are

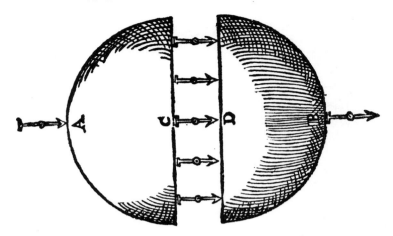

are directed as in the present diagram.   This would also happen in
the same way if the division of the stone were through the plane of
a tropick, and the mutual separation of the divided parts and the
interval between them were the same as before, when the loadstone
was divided through the plane of the æquator, and the parts separated.
For the cusps are repelled by C, are attracted by D; and the
versoria are parallel, the poles or the verticity in both ends mutually
requiring it.

*Half a terrella by itself and its directions, unlike the directions
of the two parts close to one another as shown in the figure above.*

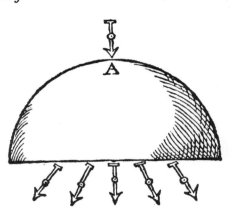

All the cusps have been touched by A; all the crosses below
except the middle one tend toward the loadstone, not straight,
but obliquely; because the pole is in the middle of the plane
which before was the plane of the æquator.   All cusps touched
by places distant from the pole move toward the pole (exactly
the same as if they had been rubbed upon the pole itself), not
toward the place where they were rubbed, wherever that may
have been in the undivided stone in some latitude between the
pole and the æquator.   And for this reason there are only two
distinctions of regions, northern and southern, in the terrella, just
as

as in the general terreftrial globe, and there is no eaftern nor weftern place; nor are there any eaftern or weftern regions, rightly fpeaking; but they are names ufed in refpect of one another toward the eaftern or weftern part of the fky.   Wherefore it does not appear that Ptolemy did rightly in his *Quadripartitum*, making eaftern and weftern diftricts and provinces, with which he improperly connects the planets, whom the common crowd of philofophizers and the fuperftitious foothfayers follow.

CHAP. X.

On Mutation of Verticity and of Magnetick
Properties, or on alteration in the power
excited by a loadftone.

FRICTION with a loadftone gives to a piece of iron a verticity ftrong enough; not, however, fo ftable that the iron may not by being rubbed on the oppofite part (not only with a more powerful loadftone, but with the fame) be changed and deprived of all its former verticity, and indued with a new and oppofite one. Take a piece of iron wire and rub each end of the wire equally with one and the fame pole of a loadftone, and let it be paffed through a fuitable cork and place it on water.   Then truly one end of the wire will be directed toward that pole of the earth toward which that end of the ftone will not turn.   But which end of the iron wire will it be?   That certainly which was rubbed laft.   Rub the other end of this again with the fame pole, and immediately *
that end will turn itfelf in the oppofite direction.   Again touch the former end of the iron wire only with the fame pole of the loadftone as before; and that end, having gained the command, immediately changes to the contrary fide.   So you will be able to change the property of the iron frequently, and that end of the wire rules which has been touched the laft.   Now then merely hold the boreal pole of the ftone for fome time near the boreal part of the wire which was laft touched, fo that it does not touch, but fo that it is removed from it by one, two, or even three digits, if the ftone have been pretty *
ftrong; and again it will change its property and will turn round to the contrary fide; which will alfo happen (albeit rather more feebly) even if the loadftone be removed to a diftance of four digits.   You will be able to do the fame thing, moreover, with both the auftral and the boreal part of the ftone in all thefe experiments.   Verticity may likewife be acquired and changed when thin plates of gold, *
filver, and glafs are interpofed between the ftone and the end of the iron or iron wire, if the ftone were rather ftrong, even if the inter-

T   mediate

mediate lamina is not touched either by the iron or the ftone.
And thefe changes of verticity take place in fmelted iron. Indeed
what the one pole of the ftone implants and excites, the other
difturbs and extinguifhes, and confers a new force. For it does not
require a ftronger loadftone to take away the weaker and fluggifh
virtue and to implant the new one; nor is iron inebriated by the
equal ftrength of loadftones, and made utterly uncertain and neutral,
as Baptifta Porta teaches; but by one and the fame loadftone, or by
loadftones endowed with equal power and might, its ftrength is, in
accordance with magnetick rules, turned round and changed, excited, repaired, or difturbed. But a loadftone itfelf, by being rubbed
on another, whether a larger or a more powerful ftone, is not difturbed
from its own property and verticity, nor does it turn round toward
the oppofite direction in its boat, or to the other pole oppofite to
that to which it inclines by its own nature and implanted verticity.
For ftrength which is innate and has been implanted for a very long
time abides more firmly, nor does it eafily yield from its ancient
holding; and that which has grown for a long time is not all of a
fudden brought to nothing, without the deftruction of the fubftance
containing it. Neverthelefs in a long interval of time a change
does take place; in one year, that is to fay, or two, or fometimes
in a few months; doubtlefs when a weaker loadftone remains lying
by a ftronger one contrary to the order of nature, namely, with
the northern pole of one loadftone adjoined to the northern pole
of another, or the fouthern to the fouthern. For fo the weaker
ftrength gradually declines with the lapfe of time.

CHAP. XI.

On the Rubbing of a piece of Iron on a Loadftone
in places midway between the poles, and upon
the æquinoctial of a terrella.

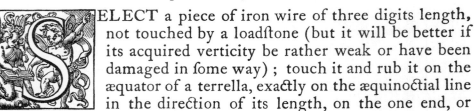 ELECT a piece of iron wire of three digits length,
not touched by a loadftone (but it will be better if
its acquired verticity be rather weak or have been
damaged in fome way); touch it and rub it on the
æquator of a terrella, exactly on the æquinoctial line
in the direction of its length, on the one end, or
the ends only, or in all its parts; place the wire touched in this
way on water in a cork fitted for it; it will fwim about doubtfully
on the waves without any acquired verticity, and the verticity previoufly implanted will be difturbed. If, however, it float by chance
toward the poles, it will be checked a little by the poles of the
earth, and will at length by the influence of the earth be indued
with verticity.

                                                            CHAP.

CHAP. XII.

In what way Verticity exifts in any Iron that has
been fmelted though not excited by a loadftone.

AVING thus far demonftrated natural and inborn caufes and powers acquired by means of the ftone, we will now examine the caufes of magnetick virtues in fmelted iron that has not been excited by a ftone. Loadftone and iron furnifh and exhibit to us wonderful fubtilities. It has been repeatedly fhown above that iron not excited by a ftone turns north and fouth; further that it has verticity, that is, fpecial and peculiar polar diftinctions, juft as a loadftone, or iron which has been rubbed upon a loadftone. This indeed feemed to us at firft wonderful and incredible; the metal of iron from the mine is fmelted in the furnace; it runs out of the furnace, and hardens into a great mafs; this mafs is divided in great workfteads, and is drawn into iron bars, from which fmiths again conftruct many inftruments and neceffary pieces of iron-work. Thus the fame mafs is varioufly worked up and transformed into very many fimilitudes. What is it, then, which

preferves

preferves its verticity, and whence is it derived? So take this firft
from the above fmithy.   Let the blackfmith beat out upon his anvil
a glowing mafs of iron of two or three ounces weight into an iron
fpike of the length of a fpan or nine inches.   Let the fmith be
* ftanding with his face to the north, his back to the fouth, fo that
the hot iron on being ftruck has a motion of extenfion to the north;
and let him fo complete his work with one or two heatings of the
iron (if that be required); let him always, however, whilft he is
ftriking the iron, direct and beat out the fame point of it toward the
north, and let him lay down that end toward the north.   Let him
in this way complete two, three, or more pieces of iron, nay, a
hundred or four hundred; it is demonftrable that all thofe which
are thus beaten out toward the north, and fo placed whilft they are
cooling, turn round on their centres; and floating pieces of iron
(being transfixed, of courfe, through fuitable corks) make a motion
in the water, the determined end being toward the north.   In the
fame way alfo pieces of iron acquire verticity from their direction
* whilft they are being beaten out and hammered or drawn out,
as iron wires are accuftomed to do toward fome point of the
horizon between eaft and fouth or between fouth and weft, or
in the oppofite direction.   Thofe, however, which are pointed or
* drawn out rather toward the eaftern or weftern point, conceive
hardly any verticity or a very undecided one.   That verticity is
efpecially acquired by being beaten out.   But a fomewhat inferior
* iron ore, in which no magnetick powers are apparent, if put in a
fire (its pofition being obferved to be toward the poles of the world
or of the earth) and heated for eight or ten hours, then cooled away
from the fire, in the fame pofition towards the poles, acquires a verticity in accordance with the pofition of its heating and cooling.   Let
* a rod of caft iron be heated red-hot in a ftrong fire, in which it lies
meridionally (that is, along the path of a meridian circle), and let
it be removed from the fire and cooled, and let it return to its former
temperature, remaining in the fame pofition as before; then from
this it will turn out that, if the fame ends have been turned to the
fame poles of the earth, it will acquire verticity, and the end which
looked toward the North on water with a cork before the heating,
if it have been placed during the heating and cooling toward the
fouth, now turns round to the fouth.   But if perchance fometimes
the rotation have been doubtful and fomewhat feeble, let it be placed
again in the fire, and when it is taken out at a red heat, let it be
perfectly cooled toward the pole from which we defire the verticity,
* and the verticity will be acquired.   Let the fame rod be heated
again in the contrary pofition, and let it be placed fo at a red heat
until it is cool; for it is from its pofition in cooling (by the operation of the verticity of the earth) that verticity is put into the iron,
and it turns round to parts contrary to its former verticity.   So
the

the end which formerly looked toward the north now turns to the
fouth.   In accordance with thefe reafonings and in thefe ways the
boreal pole of the earth gives to the end of a piece of iron turned
toward it a fouthern verticity, and that end is attracted by that pole.   ✳
And here it muft be obferved that this happens to iron not only
when it is cooled in the plane of the horizon, but alfo at any angle
to it almoft up to the perpendicular toward the centre of the earth.
So the heated iron conceives vigour and verticity from the earth
more quickly in the courfe of its return to its normal ftate, and in
its recovery, as it were (in the courfe of which it is transformed),
than by its mere pofition alone.   This is effected better and more   ✳
perfectly in winter and in colder air, when the metal returns more
certainly to its natural temperature, than in fummer and in warm
regions.   Let us fee alfo what pofition alone and a direction toward
the poles of the earth can effect by itfelf without fire and heat.
Iron rods which have been placed and fixed for a long time, twenty   ✴
or more years, from fouth to north (as they not infrequently are
fixed in buildings and acrofs windows), thofe rods, I fay, by that
long lapfe of time acquire verticity and turn round, whether hanging in the air, or floating (being placed on cork), to the pole toward
which they were pointing, and magnetically attract and repel a
balanced iron magnetick; for the long continued pofition of the
body toward the poles is of much avail.   This fact (although confpicuous by manifeft experiments) is confirmed by an incident related
in an Italian letter at the end of a book of Maeftro Filippo Cofta,
of Mantua, *Sopra le Compofitioni degli Antidoti,* written in Italian,
which tranflated runs thus: " A druggift of Mantua fhowed me
" a piece of iron entirely changed into a magnet, drawing another
" piece of iron in fuch a way that it could be compared with a load-
" ftone.   Now this piece of iron, when it had for a long time held
" up a brick ornament on the top of the tower of the church of St.
" Auguftine at Rimini, had been at length bent by the force of the
" winds, and remained fo for a period of ten years.   When the monks
" wifhed to bend it back to its former fhape, and had handed it over
" to a blackfmith, a furgeon named Maeftro Giulio Caefare difcovered
" that it was like a magnet and attracted iron."   This was caufed by
the turning of its extremities toward the poles for fo long a time.
And fo what has been laid down before about change of verticity
fhould be borne in mind; how in fact the poles of iron fpikes are
altered, when a loadftone is placed againft them only with its pole
and points toward them, even at a rather long diftance.   Clearly
it is in the fame way that that large magnet alfo (to wit, the earth
itfelf) affects a piece of iron and changes its verticity.   For, although
the iron may not touch the pole of the earth, nor any magnetick
part of the earth, yet verticity is acquired and changed; not becaufe
the poles of the earth and the point itfelf which is 39° diftant
from

from our city of London, changes the verticity at a diftance of fo
many miles; but becaufe the whole magnetick earth, that which
projects to a confiderable height, and to which the iron is near,
and that which is fituated between us and the pole, and the vigour
exifting within the orbe of its magnetick virtue (the nature of the
whole confpiring thereto), produces the verticity.   For the magnetick effluence of the earth rules everywhere within the orbe of its
virtue, and transforms bodies; but thofe things which are more
fimilar to it, and fpecially connected with it by nature, it rules and
controls; as loadftone and iron.   Wherefore in very many matters
of bufinefs and actions it is clearly not fuperftitious and idle to
obferve the pofitions and conditions of lands, the points of the
horizon and the places of the ftars.   For as when a babe is brought
forth into the light from its mother's womb, and acquires refpiration
and certain animal activities, then the planets and celeftial bodies,
according to their pofition in the univerfe, and according to that
configuration which they have with regard to the horizon and the
earth, inftil peculiar and individual qualities into the newly born;
fo that piece of iron, whilft it is being formed and lengthened out,
is affected by the common caufe (to wit, the earth); whilft it is
returning alfo from its heated condition to its former temperature,
it is imbued with a fpecial verticity in accord with its pofition.
* Rather long pieces of iron fometimes have the fame verticity
at each end; wherefore they have motions which are lefs certain
and well ordered on account of their length and of the aforefaid
proceffes, exactly as when an iron wire four feet long is rubbed at
each end upon the fame pole of a loadftone.

CHAP. XIII.

Why no other Body, excepting a magnetick, is imbued
with verticity by being rubbed on a loadftone; and why no
body is able to inftil and excite that virtue,
unlefs it be a magnetick.

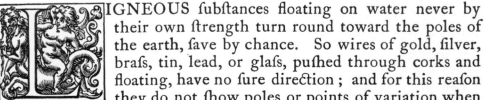
IGNEOUS fubftances floating on water never by
their own ftrength turn round toward the poles of
the earth, fave by chance.   So wires of gold, filver,
brafs, tin, lead, or glafs, pufhed through corks and
floating, have no fure direction; and for this reafon
they do not fhow poles or points of variation when
rubbed with a loadftone.   For thofe things which do not of themfelves incline toward the poles and obey the earth are alfo not ruled by
the

the touch of a loadftone; for the magnetick vigour has no entrance into their inward parts; neither is the magnetick form received by them, nor are their forms magnetically excited; nor, if it did enter, would it effect anything, becaufe in thofe bodies (mixed up with various kinds of efflorefcent humours and forms, corrupted from the original property of the earth) there are no primary qualities. But thofe prime qualities of iron are excited by the juxtapofition of a loadftone, juft as brute animals or men, when they are awakened out of fleep, move and put forth their ftrength. Here one muft marvel at a demonftrable error of B. Porta, who, while rightly oppofing a very old falfehood about the diamond, in fpeaking of a power contrary to that of the loadftone, introduces another ftill worfe opinion; that forfooth iron, when touched by a diamond, turns to the north. "If" (he fays) "you rub a fteel-Needle on a Diamond, "and then put it in a Boat, or thruft it through a reed, or hang it up "by a Thread, it will prefently turn to the North, almoft as well as "if it had been touched with the Loadftone; but fomething more "faintly. And, what is worth noting, the contrary part will turn "the iron to the South: and when I had tried this in many fteel- "Needles, and put them all into the Water, I found, that they all "ftood equi-diftant, pointing to the North." This indeed would *
be contrary to our magnetick rules. For this reafon we made an experiment with feventy excellent diamonds, in the prefence of many witneffes, on a large number of fpikes and wires, with the moft careful precautions, floating (thruft, of courfe, through their corks) on the furface of water; never, however, could we obferve this. He was deceived by the verticity acquired from the earth (as ftated above) in the fpike or wire of iron itfelf, and the iron itfelf turned afide to its own definite pole; and he, being ignorant of this, thought it was done by the diamond. But let the inveftigators of natural phenomena take heed that they are not the more deceived by their own badly obferved experiments, and difturb the commonwealth of letters with their errors and ftupidities. Diamond is fometimes defignated by the name of *Sideritis*, not becaufe it is made of iron or becaufe it draws iron, but on account of its luftre, refembling flafhing fteel; with fuch a luftre do the choiceft pieces of diamond fhine; hence by very many writers many qualities are imputed to diamond which really belong to fiderite loadftone.

CHAP.

CHAP. XIIII.

The Placing of a Loadſtone above or below a magnetick
body ſuſpended in æquilibrium changes neither the power
nor the verticity of the magnetick body.

QUIETLY to paſs this over would be improper, be-
cauſe a recent error ariſing from a defective obſerva-
tion of Baptiſta Porta muſt be overthrown; on
which he (by an unfortunate repetition) even writes
three chapters, namely, the 18th, the 31ſt, and the
42nd. For if a loadſtone or a piece of magnetick
iron, hanging in æquilibrium or floating on water, is attracted and
diſpoſed toward certain definite points, when you bring above it a
piece of iron or another loadſtone, it will not, if you afterward
put the ſame below it, turn round to the contrary parts; but the
ſame ends of the iron or the loadſtone will always be directed toward
the ſame ends of the ſtone, even if the loadſtone or the iron is ſuſpended in any way in æquilibrium or is poiſed on a needle, ſo that it
can turn round freely. He was deceived by the irregular ſhape of
ſome ſtone, or becauſe he did not arrange the experiment ſuitably.
Wherefore he is led aſtray by a vain opinion, and thinks he may
infer that, juſt as a ſtone has an arctic and antarctic pole, ſo alſo it
has a weſtern and an eaſtern, and an upper and a lower pole. So
from fooliſh ideas conceived and admitted ariſe other fallacies.

CHAP. XV.

The Poles, Æquator, Centre in an entire Loadſtone
remain and continue ſteady; by diminution and
ſeparation of ſome part they vary and
acquire other poſitions.

UPPOSE A B to be a terrella, whoſe centre is E,
and whoſe diameter (as alſo its æquinoctial circle)
is D F. If you cut off a portion (through the arctic
circle, for example), G H, it is demonſtrable that
the pole which was at A now has a poſition at I.
But the centre and the æquinoctial recede toward B
merely

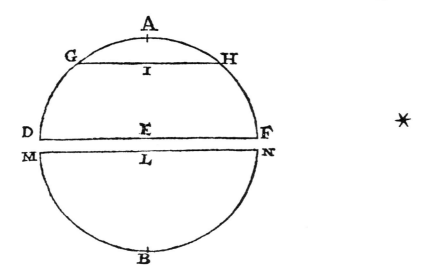

merely fo that they are always in the middle of the mafs that is
left between the plane of the arctick circle G I H and the antarctick
pole B.   Therefore the fegment of the terrella comprifed between
the plane of the former æquinoctial (that, of courfe, which was
the æquator before cutting that part away) D E F and the newly
acquired æquator M L N will always be equal to the half of that
part which was cut off, G I H A.

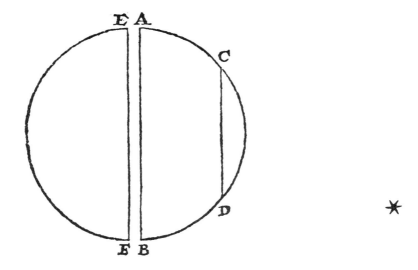

But if the portions have been taken away from the side C D, the
poles and axis will not be in the line A B, but in E F, and the axis
would be changed in the fame proportion as the æquator in the
former figure.   For thofe pofitions of forces and virtues, or rather
limits of the virtues, which are derived from the whole form, are
moved forward by change of quantity and fhape; fince all thefe
limits arife from the confpiring together of the whole and of all

U   the

the parts united ; and the verticity or the pole is not a virtue innate
in one part, or in fome definite limit, or fixed in the fubftance ;
but it is an inclination of the virtue to that part.   And juft as a
terrella feparated from the earth has no longer the earth's poles
and æquator, but individual ones of its own ; so alfo if it again be
divided, thofe limits and diftinctions of the qualities and virtues
pafs on to other parts.   But if a loadftone be divided in any way,
either along a parallel, or meridionally, fo that by the change of
fhape either the poles or the æquator move to other pofitions, if
the part cut off be merely applied in its natural pofition and
joined to the whole, even without any agglutination or cementing
together, the determining points of the virtues return again to
their former fites, as if no part of the body had been cut off.   When
a body is entire, its form remains entire ; but when the body is
leffened, a new whole is made, and there arifes a new entirety,
determined for every loadftone, however fmall, even for magnetick
gravel, and for the fineft fand.

CHAP. XVI.

If the Southern Portion of a Stone be leffened,
fomething is alfo taken away from the power
of the Northern Portion.

NOW, although the fouthern end of a magnetick iron
is attracted by a northern end, and repelled by a
fouthern, yet the fouthern portion of a ftone does
not diminifh, but increafes the potency of the boreal
part.   Wherefore if a ftone be cut in two and divided
through the arctick circle, or through the tropick of
Cancer or the æquator, the fouthern portion does not attract magnetick fubftances fo ftrongly with its pole as before ; becaufe a new
whole arifes, and the æquator is removed from its old pofition and
moves forward on account of that cutting of the ftone.   In
the former condition, fince the oppofite portion of
the ftone increafes the mafs beyond the plane
of the æquator, it ftrengthens alfo the
verticity, and the potency, and
the motion to unity.

CHAP·

CHAP. XVII.

On the Ufe and Excellence of Verforia : and how iron
verforia ufed as pointers in fun-dials, and the fine needles
of the mariners' compafs, are to be rubbed, that
they may acquire ftronger verticity.

ERSORIA prepared by the loadftone fubferve fo many actions in human life that it will not be out of place to record a better method of touching them and exciting them magnetically, and a fuitable manner of operating. Rich ores of iron and fuch as yield a greater proportion of metal are recognized by means of an iron needle fufpended in æquilibrium and magnetically prepared; and magnetick ftones, clays, and earths are diftinguifhed, whether crude or prepared. An iron needle (the foul of the mariners' compafs), the marvellous director in voyages and finger of God, one might almoft fay, indicates the courfe, and has pointed out the whole way around the earth (unknown for fo many ages). The Spaniards (as alfo the Englifh) have frequently circumnavigated (by an immenfe circuit) the whole globe by aid of the mariners' compafs. Thofe who travel about through the world or who fit at home have fun-dials. A magnetick pointer follows and fearches out the veins of ore in mines. By its aid mines are driven in taking cities; catapults and engines of war are aimed by night; it has been of fervice for the topography of places, for marking off the areas and pofition of buildings, and for excavating aqueducts for water under ground. On it depend inftruments defigned to inveftigate its own dip and variation.

When iron is to be quickened by the ftone, let it be clean and bright, disfigured by no ruft or dirt, and of the beft fteel. Let the ftone itfelf be wiped dry, and let it not be damp with any moifture, but let it be filed gently with fome fmooth piece of iron. But the hitting of the ftone with a hammer is of no advantage. By thefe means let their bare furfaces be joined, and let them be rubbed, fo that they may come together more firmly; not fo that the material fubftance of the ftone being joined to the iron may cleave to it, but they are rubbed gently together with friction, and (ufelefs parts being rubbed off) they are intimately united; whence a more notable virtue arifes in the iron that is excited. A is the beft way of touching a verforium when the cufp touches the pole and faces it; B is a moderately good way, when, though facing it, it is a little way

diftant

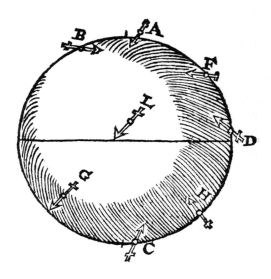

diftant from the pole; alfo in like manner C is only moderately
good, on account of the cufp being turned away from the pole;
D, which is farther diftant, is hardly fo good; F, which is prepared
croffwife along a parallel, is bad; of no virtue and entirely irrefpon-
five and feeble is the magnetick index L, which is rubbed along the
æquator; oblique and not pointing towards the pole as G, and
oblique, not pointing toward but turned away from the pole as H,
are bad.   Thefe have been placed fo that they might indicate the
diftinct forces of a round ftone.   But mechanicians very often have
a ftone tending more to a cone fhape, and more powerful on account
of that fhape, fince the pole, on which they rub their wires, is at
the apex of the projecting part.   Sometimes the ftone has on the
top and above its own pole an artificial acorn or fnout made of fteel
for the fake of its power.   Iron needles are rubbed on the top of
this; wherefore they turn toward the fame pole as if they had been
prepared on that part of the ftone with the acorn removed.   Let
the ftone be large enough and ftrong; the needle, even if it be rather
long, fhould be fufficiently thick, not very flender; with a moderate
cufp, not too fharp, although the virtue is not in the cufp itfelf
only, but in the whole piece of iron.   A ftrong large ftone is not
unfit for rubbing all needles on, excepting that fometimes by its
ftrength it occafions fome dip and difturbance in the iron in the
cafe of longer needles; fo that one which, having been touched
before, refted in æquilibrium in the plane of the horizon, now when
touched and excited dips at one end, as far as the upright pin
on which it turns permits it.   Wherefore in the cafe of longer
verforia, the end which is going to be the Boreal, before it is rubbed,
fhould be a little lighter, fo that it may remain exactly in æquilib-
* rio after it is touched.   But a needle in this way prepared does its
work

work worfe the farther it is beyond the æquinoctial circle.   Let the
prepared needle be placed in its capfule, and let it not be touched
by any other magneticks, nor remain in the near vicinity of them,
left by their oppofing forces, whether powerful or fluggifh, it fhould
become uncertain and dull.   If you also rub the other end of the
needle on the other pole of the ftone, the needle will perform its
functions more fteadily, efpecially if it be rather long.   A piece of
iron touched by a loadftone retains the magnetick virtue, excited
in it even for ages, firm and ftrong, if it is placed according to
nature meridionally and not along a parallel, and is not injured by ruft
or any external injury from the furrounding medium.   Porta wrongly
feeks for a proportion between the loadftone and the iron : becaufe,
he fays, a little piece of iron will not be capable of holding much
virtue ; for it is confumed by the great force of the loadftone.   A
piece of iron receives its own virtue fully, even if it be only of the
weight of one fcruple, whilft the mafs of the loadftone is a thoufand
pounds.   It is alfo ufelefs to make the needle rather flat at the end
that is touched, fo that it may be better and more perfectly magnetick, and that it may beft receive and hold certain magnetick particles ; fince hardly any part will ftick on a fharp point ; becaufe he
thought that it was by the adhefion of parts of the loadftone (as it
were, hairs) that the influence is imparted and conferved, though
thofe particles are merely rubbed off by the rubbing of the iron
over the fofter ftone, and the iron none the lefs points toward the
North and South, if after it is touched it be fcoured with fand or
emery powder, or with any other material, even if by long rubbing
of this kind the external parts of it are leffened and worn away.
When a needle is being rubbed, one fhould always leave off at the
end ; otherwife, if it is rubbed on the loadftone from the point
toward the middle, lefs verticity is excited in the iron, fometimes
none at all, or very little.   For where the laft contact is, there is
the pole and goal of verticity.   In order that a ftronger verticity
may be produced in the iron by rubbing on the loadftone, one ✻
ought in northern lands to turn the true northern pole of the
loadftone toward the higheft part of the fky ; on this pole that
end of the needle is going to be rubbed, which fhall afterwards turn
toward the north of the earth ; whilft it will be an advantage for
the other end of the needle to be rubbed on the fouthern pole of
the terrella turned toward the earth, and this being fo excited
will incline toward the fouth.   In fouthern regions beyond the
æquator the plan is juft the contrary.   The reafon of this diffimi-
larity is demonftrated, Book II., chap. xxxiv., in which it is fhown
(by a manifeft combination of a terrella and the earth) why the
poles of a loadftone, for different reafons, are one ftronger than the
other.   If a needle be touched between the mutually accordant ✻
poles of two loadftones, equal in power, fhape, and mafs, no ftrength
                                                                  is

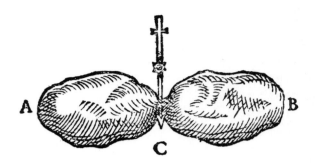

is acquired by the needle.   A and B are two loadſtones attracting
* one another, according to nature, at their diſſimilar ends ; C, the
point of a needle touched by both at once, is not excited (even if
thoſe loadſtones be connected according to nature), if they are
equal ; but if they are not equal, virtue is acquired from the ſtronger.

When a needle is being excited by a loadſtone, begin in the
middle, and draw the needle toward its end ; at the end let the
application be continued with a very gentle rubbing around the
end for ſome time ; that is to ſay, for one or two minutes ; do not
repeat the motion from the middle to the end (as is frequently
done) for in this way the verticity is injured.   Some delay is
deſirable, for although the power is imparted inſtantly, and the
iron excited, yet from the vicinity of the loadſtone and a ſuitable
delay, a more ſteady verticity ariſes, and one that is more firmly
durable in the iron.   Although an armed ſtone raiſes a greater
weight of iron than an unarmed one, yet a needle is not more
ſtrongly excited by an armed ſtone than by an unarmed one.   Let there
be two iron wires of the ſame length, wrought from the ſame wire ;
let one be excited by an armed end, the other by an unarmed end;
it is manifeſt that the ſame needles have a beginning of motion or
a ſenſible inclination at equal diſtances from the ſame armed and
unarmed loadſtone ; this is aſcertained by meaſuring with a longiſh
reed.   But objects which are more powerfully excited move more
quickly; thoſe which are leſs powerfully excited, more
feebly, and not unleſs brought rather cloſe ;
the experiment is made on water
with equal corks.

BOOK

BOOK FOURTH.

*C*HAP. I.

ON VARIATION.

DIRECTION has hitherto been fpoken of as if in
nature there were no variation ; for in the preceding natural hiftory we wifhed to omit and
neglect this, inafmuch as in a terreftrial globe, perfect and in every fenfe complete, there would be
none. Since, however, in fact, the earth's magnetick direction, owing to fome fault and flip, deviates from its
right courfe and from the meridian, we muft extract and demonftrate the obfcure and hidden caufe of that variance which has
troubled and fore racked in vain the minds of many. Thofe who
before us have written on the magnetick movements have made
no diftinction between direction and variation, but confider the
motion of magnetick iron to be uniform and fimple. Now true
direction is the motion of the magnetick body to the true meridian
and its continuance therein with its appropriate ends towards the
poles. But it very often happens at fea and on land that the magnetick iron does not point to the true pole, and that not only a verforium and magnetick pieces of iron, and the needle of a compafs,
or a mariners' compafs, but alfo a terrella in its boat, as well as ∗
iron ore, iron ftones, and magnetick earths, properly prepared,
are drawn afide and deviate towards fome point of the Horizon
very near to the meridian. For they with their poles frequently face termini away from the meridian. This variation
                                                    obferved

(obferved by means of inftruments or a nautical variation compafs)
is therefore the arc of the horizon between the common point of
interfection of it with the true meridian, and the terminus of the
deflection on the horizon or projection of the deviating needle.
That arc varies and differs with change of locality. To the terminus
of the variation is commonly affigned a great circle, called the circle
of variation, and alfo a magnetick meridian paffing through the zenith
and the point of variation on the horizon. In the northern regions
of the earth this variation is either from the north toward the
eaft or from the north toward the weft: fimilarly in the fouthern
regions it is from the fouth toward the eaft or toward the weft.
* Wherefore one fhould obferve in the northern regions of the earth
that end of the verforium or compafs which turns toward the
North; but in the fouthern regions the other end looking to the
fouth—which feamen and fciolifts for the moft part do not underftand, for in both regions they obferve only the boreal lily of the
compafs (that which faces North). We have before faid that all
the motions of the magnet and iron, all its turning, its inclination,
and its fettlement, proceed from bodies themfelves magnetical and
from their common mother the earth, which is the fource, the pro-
pagatrix, and the origin of all thefe qualities and properties.
Accordingly the earth is the caufe of this variation and inclination
toward a different point of the horizon: but how and by what
powers muft be more fully inveftigated. And here we muft at the
outfet reject that common opinion of recent writers concerning
magnetick mountains, or any magnetick rock, or any phantafmal
pole diftant from the pole of the earth, by which the motion of
the compafs or verforium is controlled. This opinion, previoufly
invented by others, Fracaftorio himfelf adopted and developed; but
it is entirely at variance with experience. For in that cafe in different places at fea and on land the point of variation would change
toward the eaft or weft in proportion and geometrical fymmetry,
and the verforium would always refpect the magnetick pole: but
experience teaches that there is no fuch definite pole or fixed ter-
* minus on the earth to account for the variation. For the arcs of
variation are changed varioufly and erratically, not only on different
meridians but on the fame meridian; and when, according to this
opinion of the moderns, the deviation fhould be more and more
toward the eaft, then fuddenly, with a fmall change of locality,
the deviation is from the north toward the weft as in the northern
regions near Nova Zembla. Moreover, in the fouthern regions,
and at fea at a great diftance from the æquator towards the antarctick
pole, there are frequent and great variations, and not only in the
northern regions, from the magnetick mountains. But the cogitations of others are ftill more vain and trifling, fuch as that of
Cortes about a moving influence beyond all the heavens; that of
                                                        Marfilius

Marfilius Ficinus about a ftar in the Bear; that of Peter Peregrinus about the pole of the world; that of Cardan, who derives it from the rifing of a ftar in the tail of the Bear; of Beffardus, the Frenchman, from the pole of the Zodiack; that of Livio Sanuto from fome magnetick meridian; that of Francifcus Maurolycus from a magnetical ifland; that of Scaliger from the heavens and mountains; that of Robert Norman, the Englifhman, from a point refpective.   Leaving therefore thefe opinions, which are at variance with common experience or by no means proved, let us feek the true caufe of the variation.   The great magnet or terreftrial globe directs iron (as I have faid) toward the north and fouth; and excited iron quickly fettles itfelf toward thofe termini.   Since, however, the globe of the earth is defective and uneven on its furface and marred by its diverfe compofition, and fince it has parts very high and convex (to the height of fome miles), and thofe uniform neither in compofition nor body, but oppofite and diffimilar: it comes to pafs that the whole of that force of the earth diverts magnetical bodies in its periphery toward the ftronger and more prominent connected magnetick parts.   Hence on the outermoft furface of the earth magnetical bodies are flightly perverted from the true meridian.   Moreover, fince the furface of the globe is divided into high lands and deep feas, into great continental lands, into ocean and vafteft feas, and fince the force of all magnetical motions is derived from the conftant and magnetick terreftrial nature which is more prevalent on the greater continent and not in the aquæous or fluid or unftable part; it follows that in certain parts there would be a magnetick inclination from the true pole eaft or weft away from any meridian (whether paffing through feas or iflands) toward a great land or continent rifing higher, that is, obvioufly toward a ftronger and more elevated magnetick part of the terreftrial globe.   For fince the diameter of the earth is more than 1,700 German miles, thofe large lands can rife from the centre of the earth more than four miles above the depth of the ocean bottom, and yet the earth will retain the form of a globe although fome-what uneven at the top.   Wherefore a magnetical body is turned afide, fo far as the true verticity, when difturbed, admits, and departs from its right (the whole earth moving it) toward a vaft prominent mafs of land as though toward what is ftronger.   But the variation does really take place, not fo much becaufe of the more prominent and imperfect terreftrial parts and continent lands as becaufe of the inæquality of the magnetick globe, and becaufe of the real earth, which ftands out more under the continent lands than under the depths of the feas.   We muft fee, therefore, how the *apodixis* of this theory can be fuftained by more definite obfervations.   Since throughout all the courfe from the coaft of Guinea to Cape Verde, the Canary Ifles, and the border of the kingdom of Morocco, and

X   thence

thence along the coafts of Spain, France, England, Belgium, Germany, Denmark, and Norway, there lie on the right hand and toward the eaft a continent and extenfive connected regions, and on the left extenfive feas and a vaft ocean lie open far and wide, it is confonant with the theory (as has been carefully obferved by many) that magnetical bodies fhould turn flightly to the Eaft from the true pole toward the ftronger and more remarkable elevations of the earth. But it is far otherwife on the eaftern fhores of northern America; for from Florida by Virginia and Norumbega to Cape Race and away to the north the verforium is turned toward the weft. But in the middle fpaces, fo to fpeak, as in the more wefterly Azores, it looks toward the true pole. That any magnetick body turns itfelf fimilarly to the fame regions of the earth is not, however, becaufe of that meridian or becaufe of the concordancy of the meridian with any magnetick pole, as the crowd of philofophizers reckon, for it is not fo
* throughout the whole of that meridian. For on the fame meridian near Brazil fomething very different occurs, as we will fhow further on. The variation (cæteris paribus) is always lefs near the æquator, greater in higher latitudes, with the limitation that it be not very
* near the pole itfelf. Hence the variation is greater on the coaft of Norway and Belgium than on the coaft of Morocco or Guinea: greater alfo near Cape Race than in the harbours of Norumbega or of Virginia. On the coaft of Guinea magnetick implements deviate by a third part of one rumbe to the Eaft: in Cape Verde Iflands by a half: on the coaft of Morocco by two thirds: in England at the mouth of the Thames by a whole rumbe: and at London by nearly eleven degrees and one third. For indeed the moving magnetick virtue is ftronger in a higher latitude; and the larger regions extending toward the poles dominate the more, as is eafily apparent anywhere on a terrella. For as in the cafe of true Direction magnetick bodies tend toward the pole (namely, toward the ftronger end, the whole earth caufing the motion), fo alfo do they incline a little toward the ftronger and higher parts by the action of the whole along with the conjoint action of iron bodies.

CHAP.

CHAP. II.

That the variation is caufed by the inæquality of the
projecting parts of the earth.

EMONSTRATION of this may manifeftly be made by means of a terrella in the following way : let there be a round loadftone fomewhat imperfect in fome part, and impaired by decay (fuch an one we had with a certain part corroded to refemble the Atlantick or great Ocean): place upon it fome fine iron wire of the length of two barleycorns, as in the following figure.   A B, a Terrella in certain parts fomewhat imperfect and of unæqual virtue on the circumference.

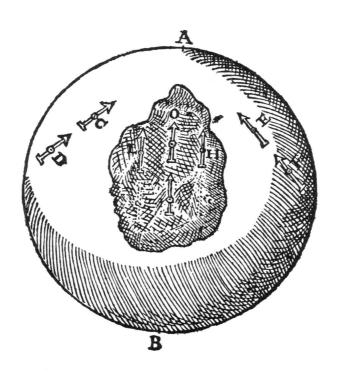

The verforia E, F, do not vary, but look directly to the pole A; for they are placed in the middle of the firm and found part of the terrella and fomewhat diftant from the imperfect part : that part of the furface which is diftinguifhed by dots and tranfverfe lines is the weaker.   The verforium O alfo does not vary (becaufe it is placed in the middle of the imperfect part), but is directed toward the pole,
juft

juft as near the weftern Azores on the earth. The verforia H and L do vary, for they incline toward the founder parts very near them. As this is manifeft in a terrella whofe furface is fenfibly rather imperfect, fo alfo is it in others whole and perfect, when often one part of the ftone has ftronger external parts, which neverthelefs do not difclofe themfelves manifeftly to the fenfes. In fuch a terrella the demonftration of the variation and the difcovery of the ftronger parts is on this wife.

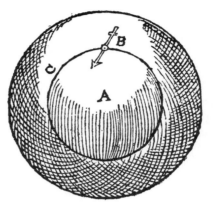

Let A be the pole, B the place of the variation, C the ftronger regions; then the horizontal verforium at B varies from the pole A toward C : fo that both the variation is fhown and the ftronger places of the loadftone recognized. The ftronger furface is alfo found by a fine iron wire of the length of two barleycorns: for fince at the pole of the terrella it rears up perpendicularly, but in other places inclines toward the æquator, if in one and the fame parallel circle it fhould be more erect in one place than in another; where the wire is raifed more upright, there the part and furface of the terrella is ftronger. Alfo when the iron wire placed over the pole inclines more to one part than to another.

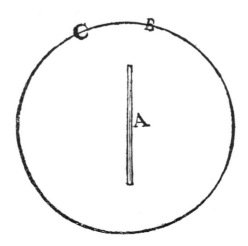

Let

Let the experiment be made by means of a fine iron wire of three digits length placed over the pole A, fo that its middle lies over the pole. Then one end is turned away from B toward C, and is not willing to lie quietly toward B; but on a terrella which is perfect all round and even it refts on the pole directed toward any point of the æquator you pleafe. Otherwife, let there be two ✳

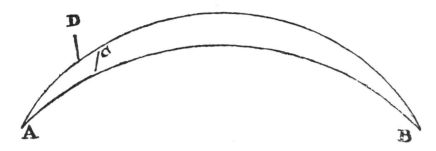

meridians meeting in the poles A B, let iron wires be reared juft at the ends D and C of the equal arcs D A and C A; then the wire at D (the ftronger region) will be more raifed up than that at C, the weaker. And thus the founder and ftronger part of the loadftone is recognized, which otherwife would not be perceived by the touch. In a terrella which is perfect, and even, and fimilar in all its parts, there is, at equal diftances from the pole, no variation. Variation is fhown by means of a terrella, a confiderable part of which, forming a furface a little higher than the reft, does, although it be not decayed and broken, allure the verforium from the true ✳ direction (the whole terrella co-operating).

A terrella uneven in furface.

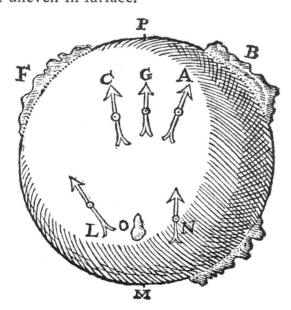

It is fhown by a fmall fpike placed over a terrella or by a fmall
verforium; for they are turned by the terrella toward the mafs that
ftands out and toward the large eminences. In the fame way on
the earth the verticity is perturbed by great continents, which are
moftly elevated above the depths of the feas and make the verforium
deviate fometimes from the right tracks (that is, from the true
meridians). On a terrella it is thus demonftrated: the end of the
verforium A is not directed ftraight to the pole P, if there be a large
protuberance B on the terrella; fo alfo the cufp C deviates from
the pole becaufe of the eminence F. In the middle between the
two eminences the verforium G collimates to the true pole becaufe,
being at equal diftances from the two eminences B and F, it turns
afide to neither, but obferves the true meridian, efpecially when the
protuberances are of equal vigour. But the verforium N on the
other fide varies from the pole M toward the eminences H, and is
not held back, ftopped, or reftrained by the fmall eminence O on the
terrella (as it were, fome ifland of land in the ocean). L, however,
being unimpeded, is directed to the pole M. The variation is
demonftrated in another way on a terrella, juft as on the earth.
Let A be the pole of the earth, B the æquator, C the parallel circle
of latitude of 30 degrees, D a great eminence fpread out toward
the pole, E another eminence fpread out from the pole toward the
æquator. It is manifeft that in the middle of D the verforium F

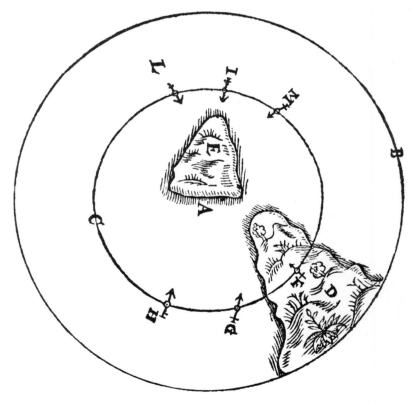

does

does not vary; while G is very greatly deflected: but H very little, becaufe it is further removed from D. Similarly alfo the verforium I placed directly toward E does not deviate from the pole: but L and M turn themfelves away from the pole A toward the eminence E.

CHAP. III.

The variation in any one place
is conftant.

NLESS there fhould be a great diffolution of a continent and a fubfidence of the land fuch as there was of the region Atlantis of which Plato and the ancients tell, the variation will continue perpetually immutable; the arc of the variation remains the fame in the fame place or region, whether it be at fea or on land, as in times paft a magnetick body has declined toward the Eaft or the Weft. The conftancy of the variation and the pointing of the verforium to a definite point on the horizon in individual regions is demonftrated by a fmall verforium placed over a terrella the furface of which is uneven: for it always deviates from the meridian by an equal arc. It is alfo fhown by the inclination of a verforium toward a fecond magnet; although in reality it is by the turning power of the whole, whether in the

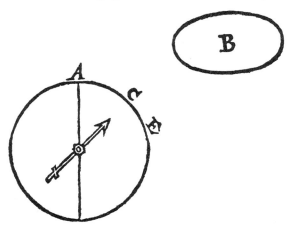

earth or in a terrella. Place upon a plane a verforium whofe cufp is directed toward the north A: place befide it a loadftone, B, at fuch a diftance that the verforium may turn afide toward B to the point C, and not beyond. Then move the needle of the verforium as often as you will (the box and the loadftone not being moved), and it will certainly always return to the point C. In the fame manner, if you

placed

placed the ſtone ſo that it may be truly directed toward E, the cuſp always reverts to E, and not to any other point of the compaſs. Accordingly, from the poſition of the land and from the diſtinctive nature of the higheſt parts of the earth (certain terrene and more magnetick eminences of the regions prevailing), the variation indeed becomes definite in one and the ſame place, but diverſe and unæqual from a change of place, ſince the true and polar direction originating in the whole terreſtrial globe is diverted ſomewhat toward certain ſtronger eminences on the broken ſurface.

CHAP. IIII.

The arc of variation is not changed equally
in proportion to the diſtance of places.

N the open ſea, when a veſſel is borne by a favourable wind along the ſame parallel, if the variation be changed by one degree in the courſe of one hundred miles, the next hundred miles do not therefore leſſen it by another degree; for the magnetick [needle] varies erratically as reſpects poſition, form, and vigour of the land, and alſo becauſe of the diſtance. As, for example, when a courſe from the Scilly Iſles to Newfoundland has proceeded ſo far that the compaſs is directed to the true pole, then, as the veſſel proceeds, in the firſt part of the courſe the variation increaſes toward the north-weſt, but rather indiſtinctly and with ſmall difference: thence, after an equal diſtance, the arc is increaſed in a greater proportion until the veſſel is not far from the continent: for then it varies moſt of all. But before it touches actual land or enters port, then at a certain diſtance the arc is again ſlightly diminiſhed. But if the veſſel in its courſe ſhould decline greatly from that parallel either toward the ſouth or the north, the magnetick [needle] will vary more or leſs, according to the poſition of the land and the latitude of the region. For (cæteris paribus) the greater the latitude the greater the variation.

CHAP.

CHAP. V.

An iſland in Ocean does not change the variation, as
neither do mines of loadſtone.

SLANDS, although they be more magnetick than the ſea, yet do not change the magnetick directions or variations. For ſince direction is a motion derived from the power of the whole earth, not from the attraction of any hill but from the diſpoſing and turning power of the whole; ſo variation (which is a perturbation of the direction) is an aberration of the real turning power ariſing from the great inæqualities of the earth, in conſequence of which it, of itſelf, ſlightly diverts movable magneticks toward thoſe which are the largeſt and the more powerful. The cauſe now ſhown may ſuffice to explain that which ſome ſo wonder at about the Iſland of Elba (and although this is productive of loadſtone, yet the verſorium (or mariners' compaſs) makes no ſpecial inclination toward it whenever veſſels approach it in the Tyrrhenian ſea); and the following cauſes are alſo to be conſidered, viz.: that the virtue of ſmaller magnetick bodies extends ſcarcely or not at all of itſelf beyond their own mines: for variation does not occur becauſe of attraction, as they would have it who have imagined magnetick poles. Beſides, magnetick mines are only agnate to the true earth, not innate: hence the whole globe does not regard them, and magneticks are not borne to them, as is demonſtrated by the diagram of eminences.

CHAP. VI.

That variation and direction ariſe from the diſponent
power of the earth, and from the natural magnetick tendency
to rotation, not from attraction, or from coition,
or from other occult cauſe.

WING to the loadſtone being ſuppoſed (amongſt the crowd of philoſophizers) to ſeize and drag, as it were, magnetick bodies; and ſince, in truth, ſcioliſts have remarked no other forces than thoſe ſo oft beſung of attractive ones, they therefore deem every motion toward the north and ſouth to be cauſed by ſome alluring and inviting quality. But the Engliſhman, Ro-
bert

Y

bert Norman, firſt ſtrove to ſhow that it is not cauſed by attraction:
wherefore, as if tending toward hidden principles, he imagined a
point reſpective, toward which the iron touched by a loadſtone
would ever turn, not a *point attractive*; but in this he erred greatly,
although he effaced the former error about attraction.   He, however, demonſtrates his opinion in this way:

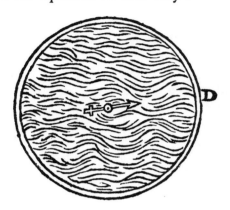

Let there be a round veſſel filled with water: in the middle of the
ſurface of the water place a ſlender iron wire on a perfectly round
cork, ſo that it may juſt float in æquilibrium on the water; let
the wire be previouſly touched by a magnet, ſo that it may more
readily ſhow the point of variation, the point D as it were: and
let it remain on the ſurface for ſome time.   It is demonſtrable that
the wire together with the cork is not moved to the ſide D of the
veſſel: which it would do if an attraction came to the iron wire by
D: and the cork would be moved out of its place.   This aſſertion
of the Engliſhman, Robert Norman, is plauſible and appears to do
away with attraction becauſe the iron remains on the water not
moving about, as well in a direction toward the pole itſelf (if the
direction be true) as in a variation or altered direction; and it is
moved about its own centre without any transference to the edge
of the veſſel.   But direction does not ariſe from attraction, but from
the diſpoſing and turning power which exiſts in the whole earth,
not in the pole or in ſome other attracting part of the ſtone, or in
any maſs riſing above the periphery of the true circle ſo that a
variation ſhould occur becauſe of the attraction of that maſs.   Moreover, it is the directing power of the loadſtone and iron and its
natural power of turning around the centre which cauſe the motion
of direction, and of conformation, in which is included alſo the
motion of the dip.   And the terreſtrial pole does not attract as if
the terrene force were implanted only in the pole, for the magnetick force exiſts in the whole, although it predominates and excels
at the pole.   Wherefore that the cork ſhould reſt quieſcent in the
middle and that the iron excited by a loadſtone ſhould not be moved
toward the ſide of the veſſel are agreeable to and in conformity
with

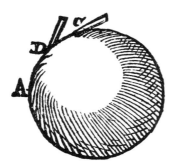

with the magnetick nature, as is demonſtrated by a terrella: for an iron ſpike placed on the ſtone at C clings on at C, and is not pulled ✳ further away by the pole A, or by the parts near the pole: hence it perſiſts at D, and takes a direction toward the pole A; neverthe-leſs it clings on at D and dips alſo at D in virtue of that turning power by which it conforms itſelf to the terrella: of which we will ſay more in the part *On Declination*.

CHAP. VII.

Why the variation from that lateral cauſe is not

greater than has hitherto been obſerved, having been
rarely ſeen to reach two points of the mariners'
compaſs, except near the pole.

HE earth, by reaſon of lateral eminences of the ſtronger globe, diverts iron and loadſtone by ſome degrees from the true pole, or true meridian. As, for example, with us Engliſh at London it varies eleven degrees and $\frac{1}{3}$: in ſome other places the variation is a little greater, but in no other region is the end of the iron ever moved aſide very much more from the meridian. For as the iron is always directed by the true verticity of the earth, ſo the polar nature of the continent land (juſt as of the whole terrene globe) acts toward the poles: and even if that maſs divert magnetick bodies from the meridian, yet the verticity of thoſe lands (as alſo of the whole earth) controls and diſpoſes them ſo that they do not turn toward the Eaſt by any greater arc. But it is not eaſy to determine by any general method how great the arc of variation is in all places, and how many degrees and minutes it ſubtends on the horizon, ſince it becomes greater or leſs

from

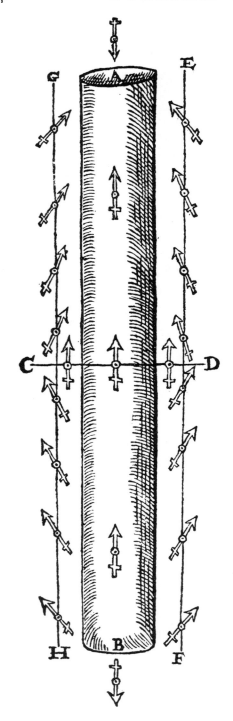

from diverfe caufes. For both the ftrength of true verticity of the place and of the elevated regions, as well as their diftances from the given place and from the poles of the world, muft be confidered and compared; which indeed cannot be done exactly: neverthelefs by our method the variation becomes fo known that no grave error will perturb the courfe at fea. If the pofitions of the lands were uniform and ftraight along meridians, and not defective and rugged, the variations near lands would be fimple; fuch as appear in the following figure.

This is demonftrated by a long loadftone the poles of which are in the ends A B; let C D be the middle line and the æquinoctial, and let G H and E F (the lines) be for meridians on which verforia are difpofed, the variations of which are greater at a greater diftance from the æquator. But the inequalities of the maritime parts of the habitable earth, the enormous promontories, the very wide gulfs, the mountainous and more elevated regions, render the variations more unequal, or fudden, or more obfcure; and, moreover, lefs certain and more inconftant in the higher latitude.

CHAP.

CHAP. VIII.

On the conſtruction of the common mariners'
compaſs, and on the diverſity of the compaſſes
of different nations.

IN a round hollow wooden bowl, all the upper part of which is cloſed with glaſs, a verſorium is placed upon a rather long pin which is fixed in the middle. The covering prevents the wind, and the motion of air from any external cauſe. Through the glaſs everything within can be diſcerned. The verſorium is circular, conſiſting of ſome light material (as card), to the under part of which the magnetick pieces of iron are attached. On the upper part 32 ſpaces (which are commonly called *points*) are aſſigned to the ſame number of mathematical intervals in the horizon or winds which are diſtinguiſhed by certain marks and by a lily indicating the north. The bowl is ſuſpended in the plane of the horizon in æquilibrium in a braſs ring which alſo is itſelf ſuſpended tranſverſely in another ring within a box ſufficiently wide with a leaden weight attached ; hence it conforms to the plane of the horizon even though the ſhip be toſſed to and fro by the waves. The iron works are either a pair with their ends united, or elſe a ſingle one of a nearly oval ſhape with project-ing ends, which does its work more certainly and more quickly. This is to be fitted to the cardboard circle ſo that the centre of the circle may be in the middle of the magnetick iron. But inaſmuch as variation ariſes horizontally from the point of the meridian which cuts the horizon at right angles, therefore on account of the variation the makers in different regions and cities mark out the mariners' compaſs in different ways, and alſo attach in different ways the magnetick needles to the cardboard circle on which are placed the 32 diviſions or points. Hence there are commonly in Europe 4 different conſtructions and forms. Firſt that of the States on the Mediterranean Sea, Sicily, Genoa, and the Republick of Venice. In all theſe the needles are attached under the roſe or lily on the cardboard verſorium, ſo that (where there is no varia-tion) they are directed to the true north and ſouth points. Where-fore the north part marked with the lily always ſhows exactly the point of variation when the apex itſelf of the lily on the movable circle, together with the ends of the magnetick wires attached below, reſts at the point of variation. Yet another is that of Dantzig, and throughout the Baltic Sea, and the Belgian provinces;

in

in which the iron works fixed below the circle diverge from the
lily ¼ of a rumbe to the eaſt.   For navigation to Ruſſia the diver-
gency is ⅔.   But the compaſſes which are made at Seville, Liſbon,
Rochelle, Bordeaux, Rouen, and throughout all England have an
interval of ½ a rumbe.   From thoſe differences moſt ſerious errors
have ariſen in navigation, and in the marine ſcience.   For as ſoon as
the bearings of maritime places (ſuch as promontories, havens, iſlands)
have been firſt found by the aid of the mariners' compaſs, and the
times of ſea-tide or high water determined from the poſition of
the moon over this or that point (as they ſay) of the compaſs, it
muſt be further inquired in what region or according to the cuſtom
of what region that compaſs was made by which the bearings of
thoſe places and the times of the ſea-tides were firſt obſerved and
diſcovered.   For one who ſhould uſe the Britiſh compaſs and ſhould
follow the directions of the marine charts of the Mediterranean Sea
would neceſſarily wander very much out of the ſtraight courſe.   So
alſo he that ſhould uſe the Italian compaſs in the Britiſh, German,
or Baltic Sea, together with marine charts that are made uſe of in
thoſe parts, will often ſtray from the right way.   Theſe different conſtructions have been made on account of the diſſimilar variations, ſo
that they might avoid ſomewhat ſerious errors in thoſe parts of the
world.   But Pedro Nuñez ſeeks the meridian by the mariners'
compaſs, or verſorium (which the Spaniſh call the needle), without
taking account of the variation : and he adduces many geometrical
demonſtrations which (becauſe of his ſlight uſe and experience in
matters magnetical) reſt on utterly vicious foundations.   In the
ſame manner Pedro de Medina, ſince he did not admit variation,
has disfigured his *Arte de Navegar* with many errors.

CHAP. IX.

Whether the terreſtrial longitude can be found from
the variation.

GRATEFUL would be this work to ſeamen, and
would bring the greateſt advance to Geography. But
B. Porta in chap. 38 of book 7 is mocked by a vain
hope and fruitleſs opinion.   For when he ſuppoſes
that the magnetick needle would follow order and
proportion in moving along meridians, ſo that " the
" neerer it is to the eaſt, the more it will decline from the Meridian
" line, toward the eaſt; and the neerer it comes to the weſt, the
point

" point of the needle will decline the more to the weſt " (which is
totally untrue), he thinks that he has diſcovered a true index of
longitude. But he is miſtaken. Nevertheleſs, admitting and aſſum-
ing theſe things (as though they were perfectly true), he makes a
large compaſs indicating degrees and minutes, by which theſe proportional changes of the verſorium might be obſerved. But thoſe
very principles are falſe, and ill conceived, and very ill conſidered ;
for the verſorium does not turn more to the eaſt becauſe a journey
is made toward the eaſt : and although the variation in the more
weſterly parts of Europe and the adjoining ocean is to the eaſt and
beyond the Azores is changed a little to the weſt, yet the variation
is, in various ways, always uncertain, both on account of longitude
and of latitude, and becauſe of the approach toward extenſive tracts
of land, and alſo becauſe of the form of the dominant terreſtrial
eminences ; nor does it, as we have before demonſtrated, follow the
rule of any particular meridian. It is with the ſame vanity alſo that
Livio Sanuto ſo greatly torments himſelf and his readers. As for
the fact that the crowd of philoſophizers and ſailors ſuppoſe that the
meridian paſſing through the Azores marks the limits of variation,
ſo that on the other and oppoſite ſide of that meridian a magnetick
body neceſſarily reſpects the poles exactly, which is alſo the opinion of
Joannes Baptiſta Benedictus and of many other writers on navigation,
it is by no means true. Stevinus (on the authority of Hugo Grotius)
in his *Havenfinding Art* diſtinguiſhes the variation according to the
meridians : " It may be ſeene in the Table of variations, that in *Coruo*
" the Magneticall needle pointeth due North : but after that, the more
" a man ſhal goe towards the Eaſt, ſo much the more alſo ſhall he
" ſee the needle varie towards the Eaſt [ἀνατολίζειν], till he come one
" mile to the Eaſtward from *Plimouth*, where the variation comming
" to the greateſt is 13 degr. 24 min. From hence the Northeaſting
" [Anatoliſmus] beginneth to decreaſe, til you come to *Helmſhude*
" (which place is Weſtward from the North Cape of Finmark) where
" againe the needle pointeth due North. Now the longitude from
" *Coruo* to *Helmſhude* is 60 degr. Which things being well weighed,
" it appeareth that the greateſt variation [Chalyboclyſis] 13 degr. 24
" minutes at *Plimmouth* (the longitude whereof is 30 degr.) is in the
" midſt betweene the places where the needle pointeth due North."
But although this is in ſome part true in theſe places, yet it is by no
means true that along the whole of the meridian of the iſland of
Corvo the verſorium looks truly to the north ; nor on the meridian
of Plymouth is the variation in other places 13 deg. 24 min.—nor
again in other parts of the meridian of Helmſhuda does it point to
the true pole. For on the meridian paſſing through Plymouth in
Latitude 60 degrees the North-eaſterly variation is greater : in Latitude 40 deg. much leſs ; in Latitude 20 deg. very small indeed.
On the meridian of Corvo, although there is no variation near the
iſland

ifland, yet in Latitude 55 degrees the variation is about $\frac{1}{2}$ a rumbe to the North-weft; in Latitude 20 deg. the verforium inclines $\frac{1}{4}$ of a rumbe toward the Eaft. Confequently the limits of variation are not conveniently determined by means of great circles and meridians, and much lefs are the ratios of the increment or decrement toward any part of the heavens properly inveftigated by them. Wherefore the rules of the abatement or augmentation of Northeafting or Northwefting, or of increafing or decreafing the magnetick deviation, can by no means be difcovered by fuch an artifice. The rules which follow later for variation in fouthern parts of the earth inveftigated by the fame method are altogether vain and abfurd. They were put forth by certain Portuguefe mariners, but they do not agree with the obfervations, and the obfervations themfelves are admitted to be bad. But the method of haven-finding in long and diftant voyages by carefully obferved variation (fuch as was invented by Stevinus, and mentioned by Grotius) is of great moment, if only proper inftruments are in readi-nefs, by which the magnetick deviation can be afcertained with certainty at fea.

CHAP. X.

Why in various places near the pole the variations
are much more ample than in a
lower latitude.

VARIATIONS are often flight, and generally null, when the verforium is at or near the earth's æquator. In a higher Latitude of 60, 70 or 80 deg. there are not feldom very wide variations. The caufe of this is to be fought partly from the nature of the earth and partly from the difpofition of the verforium. The earth turns magnetick bodies and at the æquator directs them ftrongly toward the pole: at the poles there is no direction, but only a ftrong coition through the congruent poles. Direction is therefore weaker near the poles, becaufe by reafon of its own natural tendency to turn, the verforium dips very much, and is not ftrongly directed. But fince the force of thofe elevated lands is more vigorous, for the virtue flows from the whole globe, and fince alfo the caufes of variation are nearer, therefore the verforium deflects the more from its true direction toward thofe eminences. It muft alfo be known that the direction of the verforium on its pin along the plane of the Horizon is much ftronger at the æquator than anywhere elfe by reafon of the difpofition of the
verforium;

verforium; and this direction falls off with an increafe of latitude. For on the æquator the verforium is, following its natural property, directed along the plane of the horizon; but in other places it is, contrary to its natural property, compelled into æquilibrium, and remains there, compelled by fome external force: becaufe it would, according to its natural property, dip below the horizon in proportion to the latitude, as we fhall demonftrate in the book *On Declination.* Hence the direction falls off and at the pole is itfelf nothing: and for that reafon a feebler direction is eafily vanquifhed by the ftronger caufes of variation, and near the pole the verforium deflects the more from the meridian. It is demonftrated by means of a terrella: if an iron wire of two digits length be placed on its æquator, it will be ftrongly and rapidly directed toward the poles along the meridian, but more weakly fo in the mid-intervals; while near the poles one may difcern a precipitate variation.

CHAP. XI.

Cardan's error when he feeks the diftance of the
centre of the earth from the centre of the cofmos by the
motion of the ftone of Hercules; in his
book 5, On Proportions.

NE may very eafily fall into miftakes and errors when one is fearching into the hidden caufes of things, in the abfence of real experiments, and this is eafily apparent from the crafs error of Cardan; who deems himfelf to have difcovered the diftances of the centres of the cofmos and of the earth through a variation of the magnetick iron of 9 degrees. For he reckoned that everywhere on the earth the point of variation on the Horizon is always diftant nine degrees from the true north, toward the eaft: and from thence he forms, by a moft foolifh error, his demonftrative ratio of the feparate centres.

CHAP.

CHAP. XII.

On the finding of the amount of variation : how great
is the arc of the Horizon from its arctick or antarctick
interfection of the meridian, to the point
refpective of the magnetick needle.

IRTUALLY the true meridian is the chief foundation of the whole matter : when that is accurately
known, it will be eafy by a mariners' compafs (if
its conftruction and the mode of attachment of the
magnetick iron works are known) or by fome
other larger horizontal verforium to exhibit the
arc of variation on the Horizon.   By means of a fufficiently large
nautical variation compafs (two equal altitudes of the fun being
obferved before and after midday), the variation becomes known from
the fhadow ; the altitude of the fun is obferved either by a ftaff or
by a rather large quadrant.

On land the variation is found in another way which is
eafier, and, becaufe of the larger fize of the inftrument, more
accurate.   Let a thick fquared board be made of fome fuitable
wood, the furface of which is two feet in length and fixteen
inches in width : defcribe upon it fome femicircles as in the following figure, only more in number.   In the centre let a brafs ftyle
be reared perpendicularly : let there be alfo a movable pointer
reaching from the centre to the outmoft femicircle, and a magnetick
verforium in a cavity covered over with glafs : then let the board
be exactly adjufted to the level of the Horizon by the plane inftrument with its perpendicular ; and turn the lily of the inftrument
toward the north, fo that the verforium may reft truly over the
middle line of the cavity, which looks toward the point of variation on the Horizon.   Then at fome convenient hour in the morn-
ing (eight or nine, for inftance) obferve the apex of the fhadow
thrown by the ftyle when it reaches the neareft femicircle and
mark the place of the apex of this fhadow with chalk or ink : then
bring round the movable index to that mark, and obferve the
degree on the Horizon numbered from the lily, which the index
fhows.   In the afternoon fee when the end of the fhadow fhall
again reach the periphery of the fame femicircle, and, bringing the
index to the apex of the fhadow, feek for the degree on the other
fide of the lily.   From the difference of the degrees becomes known
the

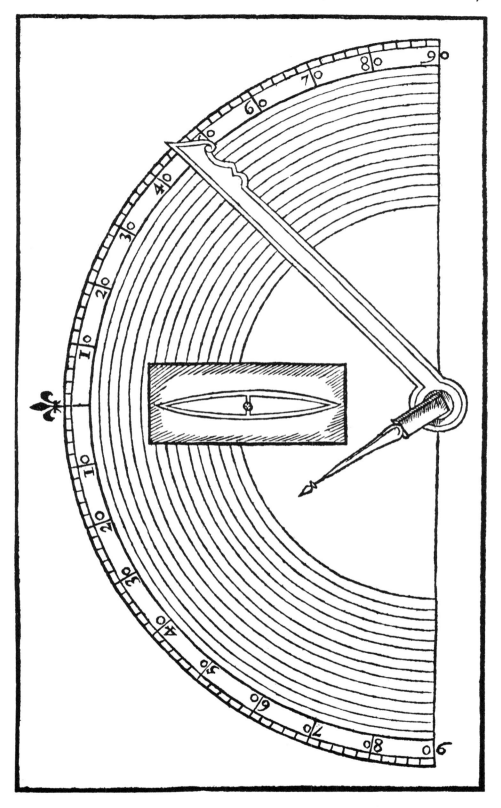

the variation; the lefs being taken from the greater, half the remainder is the arc of variation.   The variation is fought by many
other inftruments and methods in conjunction with a convenient
mariners' compafs; alfo by a globe, by numbers, and by the ratios
of triangles and fines, when the latitude is known and one obfervation is made of the fun's altitude : but thofe ways and methods are
of lefs ufe, for it is fuperfluous to try to find in winding and round-
about ways what can be more readily and as accurately found in a
fhorter one.   For the whole art is in the proper ufe of the inftruments by which the fun's place is expeditioufly and quickly taken
(fince it does not remain ftationary, but moves on) : for either the
hand trembles or the fight is dim, or the inftrument makes an error.
Befides, to obferve the altitude on both fides of the meridian is
juft as expeditious as to obferve on one fide only and at the fame
time to find the elevation of the pole.   And he who can take one
altitude by the inftrument can alfo take another; but if the one
altitude be uncertain, then all the labour with the globe, numbers,
fines and triangles is loft; neverthelefs thofe exercifes of ingenious
mathematicians are to be commended.   It is eafy for anyone, if he
ftand on land, to learn the variation by accurate obfervations and
fuitable inftruments, efpecially in a nearly upright fphere; but on
the fea, on account of the motion and the reftleffnefs of the waters,
exact experiments in degrees and minutes cannot be made : and
with the ufual inftruments fcarcely within the third or even the
half of a rumbe, efpecially in a higher latitude; hence fo many
falfe and bad records of the obfervations of navigators.   We have,
however, taken care for the finding of the deviation by a fufficiently
convenient and ready inftrument, by means of the rifing of certain
ftars, by the rifing or fetting of the fun, and in northern regions by
the Pole Star : for the variation is learned with greater certainty
even by the fkilful with an inftrument which is at once fimple and
lefs fenfitive to the waves of the fea.   Its conftruction is as follows.

Let an inftrument be made of the form of a true and meridional
mariners' compafs of at leaft one foot in diameter (with a verforium
which is either nude or provided with a cardboard circle) : let the
limb be divided into four quadrants, and each quadrant into 90
degrees.   The movable compafs-box (as is ufual in the nautical
inftrument) is to be balanced below by a heavy weight of fixteen
pounds.   On the margin of the fufpended compafs-box, where oppofite quadrants begin, let a half-ring rifing in an angular frame in
the middle be raifed (with the feet of the half-ring fixed on either
fide in holes in the margin) fo that the top of the frame may be
perpendicular to the plane of the compafs; on its top let a rule
fixteen digits in length be faftened at its middle on a joint like
a balance beam, fo that it may move, as it were, about a central
axis.   At the ends of the rule there are fmall plates with holes,
                                                       through

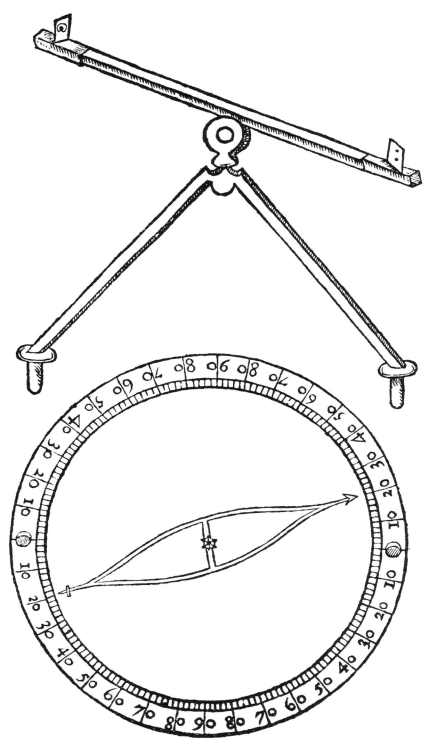

through which we can obferve the fun or ftars. The variation is beft obferved and expeditioufly by this inftrument at the equinoxes by the rifing or fetting fun. But even when the fun is in other parts of the zodiack, the deviation becomes known when we have the altitude of the pole: that being known, one can learn the amplitude on the Horizon and the diftance from the true eaft both of the fun and of the following fixed ftars by means of a globe, or tables, or an inftrument. Then the variation readily becomes known by counting from the true eaft the degrees and minutes of the amplitude at rifing. Obferve the preceding ftar of the three in the Belt of Orion as foon as it appears on the horizon; direct the inftrument toward it and obferve the verforium, for fince the ftar has its rifing in the true eaft about one degree toward the fouth, it can be feen how much the verforium is diftant from the meridian, account being taken of that one degree. You will alfo be able to obferve the arctick pole ftar when it is on the meridian, or at its greateft diftance from the meridian of about three degrees (the pole ftar is diftant 2 deg. 55 min. from the pole, according to the obfervations of Tycho Brahe), and by the inftrument you will learn the variation (if the ftar be not on the meridian) by adding or fubtracting, *fecundum artem*, the proper reduction [*proftaphærefis*] of the ftar's diftance from the meridian. You will find when the pole ftar is on the meridian by knowing the fun's place and the hour of the night: for this a practifed obferver will eafily perceive without great error by the vifible inclination of the conftellation: for we do not take notice of a few minutes, as do fome who, when they toil to track the minutes of degrees at fea, are in error by a nearly whole rumbe. A practifed obferver will, in the rifing of fun or ftars, allow fomething for refraction, fo that he may be able to ufe a more exact calculation.

Bright and confpicuous ftars which are

not far diftant from the æquator which it will be ufeful to obferve at their rifing and fetting: the amplitude at the Horizon on rifing being known from the altitude of the pole and from the declination of the ftars, by means of a globe, or tables, or an inftrument whence the variation is perceived by technical calculation.

Oculus

	Right Ascension		Declination	
Oculus Tauri	62°	55'	15°	53' N
Sinister humerus Orionis	72°	24'	4°	5' N
Dexter humerus Orionis	83°	30'	6°	19' N
Præcedens in cingulo Orionis	77°	46'	1°	16' S
Canis major	97°	10'	15°	55' S
Canis minor	109°	41'	5°	55' N
Lucida Hydræ	137°	10'	5°	3' S
Caput Geminorum australe	110°	21'	28°	30' N
Caput boreale	107°	4'	32°	10' N
Cor Leonis	146°	8'	13°	47' N
Cauda Leonis	171°	38'	16°	30' N
Spica Virginis	195°	44'	8°	34' S
Arcturus	29°	13'	21°	54' N
Cor Aquilæ	291°	56'	7°	35' N

An instrument for finding the amplitude

at rising on the horizon.

DESCRIBE the circumference of a circle and let it be divided into quadrants by two diameters interfecting each other at right angles at its centre. One of these will reprefent the æqui-noctial circle, the other the axis of the world. Let each of these quadrants be divided (in the accuftomed way) into 90 degrees; on every fifth or tenth of which at each end of each diameter and on each fide let marks (fhowing the numbers) be infcribed on the two limbs or margins made for that purpofe outfide the circumference. Then from each degree ftraight lines are drawn parallel to the æquator. You will then prepare a rule or alhidade equal to the diameter of that circle and divided throughout into the fame parts into which the diameter of the circle reprefenting the axis of the world is divided. Let there be left a fmall appendage attached to the middle of the rule, by which the middle of the fiducial line itfelf of the rule may be connected with the centre of the circle: but to every fifth or tenth part of that rule let numbers be attached proceeding from the centre toward each fide. This circle reprefents the plane of the meridian; its centre the actual point of eaft or weft, i.e., the common interfection of the horizon and æquator; all thofe lines æquidiftant from the æquator denote the parallels of the fun and ftars; the fiducial line of the rule or alhidade reprefents the horizon; and its parts fignify the degrees of the horizon, beginning from the point of fetting or of rifing.

Therefore

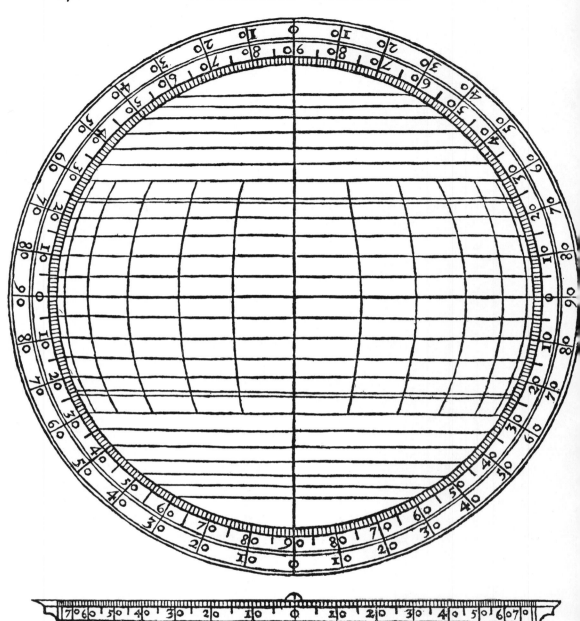

Therefore if the fiducial line of the rule be applied to the given
latitude of the place reckoned from either end of that diameter
which reprefents the axis of the world; and if further the given
declination of the fun or of fome ftar from the æquator (lefs than
the complement of the latitude of the place) be found on the limb
of the inftrument; then the interfection of the parallel drawn from
that point of the declination with the horizon, or with the fiducial
line of the rule or alhidade, will indicate for the given latitude of
the place the amplitude at rifing of the given ftar or the fun.

CHAP.

CHAP. XIII.

The obfervations of variation by feamen vary, for the
moft part, and are uncertain: partly from error and inexperience,
and the imperfections of the inftruments: and partly
from the fea being feldom fo calm that the
fhadows or lights can remain quite
fteady on the inftruments.

AFTER the variation of the compafs had firft been noticed, fome more diligent navigators took pains to inveftigate in various ways the difference of afpect of the mariners' compafs. Yet, to the great detriment of the nautical art, this has not been done fo exactly as it ought to have been. For either being fomewhat ignorant they have not underftood any accurate method or they have ufed bad and abfurd inftruments, or elfe they merely follow fome conjecture arifing from an ill-formed opinion as to fome prime meridian or magnetick pole; whilft others again tranfcribe from others, and parade thefe obfervations as their own; and they who, very unfkilful themfelves, firft of all committed their obfervations to writing are, as by the prerogative of time, held in efteem by others, and their pofterity does not think it fafe to differ from them. Hence in long navigations, efpecially to the Eaft Indies, the records by the Portuguefe of the deviating compafs are feen to be unfkilful: for whoever reads their writings will eafily underftand that they are in error in very many things, and do not rightly underftand the conftruction of the Portuguefe compafs (the lily of which diverges by half a rumbe from the needles toward the weft), nor its ufe in taking the variation. Hence, while they fhow the variation of the compafs in different places, it is uncertain whether they meafure the deviation by a true meridional compafs or by fome other whofe needles are difplaced from the lily. The Portuguefe (as is patent in their writings) make ufe of the Portuguefe compafs, whofe magnetick needles are fixed afide from the lily by half of one rumbe toward the eaft. Moreover on the fea the obfervation of the variation is a matter of great difficulty, on account of the motion of the fhip and the uncertainty of the deviation, even with the more fkilful obfervers, if they ufe the beft made inftruments hitherto known and ufed. Hence there arife different opinions concerning the magnetick deviation: as, for inftance, near the Ifland of St. Helena the Portuguefe Rodriguez de

Lagos

Lagos meaſures half a rumbe. The Dutch in their nautical log fix it at a whole rumbe. Kendall, the expert Engliſhman, with a true meridional compaſs admits only a ſixth part of a rumbe. A little to the Eaſt of Cape Agulhas Diego Alfonſo makes no variation, and ſhows by an Aſtrolabe that the compaſs remains in the true meridian. Rodriguez ſhows that the compaſs at Cape Agulhas has no variation if it is of Portugueſe conſtruction, in which the needles are inclined half a rumbe to the Eaſt. And there is the ſame confuſion, negligence, and vanity in very many other inſtances.

CHAP. XIIII.

On the variation under the æquinoctial line,
and near it.

N the North the magnetick needle varies becauſe of the Boreal eminences of the continent ; in the South becauſe of the Auſtral ; at the æquator, if the regions on both ſides were equal, there would be no variation. But becauſe this rarely happens ſome variation is often obſerved under the æquator; and even at ſome diſtance from the æquator of three or 4 degrees toward the North, there may be a variation ariſing from the ſouth, if thoſe very wide and influential ſouthern continents be ſomewhat near on one ſide.

CHAP. XV.

The variation of the magnetick needle in the great
Æthiopick and American ſea, beyond
the æquator.

ISCOURSE hath already been had of the mode and reaſon of the variation in the great Atlantick Ocean : but when one has advanced beyond the æquator off the eaſt coaſt of Brazil the magnetick needle turns aſide toward the mainland, namely, with that end of it which points to the ſouth; ſo that with that end of the verſorium it deviates from the true meridian toward the weſt ; which navigators obſerve at the other end and ſuppoſe a variation to occur toward the eaſt. But throughout the whole way from the firſt promontory on the eaſt of Brazil, by Cape

Cape St. Auguftine and thence to Cape Frio, and further ftill to the mouth of the Strait of Magellan, the variation is always from the fouth toward the weft with that end of the verforium which tends toward the antarctick pole.   For it is always with the accordant end that it turns toward a continent.   The variation, however, occurs not only on the coaft itfelf, but at fome diftance from land, fuch as a fpace of fifty or fixty German miles or even more.   But when at length one has progreffed far from land, then the arc begins to diminifh : for the magnetick needle turns afide the lefs toward what is too far off, and is turned afide the lefs from what is prefent and at hand, fince it enjoys what is prefent.   In the Ifland of St. Helena (the longitude of which is lefs than is commonly marked on charts and globes) the verforium varies by one degree or nearly two.   The Portuguefe and others taught by them, who navigate beyond the Cape of Good Hope to the Indies, fet a courfe toward the Iflands of Triftan d'Acunha, in order that they may enjoy more favourable winds ; in the former part of their courfe the change of variation is not great ; but after they have approached the iflands the variation increafes ; and clofe to the iflands it is greater than anywhere elfe in the whole courfe.   For the end of the ver-forium tending to the fouth (in which lies the greateft fource of the variation) is caught and allured toward the fouth-weft by the great promontory of the fouthern land.   But when they pro-ceed onward toward the Cape of Good Hope the variation diminifhes the more they approach it.   But on the prime meridian in the latitude of 45 degrees, the verforium tends to the fouth-eaft : and one who navigates near the coaft from Mani-congo to the tropick, and a little beyond, will perceive that the verforium tends from the fouth to the eaft, although not much.   At the promontory of Agulhas it preferves flightly the variation which it fhowed near the iflands of d'Acunha, which neverthelefs is very much diminifhed becaufe of the greater remote-nefs from the caufe of variation, and confequently there the fouthern end of the verforium does not yet face exactly to the pole.

CHAP. XVI.

On the variation in Nova Zembla.

ARIATIONS in parts near the pole are greater (as has been fhown before) and alfo have fudden changes, as in former years the Dutch explorers obferved not badly, even if thofe obfervations were not exact—which indeed is pardonable in them ; for with the ufual inftruments it is with difficulty
that

that the truth becomes known in fuch a high latitude (of about 80 degrees). Now, however, from the deviation of the compafs the reafon for there being an open courfe to the eaft by the Arctick Ocean appears manifeft; for fince the verforium has fo ample a variation toward the north-weft, it is demonftrable that a continent does not extend any great diftance in the whole of that courfe toward the eaft. Therefore with the greater hope can the fea be attempted and explored toward the eaft for a paffage to the Moluccas by the north-eaft than by the north-weft.

CHAP. XVII.

Variation in the Pacifick Ocean.

PASSING the Strait of Magellan the deviation on the fhore of Peru is toward the fouth-eaft, *i.e.*, from the fouth toward the eaft. And a fimilar deflection would be continued along the whole coaft of Peru as far as the æquator. In a higher latitude up to 45 deg. the variation is greater than near the æquator; and the deflection toward the fouth-eaft is in nearly the fame proportion as was the deviation from the fouth toward the weft on the eaftern fhore of South America. From the æquator toward the North there is little or no variation until one comes to New Galicia; and thence along the whole fhore as far as Quivira the inclination is from the north toward the eaft.

CHAP. XVIII.

On the variation in the Mediterranean Sea.

SICILIAN and Italian failors think that in the Sicilian Sea and toward the eaft up to the meridian of the Peloponnefus (as Francifcus Maurolycus relates) the magnetick needle " græcizes," that is, turns from the pole toward what is called the greek wind or Boreas; that on the fhore of the Peloponnefus it looks toward the true pole; but that when they have proceeded further eaft, then it " miftralizes," becaufe it tends from the pole toward the miftral or north-weft wind: which agrees with our rule for the variation. For as the Mediterranean Sea is extended toward the weft from that meridian, fo on the fide

toward

toward the eaſt the Mediterranean Sea lies open as far as Paleſtine; as toward North and Eaſt lie open the whole Archipelago and the neighbouring Black Sea. From the Peloponneſus toward the north pole the meridian paſſes through the largeſt and moſt elevated regions of all Europe; through Achaia, Macedonia, Hungary, Tranſylvania, Lithuania, Novogardia, Corelia and Biarmia.

CHAP. XIX.

The variation in the interior of large
Continents.

OST of the great ſeas have great variations; in ſome parts, however, they have none, but the true directions are toward the pole. On continents, alſo, the magnetick needle often deviates from the meridian, as on the edge of the land and near the borders; but it is generally accuſtomed to deviate by a ſomewhat ſmall arc. In the middle, however, of great regions there are no variations. Hence in the middle lands of Upper Europe, in the interior of Aſia, and in the heart of Africa, of Peru, and in the regions of North or Mexican America, the verſorium reſts in the meridian.

CHAP. XX.

Variation in the Eaſtern Ocean.

ARIATION in the Eaſtern Ocean throughout the whole voyage to Goa and the Moluccas is obſerved by the Portugueſe; but they err greatly in many things, following, as they do, the firſt obſervers who note down variations in certain places with ill-adapted inſtruments, and by no means accurate obſervations, or by ſome conjectures. As, for inſtance, in Brandöe Iſland, they make the verſorium deviate by 22 degrees to the north-weſt. For in no region or place in the whole world, of not greater latitude, is there ſo great a deviation; and, in reality, there the deviation is ſlight. Alſo when they make out that at Moſambique the compaſs deviates by one rumbe to the north-weſt, it is falſe; even though they uſe (as they are accuſtomed to do) the Portugueſe compaſs: for beyond all doubt on the ſhore of Moſam-
bique

bique the verforium inclines ¼ rumbe or even more to the south-west. Very wrongly alfo beyond the æquator in the courfe to Goa they make the little compafs incline by 1½ rumbe to the weft: whereas they fhould rather have faid that in the firft part of the courfe the Portuguefe compafs inclines by 1 rumbe: but that the true meridional compafs inclines by ½ rumbe only. In order that the amount of variation in the Eaftern Ocean may be accurately fettled in moft places by our rules, there is needed a more exact and truer furvey of the fouthern land, which fpreads out from the fouth to the æquinoctial more than is commonly defcribed on maps and globes.

CHAP. XXI.

How the deviation of the verforium is augmented and *diminifhed by reafon of the diftance of places.*

IN the middle of great and continent lands there is no variation. Nor, generally, in the middle of very great feas. On the margin of thofe lands and feas the variation is often ample, yet not fo great as at a little further diftance on the fea. As, for example, near Cape St. Auguftine the compafs varies; but at 50 miles from land toward the Eaft it varies more; and 80 miles off it varies ftill more; and yet ftill more at a diftance of 100 miles. But from a diftance of 100 miles the diminutions of deviation are flower, when they are navigating toward the mainland, than at a diftance of 80 miles, and at a diftance of 80 miles than at 50: for the deviations change and are diminifhed rather more fwiftly the more they approach and draw near land than when at a great diftance off. As, for inftance, navigating toward Newfoundland the change of variation is more rapid (that is, it decreafes a degree in a fmaller arc of the courfe on the parallel) when they are not far from land than when they are a hundred miles diftant: but when travelling on land toward the interiors of regions the changes are flower in the firft parts of the journey than when they come more into the interior.

The ratio of the arcs on a parallel circle, when a verforium is moved toward continents which extend to the pole, correfponds with the degrees of variation. Let A be the pole; B the eminences of the dominant lands; at C there is no variation caufed by B, for it is too far away; at D the variation is very great becaufe the verforium is allured or turned by the whole earth toward the eminent
land

land B; and moreover it is not hindered, or reſtrained or brought back to the pole by the verticity of the earth; but, tending of its own nature to the pole, it is neverthelefs deflected from it by reaſon of the fite, or poſition, and convenient diſtance of the dominant and high lands.

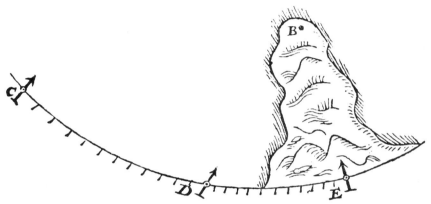

Now from C toward D the variation increaſes; the verſorium, however, does not deviate ſo rapidly in the firſt ſpaces as near D: for more miles are traverſed on the parallel circle C D, near C, in order that the verſorium may deviate by one degree from the pole A, than near D. So alſo in order that the variation may be diminiſhed from D toward E more miles are required near D than near E. Thus the deviations become equal in unequal courſes, whether the variation be increaſing or decreaſing; and yet the variation decreaſes by leſſer intervals than it in-creaſes. There intervene, however, many other cauſes which perturb this proportion.

BOOK

BOOK FIFTH.

*C*HAP I.

ON DECLINATION.

I N due courſe we have now come to that notable experiment, and remarkable motion of magnetick bodies dipping below the horizon by their own rotatory nature; by the knowledge of which is revealed a unity, a concordancy, and a mutual agreement between the terreſtrial globe and the loadſtone (or the magnetick iron), which is wonderful in itſelf, and is made manifeſt by our teaching. This motion we have made known in many ſtriking experiments, and have eſtabliſhed its rules; and in the following pages we ſhall demonſtrate the cauſes of it, in ſuch a way that no ſound, logical mind can ever rightly ſet at nought or diſprove our chief magnetick principles. Direction, as alſo variation, is demonſtrated in a horizontal plane, when a balanced magnetick needle comes to reſt at ſome definite point; but declination is ſeen to be the motion of a needle, ſtarting from that point of the horizon, firſt balanced on its own axis, then excited by a loadſtone, one end or pole of it tending toward the centre of the earth. And we have found that it takes place in proportion to the latitude of each region. But that motion ariſes in truth, not from any motion from the horizon toward the centre of the earth, but from the turning of the whole magnetick body toward the whole of the earth, as we ſhall ſhow hereafter. Nor does the iron dip from the horizontal in ſome oblique ſphere, according to the number of degrees of elevation of the pole in the given region, or by an equal arc in the quadrant, as will appear hereafter.

Inſtrument

Instrument of the Declination.

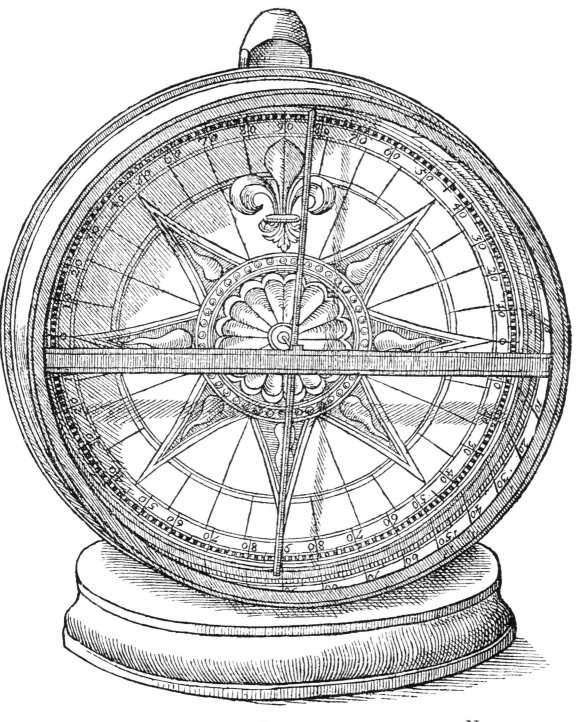

B B   Now

Now how much it dips at every horizon may be afcertained in the firft place by a contrivance, which, however, is not fo eafily made as is that in dials for meafuring time, in which the needle turns to the points of the horizon, or in the mariners' compafs. From a plank of wood let a fmooth and circular inftrument be prepared, at leaft fix digits in diameter, and affix this to the fide of a fquare pillar, which ftands upright on a wooden bafe. Divide the periphery of this inftrument into 4 quadrants: then each quadrant into 90 degrees. At the centre of the inftrument let there be placed a brafs peg, at the centre of the end of which let there be a fmall hollow, well polifhed. To this wooden inftrument let a brafs circle or ring be fixed, about two digits in width, with a thin plate or flat rod of the fame metal, reprefenting the horizon, fixed acrofs it, through the middle of the circle. In the middle of the horizontal rod let there be another hollow, which fhall be exactly oppofite the centre of the inftrument, where the former hollow was made. Afterward let a needle be fafhioned out of fteel, as verforia are accuftomed to be made. Divide this at right angles by a thin iron axis (like a crofs) through the very middle and centre of the wire and the crofs-piece. Let this dipping-needle be hung (with the ends of the crofs refting in the aforefaid holes) fo that it can move freely and evenly on its axis in the moft perfect æquilibrium, fo accurately that it turns away from no one point or degree marked on the circumference more than from another, but that it can reft quite eafily at any. Let it be fixed upright to the front part of the pillar, whilft at the edge of the bafe is a fmall verforium to fhow direction. Afterward touch the iron, fufpended by this ingenious method, on both ends with the oppofite ends of a loadftone, according to the fcientifick method, but rather carefully, left the needle be twifted in any way; for unlefs you prepare everything very fkilfully and cleverly, you will fecure no refult. Then let another brafs ring be prepared, a little larger, fo as to contain the former one; and let a glafs or a very thin plate of mica be fitted to one fide of it. When this is put over the former ring, the whole fpace within remains inclofed, and the verforium is not interfered with by duft or winds. Difpofe the inftrument, thus completed, perpendicularly on its bafe, and with the fmall verforium horizontal, in fuch a way that, while ftanding perpendicularly, it may be directed toward the exact magnetical point refpective. Then the end of the needle which looks toward the north dips below the horizon in northern regions, whilft in fouthern regions the end of the needle which looks toward the fouth tends toward the centre of the earth, in a certain proportion (to be explained afterward) to the latitude of the diftrict in queftion, from the æquator on either fide. The needle, however, muft be rubbed on

a

a powerful loadſtone; otherwiſe it does not dip to the true point, or
elſe it goes paſt it, and does not always reſt in it. A larger inſtrument
may alſo be uſed, whoſe diameter may be 10 or 12 digits; but in ſuch
an inſtrument more care is needed to balance the verſorium truly.
Care muſt be taken that the needle be of ſteel; alſo that it be ſtraight;
likewiſe that both ends of the croſs-piece be ſharp and fixed at right
angles to the needle, and that the croſs-piece paſs through the centre
of the needle. As in other magnetical motions there is an exact
agreement between the earth and the ſtone, and a correſpondence
manifeſtly apparent to our ſenſes by means of our experiments; ſo
in this declination there is a clear and evident concordance of the
terreſtrial globe with the loadſtone. Of this motion, ſo important
and ſo long unknown to all men, the following is the ſure and true
cauſe. A magnet-ſtone is moved and turned round until one of
its poles being impelled toward the north comes to reſt toward
a definite point of the horizon. This pole, which ſettles toward
the north (as appears from the preceding rules and demonſtrations),
is the ſouthern, not the boreal; though all before us deemed it
to be the boreal, on account of its turning to that point of the
horizon. A wire or verſorium touched on this pole of the ſtone turns
to the ſouth, and is made into a boreal pole, becauſe it was touched
by the ſouthern terminal of the ſtone. So if the cuſp of a verſorium
be excited in a ſimilar manner, it will be directed toward the
ſouthern pole of the earth, and will adjuſt itſelf alſo to it; but the
croſs (the other end) will be ſouthern, and will turn to the north of
the earth (the earth itſelf being the cauſe of its motion); for ſo
direction is produced from the diſpoſition of the ſtone or of the
excited iron, and from the verticity of the earth. But declination
takes place when a magnetick is turned round toward the body of
the earth, with its ſouthern end toward the north, at ſome latitude
away from the æquator. For this is certain and conſtant, that
exactly under the cœleſtial æquator, or rather over the æquator of
the terreſtrial globe, there is no declination of a loadſtone or of iron;
but in whatever way the iron has been excited or rubbed, it ſettles
in the declination inſtrument preciſely along the plane of the
horizon, if it were properly balanced before. Now this occurs
thus becauſe, when the magnetick body is at an equal diſtance from
either pole, it dips toward neither by its own verſatory nature, but
remains evenly directed to the level of the horizon, as if it were
reſting on a pin or floating free and unhindered on water. But
when the magnetick ſubſtance is at ſome latitude away from
the æquator, or when either pole of the earth is raiſed (I do not
ſay raiſed above the viſible horizon, as the commonly imagined
pole of the revolving univerſe in the ſky, but above the horizon or
its centre, or its proper diameter, æquidiſtant from the plane of the
viſible horizon, which is the true elevation of the terreſtrial pole),
then

then declination is apparent, and the iron inclines toward the body of the earth in its own meridian.   Let A B, for example, be the vifible horizon of a place; C D the horizontal through the earth, dividing it into equal parts; E F the axis of the earth; G the pofition of the place.   It is manifeft that the boreal pole E is elevated above the point C by as much as G is diftant from the

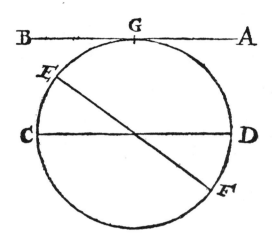

æquator.   Wherefore, fince at E the magnetick needle ftands per-pendicularly in its proper turning (as we have often fhown before), fo now at G there is a certain tendency to turn in proportion to the latitude (the magnetick dipping below the plane of the horizon), and the magnetick body interfeɛts the horizon at unequal angles, and exhibits a declination below the horizon.   For the fame reafon, if the declinatory needle be placed at G, its fouthern end, the one namely which is direɛted toward the North, dips below the plane of the vifible horizon A B.   And fo there is the greateft difference between a right fphere and a polar or parallel fphere, in which the pole is at the very Zenith.   For in a right fphere the needle is parallel to the plane of the horizon; but when the cœleftial pole is vertically overhead, or when the pole of the earth is itfelf the place of the region, then the needle is perpendicular to the horizon.   This is fhown by a round ftone.   Let a fmall dipping-needle, of two digits length (rubbed with a magnet), be hung in the air like a balance, and let the ftone be carefully placed under it; and firft let the terrella be at right angles, as in a right fphere, and as in the firft figure; for fo the magnetick needle will remain in æquilibrium. But in an oblique pofition of the terrella, as in an oblique fphere, and in the fecond figure, the needle dips obliquely at one end toward the near pole, but does not reft on the pole, nor is its dip ruled by the pole, but by the body and mafs of the whole; for the

dip

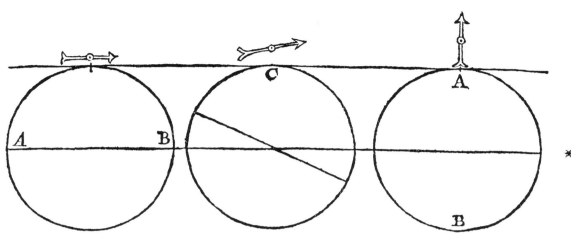

dip in higher latitudes paſſes beyond the pole. But in the third
poſition of the terrella the needle is perpendicular; becauſe the
pole of the ſtone is placed at the top, and the needle tending ſtraight
toward the body reaches to the pole. The croſs in the preceding
figures always turns toward the boreal pole of the terrella, having
been touched by the boreal pole of the terrella; the cuſp of the
needle, having been touched by the ſouthern pole of the ſtone, turns
to the ſouth. Thus one may ſee on a terrella the level, oblique,
and perpendicular poſitions of a magnetick needle.

CHAP. II.

Diagram of declinations of the magnetick needle, when
excited, in the various poſitions of the ſphere, and horizons
of the earth, in which there is no varia-
tion of the declination.

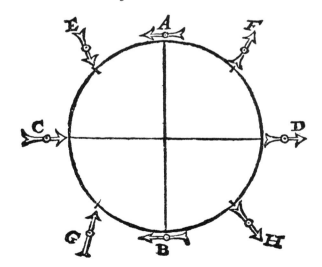

S æquator let A B be taken, C the north pole, D the ſouth, E G dipping-needles in the northern, H F in the ſouthern part of the earth or of a terrella. In the diagram before us all the cuſps have been touched by the true Arctick pole of the terrella.

Here we have the level poſition of the magnetick needle on the æquator of the earth and the ſtone, at A and B, and its perpendicular poſition at C, D, the poles; whilſt at the places midway between, at a diſtance of 45 degrees, the croſſes of the needle dip toward the ſouth, but the cuſps juſt as much toward the north. Of which thing the reaſon will become clear from the demonſtrations that follow.

✱ *Diagram of the rotation and declination of a terrella*
conforming to the globe of the earth, for a
latitude of 50 degrees north.

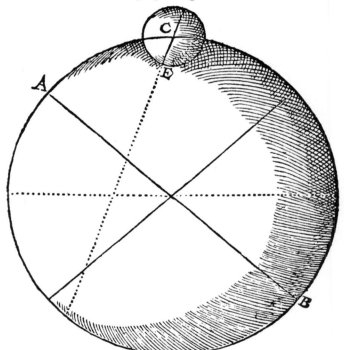

A is the boreal pole of the earth or of a rather large terrella, B the ſouthern, C a ſmaller terrella, E the ſouthern pole of the ſmaller terrella, dipping in the northern regions. The centre C is placed on the ſurface of the larger terrella, becauſe the ſmaller terrella ſhows ſome variation on account of the length of the axis; inappreciable, however, on the earth. Juſt as a magnetick needle dips in a regional latitude of 50 degrees, ſo alſo the axis of a ſtone (of a ſpherical ſtone, of courſe) is depreſſed below the horizon, and its natural auſtral pole falls, and its boreal pole is raiſed on the
south

fouth toward the Zenith.   In the fame way alfo a circular difc of iron behaves, which has been carefully touched at oppofite parts on its circumference; but the magnetical experiments are lefs clear on account of the feebler forces in round pieces of iron.

Variety in the declinations of iron fpikes at various latitudes of a terrella.

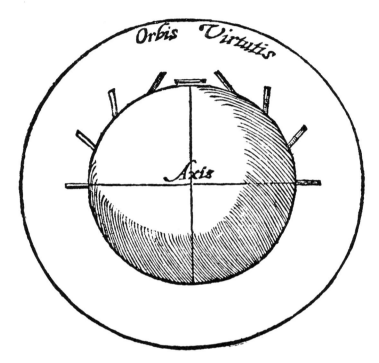

The declination of a magnetick needle above a terrella is fhown by means of feveral equal iron wires, of the length of a barleycorn, arranged along a meridian.   The wires on the æquator are directed by the virtue of the ftone toward the poles, and lie down upon its body along the plane of its horizon.   The nearer they are brought to the poles, the more they are raifed up by their verfatory nature. At the poles themfelves they point perpendicularly toward the very centre.   But iron fpikes, if they are of more than a due length, are not raifed ftraight up except on a vigorous ftone.

CHAP. III.

An indicatory inftrument, fhowing by the virtue of a ✳

ftone the degrees of declination from the horizon
of each feveral latitude.

Defcription

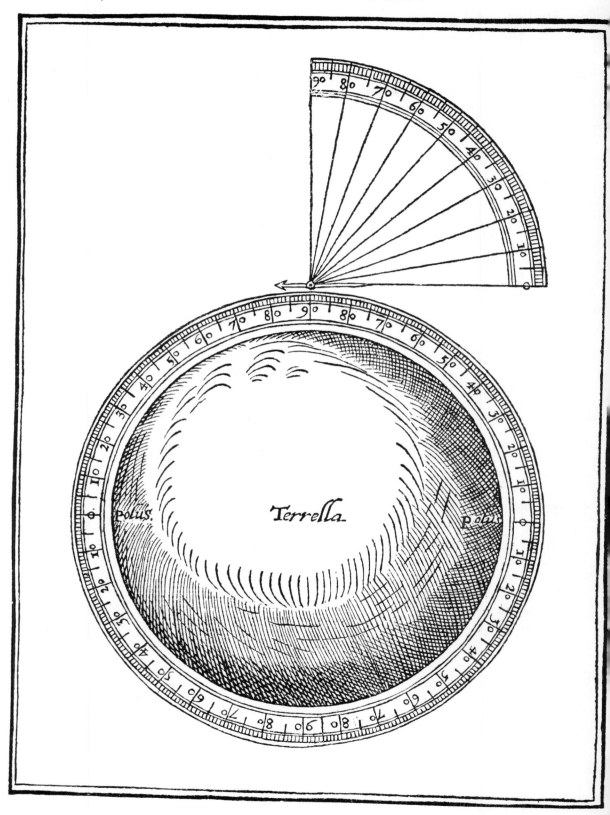

Defcription of the Inftrument, and its ufe.

AKE a terrella of the beft ftrong loadftone, and homogeneous throughout, not weakened by decay or by a flaw in any parts; let it be of a fair fize, fo that its diameter is fix or feven digits; and let it be made exactly fpherical. Having found its poles according to the method already fhown, mark them with an iron tool; then mark alfo the æquinoctial circle. Afterwards in a thick fquared block of wood, one foot in fize, make a hemifpherical hollow, which fhall hold half of the terrella, and fuch that exactly one half of the ftone fhall project above the face of the block. Divide the limb clofe to this cavity (a circle having been drawn round it for a meridian) into 4 quadrants, and each of thefe into 90 degrees. Let the terminus of the quadrants on the limb be near the centre of a quadrant defcribed on the block, alfo divided into 90 degrees. At that centre let a fhort, flender verforium (its other end being rather fharp and elongated like a pointer) be placed in æquilibrio on a fuitable pin. It is manifeft that when the poles of the ftone are at the ftarting points of the quadrants, then the verforium lies ftraight, as if in æqui-librio, over the terrella. But if you move the terrella, fo that the pole on the left hand rifes, then the verforium rifes on the meridian in proportion to the latitude, and turns itfelf as a mag-netick body; and on the quadrant defcribed on the flat furface of the wood, the degree of its turning or of the declination is fhown by the verforium. The rim of the cavity reprefents a meridional circle, to which correfponds fome meridian circle of the terrella, fince the poles on both fides are within the circumference of the rim itfelf. Thefe things clearly always happen on the fame plan on the earth itfelf when there is no variation; but when there is variation, either in the direction or in the declination (a difturb-ance, as it were, in the true turning, on account of caufes to be explained later), then there is fome difference. Let the quadrant be near the limb, or have its centre on the limb itfelf, and let the verforium be very fhort, fo as not to touch the terrella, becaufe with a verforium that is longer or more remote, there is fome error; for it has a motion truly proportionate to the terrella only on the furface of the terrella. But if the quadrant, being far diftant from the terrella, were moved within the orbe of virtue of the ter-rella toward the pole on fome circle concentrick with the terrella, then the verforium would indicate the degrees of declination on the quadrant, in proportion to and fymmetrically with that circle, not with the terrella.

c c   CHAP.

CHAP. IIII.

Concerning the length of a verforium convenient
for declination on a terrella.

ECLINATION being inveftigated on the earth itfelf by means of a declination inftrument, we may ufe either a fhort or a very long verforium, if only the magnetick virtue of the ftone that touches it is able to permeate through the whole of its middle and through all its length.   For the greateft length of a verforium has no moment or perceptible proportion to the earth's femi-diameter.   On a terrella, however, or in a plane near a meridian of a terrella, a fhort verforium is defirable, of the length, fay, of a barleycorn ; for longer ones (becaufe they reach further) dip and turn toward the body of the terrella fuddenly and irregularly in the firft degrees of declination. For example, as foon as the long verforium is moved forward from the æquator A to C, it catches on the ftone with its cufp (as if with

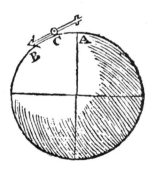

a long extended wing), when the cufp reaches to the parts about B, which produce a greater rotation than at C. And the extremities of longer wires alfo and rods turn irregularly, juft as iron wires and balls of iron and other orbicular loadftones are likewife turned about irregularly by a long non-orbicular loadftone.   Juft fo magneticks or iron bodies on the furface of a terrella ought not to have too long an axis, but a very fhort one ; fo that they may make a declination on the terrella truly and naturally proportionate to that on the earth. A long verforium alfo clofe to a terrella with difficulty ftands fteady in a horizontal direction on a right fphere, and, beginning to waver, it dips immediately to one fide, efpecially the end that was touched, or (if both were touched) the one which felt the ftone laft.

CHAP.

CHAP. V.

That declination does not arife from the attraction
of the loadftone, but from a difpofing and
rotating influence.

IN the univerfe of nature that marvellous provifion of its Maker fhould be noticed, whereby the principal bodies are reftrained within certain habitations and fenced in, as it were (nature controlling them). For this reafon the ftars, though they move and advance, are not thrown into confufion. Magnetical rotations alfo arife from a difpofing influence, whether in greater and dominating quantity, or in a fmaller, and compliant quantity, even though it be very fmall. For the work is not accomplifhed by attraction, but by an incitation of each fubftance, by a motion of agreement toward fixed bounds, beyond which no advance is made. For if the verforium dipped by reafon of an attractive force, then a terrella made from a very ftrong magnetick ftone would caufe the verforium to turn toward itfelf more than one made out of an average ftone, and a piece of iron touched with a vigorous loadftone would dip more. This, however, never happens. Moreover, an iron fnout placed on a meridian in any latitude does not raife a fpike more toward the perpendicular than the ftone itfelf, alone and unarmed; although when thus equipped, it plucks up and raifes many greater weights. But if a loadftone be fharper toward one pole, toward the other blunter, the fharp end or pole allures a magnetick needle more ftrongly, the blunt, thick end makes it rotate more ftrongly; but an orbicular ftone makes it rotate ftrongly and truly, in accordance with magnetick rules and its globular form. A long ftone, on the other hand, extended from pole to pole, moves a verforium toward it irregularly; for in this cafe the pole of the verforium always looks down on the pole itfelf. Similarly alfo, if the loadftone have been made in the fhape of a circle, and its poles are on the circumference, whilft the body of it is plane, not globular, if the plane be brought near a verforium, the verforium does not move with the regular magnetick rotation, as on a terrella; but it turns looking always toward the pole of the loadftone, which has its feat on the circumference of the plane. Moreover, if the ftone caufed the verforium to rotate by attracting it, then in the firft degrees of latitude, it would attract the end of a fhort verforium toward the body itfelf of the terrella; yet it does not fo attract it that they are brought into contact and unite; but the verforium rotates juft fo far as nature demands, as is clear from this example.

For

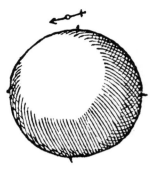

For the cufp of a verforium placed in a low latitude does not touch
the ftone or unite with it, but only inclines toward it. Moreover,
when a magnetick body rotates in dipping, the pole of the verforium
is not ftayed or detained by the pole of the earth or terrella; but
it rotates regularly, and does not ftop at any point or bound, nor
point ftraight to the pole toward which the centre of the verforium
is advancing, unlefs on the pole itfelf, and once only between the
pole and the æquator; but it dips as it advances, according as the
change of pofition of its centre gives a reafon for its inclination in
accordance with rules magnetical. The declination of a magnetick
needle in water alfo, as demonftrated in the following pages, is a
fixed quantity; the magnetick needle does not defcend to the
bottom of the veffel, but remains fteady in the middle, rotated on
its centre according to its due amount of declination. This would
not happen, if the earth or its poles by their attraction drew down
the end of the magnetick needle, fo that it dipped in this way.

CHAP. VI.

On the proportion of declination to latitude, and
the caufe of it.

CONCERNING the making of an inftrument for
finding declination, the caufes and manner of
declination, and the different degrees of rotation
in different places, the inclination of the ftone, and
concerning an inftrument indicating by the influence of a ftone the degree of declination from
any horizon we have already fpoken. Then we fpoke about needles
on the meridian of a ftone, and their rotation fhown for various
latitudes by their rife toward the perpendicular. We muft now,
however, treat more fully of the caufes of the degree of that inclination. Whilft a loadftone and a magnetick iron wire are moved
along a meridian from the æquator toward the pole, they rotate
toward a round loadftone, as alfo toward the earth with a circular
movement. On a right horizon (juft as alfo on the æquinoctial of
the

the ftone) the axis of the iron, which is its centre line, is a line parallel to the axis of the earth. When that axis reaches the pole, which is the centre of the axis, it ftands in the fame ftraight line with the axis of the earth. The fame end of the iron which at the æquator looks fouth turns to the north. For it is not a motion of centre to centre, but a natural turning of a magnetick body to a magnetick body, and of the axis of the body to the axis; it is not in confequence of the attraction of the pole itfelf that the iron points to the earth's polar point. Under the æquator the magnetick needle remains in æquilibrio horizontally; but toward the pole on either fide, in every latitude from the beginning of the firft degree right up to the ninetieth, it dips. The magnetick needle does not, however, in proportion to any number of degrees or any arc of latitude fall below the horizon juft that number of degrees or a fimilar arc, but a very different one: becaufe this motion is not really a motion of declination, but is in reality a motion of rotation, and it obferves an arc of rotation according to the arc of latitude. Therefore a magnetick body A,

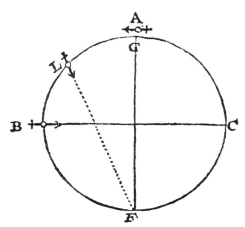

while it is advancing over the earth itfelf, or a little earth or terrella, from the æquinoctial G toward the pole B, rotates on its own centre, and halfway on the progrefs of its centre from the æquator to the pole B it is pointing toward the æquator at F, midway between the two poles. Much more quickly, therefore, muft the verforium rotate than its centre advances, in order that by rotating it may face ftraight toward the point F. Wherefore the motion of this rotation is rapid in the firft degrees from the æquator, namely, from A to L; but more tardy in the later degrees from L to B, when facing from the æquator at F to C. But if the declination were equal to the latitude (i.e., always juft as many degrees from the horizon, as the centre of the verforium has receded from the æquator), then the magnetick needle would be following fome potency and peculiar virtue of the centre, as if it
were

were a point operating by itfelf. But it pays regard to the whole, both its mafs, and its outer limits ; the forces of both uniting, as well of the magnetick verforium as of the earth.

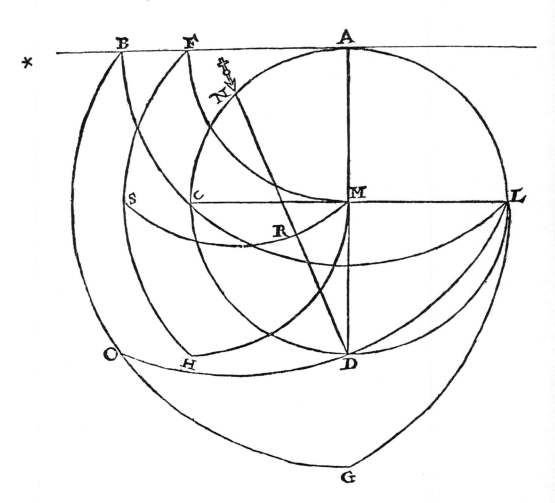

CHAP. VII.

Explanation of the diagram of the rotation of
a magnetick needle.

UPPOSE A C D L to be the body of the earth or of a terrella, its centre M, Æquator A D, Axis C L, A B the Horizon, which changes according to the place. From the point F on a Horizon diftant from the æquator A by the length of C M, the femi-diameter of the earth or terrella, an arc is defcribed to H as the limit of the quadrants of declination ; for

all

all the quadrants of declination ferving the parts from A to C begin from that arc, and terminate at M, the centre of the earth. The femi-diameter of this arc is a chord drawn from the æquator A to the pole C ; and a line produced along the horizon from A to B, equal to that chord, gives the beginning of the arc of the limits of arcs of rotation and revolution, which is continued as far as G. For juft as a quadrant of a circle about the centre of the earth (whofe beginning is on the horizon, at a diftance from the æquator equal to the earth's femi-diameter) is the limit of all quadrants of declination drawn from each feveral horizon to the centre ; fo a circle about the centre from B, the beginning of the firft arc of rotation, to G is the limit of the arcs of rotation. The arcs of rotation and revolution of the magnetick needle are intermediate between the arcs of rotation B L and G L. The centre of the arc is the region itfelf or place in which the obfervation is being made ; the beginning of the arc is taken from the circle which is the limit of rotations, and it ftops at the oppofite pole ; as, for example, from O to L, in a latitude of 45 degrees. Let any arc of rotation be divided into 90 equal parts from the limit of the arcs of rotation toward the pole ; for whatever is the degree of latitude of the place, the part of the arc of rotation which the magnetick pole on or near the terrella or the earth faces in its rotation is to be numbered fimilarly to this. The ftraight lines in the following larger diagram fhow this. The magnetick rotation at the middle point in a latitude of 45 degrees is directed toward the æquator, in which cafe alfo that arc is a quadrant of a circle from the limit to the pole ; but previous to this all the arcs of rotation are greater than a quadrant, whilft after it they are fmaller ; in the former the needle rotates more quickly, but in the fucceeding pofitions gradually more flowly. For each feveral region there is a fpecial arc of rotation, in which the limit to which the needle rotates is according to the number of degrees of latitude of the place in queftion ; fo that a ftraight line drawn from the place to the point on that arc marked with the number of degrees of latitude fhows the magnetick direction, and indicates the degree of declination at the interfection of the quadrant of declination which ferves the given place. Take away the arc of the quadrant of declination drawn from the centre to the line of direction ; that which is left is the arc of declination below the horizon. As, for example, in the rotation of the verforium N, whofe line refpective proceeds to D, from the quadrant of declination, S M, take away its arc R M ; that which is left is the arc of declination : how much, that is, the needle dips in the latitude of 45 degrees.

CHAP.

CHAP. VIII.

Diagram of the rotation of a magnetick needle, in-
dicating magnetical declination in all latitudes, and
from the rotation and declination, the
latitude itself.

IN the more elaborate diagram a circle of rotations and a circle of declinations are adjufted to the body of the earth or terrella, with a firft, a laft, and a middle arc of rotation and declination. Now from each fifth divifion of the arc which limits all the arcs of rota- tion (and which are underftood as divided into 90 equal parts) arcs are drawn to the pole, and from every fifth degree of the arc limiting the quadrants of declination, quadrants are drawn to the centre; and at the fame time a fpiral line is drawn, in- dicating (by the help of a movable quadrant) the declination in every latitude.   Straight lines fhowing the direction of the needle are drawn from thofe degrees which are marked on the meridian of the earth or a terrella to their proper arcs and the correfponding points on thofe arcs.

To afcertain the elevation of the pole or the latitude of a place any-
where in the world, by means of the following diagram, turned into
a magnetick inftrument, without the help of the cœleftial
bodies, fun, planets, or fixed ftars, in fog
and darknefs.

WE may fee how far from unproductive magnetick philofophy is, how agreeable, how helpful, how divine! Sailors when toffed about on the waves with continuous cloudy weather, and unable by means of the cœleftial luminaries to learn anything about the place or the region in which they are, with a very flight effort and with a fmall inftrument are comforted, and learn the latitude of the place.   With a declination inftrument the degree of declination of the magnetick needle below the horizon is obferved; that degree is noted on the inner arc of the quadrant, and the quad- rant is turned round about the centre of the inftrument until that degree on the quadrant touches the fpiral line; then in the open fpace B at the centre of the quadrant the latitude of the region on
the

Place this betwixt the 200 and 201 folioes

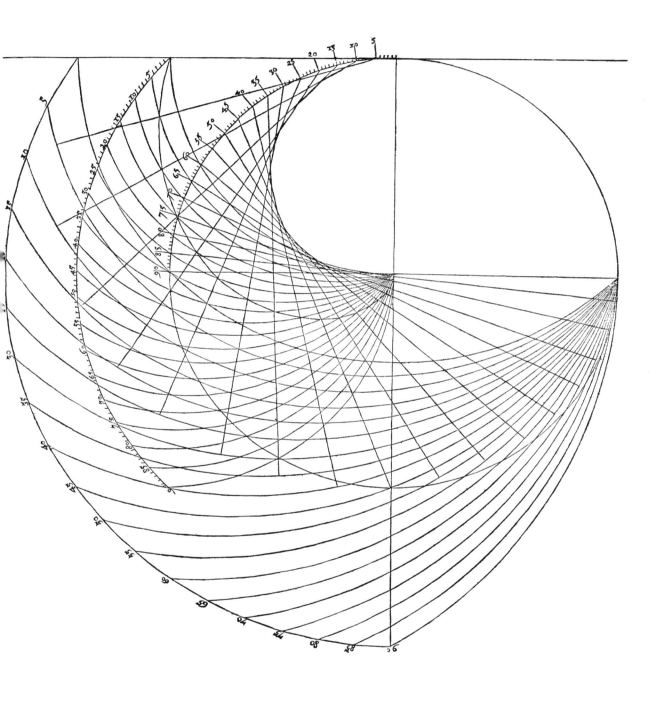

the circumference of the globe is difcerned by means of the fiducial line A B.   Let the diagram be fixed on a fuitable flat board, and let the centre of the corner A of the quadrant be faftened to the centre of it, fo that the quadrant may rotate on that centre.   But it muft be underftood that there is alfo in certain places a variation in the declination on account of caufes already mentioned (though not a large one), which it will be an affiftance alfo to allow for on a likely eftimate; and it will be efpecially helpful to obferve this variation in various places, as it feems to prefent greater difficulty than the variation in direction; but it is eafily learnt with a declination inftrument, when it dips more or lefs than the line in the diagram.

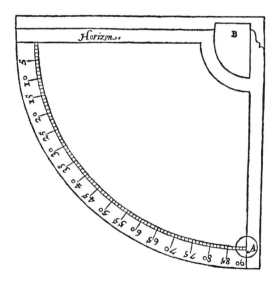

To obferve magnetick declination at fea.

SET upon our variation inftrument a declination inftrument; a wooden difc being placed between the round movable

compaſs and the declination inſtrument: but firſt remove the verſorium, left the verſorium ſhould interfere with the dipping needle.
In this way (though the ſea be rough) the compaſs box will remain
upright at the level of the horizon. The ſtand of the declination
inſtrument muſt be directed by means of the ſmall verſorium at its
baſe, which is ſet to the point reſpective of the variation, on the
great circle of which (commonly called the magnetick meridian),
the plane of the upright box is arranged; thus the declinatorium
(by its verſatory nature) indicates the degree of declination.

In a declination inſtrument the magnetick needle, which
*in a meridional poſition dips, if turned
along a parallel hangs perpendicularly.*

IN a proper poſition a magnetick needle, while by its rotatory
nature conformed to the earth, dips to ſome certain degree
below the horizon on an oblique ſphere. But when the plane of
the inſtrument is moved out of the plane of the meridian, the
magnetick needle (which tends toward the pole) no longer remains
at the degree of its own declination, but inclines more toward the
centre; for the force of direction is ſtronger than that of declination, and all power of declination is taken away, if the plane of the
inſtrument is on a parallel. For then the magnetick needle, becauſe
it cannot maintain its due poſition on account of the axis being
placed tranſverſely, faces down perpendicularly to the earth; and it
remains only on its own meridian, or on that which is commonly
called the magnetick meridian.

CHAP. IX.

Demonſtration of direction, or of variation from the
true direction, at the ſame time with declination, by
means of only a ſingle motion in water, due
to the diſpoſing and rotating virtue.

* FIX a ſlender iron wire of three digits length through
a round cork, ſo that the cork may ſupport the
iron in water. Let this water be in a good-ſized
glaſs vaſe or bowl. Pare the round cork little by
little with a very ſharp knife (ſo that it may remain
round), until it will ſtay motionleſs one or two digits
below the ſurface of the water; and let the wire be evenly balanced.
Rub

Rub one end of the wire thus prepared on the boreal end of a loadftone and the other on the fouthern part of the ftone (very fkilfully,
fo that the cork may not be moved ever fo little from its place)
and again place it in the water; then the wire will dip with a
circular motion on its own centre below the plane of the horizon,
in proportion to the latitude of the region; and, even while dipping,
will alfo fhow the point of variation (the true direction being
perturbed). Let the loadftone (that with which the iron is rubbed)
be a ftrong one, fuch as is needed in all experiments on magnetick
declination. When the iron, thus put into the water and prepared
by means of the loadftone, has fettled in the dip, the lower end
remains at the point of variation on the arc of a great circle or
magnetick meridian paffing through the Zenith or vertex, and the
point of variation on the horizon, and the loweft point of the
heavens, which they call the Nadir. This fact is fhown by placing
a rather long magnetick verforium on one fide a little way from the
vafe. This is a demonftration of a more abfolute conformity of a
magnetick body with the earth's body as regards unity; in it is made
apparent,

apparent, in a natural manner, the direction, with its variation, and the declination. But it muſt be underſtood that as it is a curious and difficult experiment, ſo it does not remain long in the middle of the water, but ſinks at length to the bottom, when the cork has imbibed too much moiſture.

CHAP. X.

On the variation of the declination.

DIRECTION has been ſpoken of previously, and alſo variation, which is like a kind of dragging aſide of the direction. Now in declination ſuch irregular motion is alſo noticed, when the needle dips beyond the proper point or when ſometimes it does not reach its mark. There is therefore a variation of declination, being the arc of a magnetick meridian between the true and apparent declination. For as, on account of terreſtrial elevations, magnetick bodies are drawn away from the true meridian, ſo alſo the needle dips (its rotation being increaſed a little) beyond its genuine poſition. For as variation is a deviation of the direction, ſo alſo, owing to the ſame cauſe, there is ſome error of declination, though often very ſlight. Sometimes, alſo, when there is no variation of direction in the horizontal, there may neverthelefs be variation of the declination; namely, either when more vigorous parts of the earth crop out exactly meridionally, *i.e.*, under the very meridian; or when thoſe parts are leſs powerful than nature in general requires; or when the virtue is too much intenſified in one part, or weakened in another, juſt as one may obſerve in the vaſt ocean. And this diſcrepant nature and varying effect may be eaſily feen in certain parts of almoſt any round loadſtone. Inæquality of power is recognized in any part of a terrella by trial of the demonſtration in chap. 2 of this book. But the effect is clearly demonſtrated by the in- ſtrument for ſhowing declination in chap. 3 of this book.

CHAP.

CHAP. XI.

On the eſſential magnetick activity ſphærically
effuſed.

DISCOURSE hath often been held concerning the ✱
poles of the earth and of the ſtone, and concerning
the æquinoctial zone ; whilſt lately we have been
ſpeaking about the declining of magneticks toward
the earth and toward the terrella, and the cauſes of
it.   But while by various and complicated devices
we have laboured long and hard to arrive at the cauſe of this
declination, we have by good fortune found out a new and admirable (beyond the marvels of all virtues magnetical) ſcience of the
orbes themſelves.   For ſuch is the power of magnetick globes,
that it is diffuſed and extended into orbes outſide the body itſelf,
the form being carried beyond the limits of the corporeal ſubſtance ;
and a mind diligently verſed in this ſtudy of nature will find the
definite cauſes of the motions and revolutions.   The ſame powers
of a terrella exiſt alſo within the whole orbe of its power ; and
theſe orbes at any diſtance from the body of the terrella have in
themſelves, in proportion to their diameter and the magnitude of
their circumference, their own limits of influences, or points wherein
magnetick bodies rotate ; but they do not look toward the ſame
part of the terrella or the ſame point at any diſtance from the ſame
(unleſs they be on the axis of the orbes and of the terrella) ; but
they always tend to thoſe points of their own orbes, which are diſtant by ſimilar arcs from the common axis of the orbes.   As, for
example, in the following diagram, we ſhow the body of a terrella,
with its poles and æquator ; and alſo a verſorium on three other
concentrick orbes around the terrella at ſome diſtance from it.   In
theſe orbes (as in all thoſe which we may imagine without end) the
magnetick body or verſorium conforms to its own orbe in which
it is located, and to its diameter and poles and æquator, not to thoſe
of the terrella ; and it is by them and according to the magnitude
of their orbes that the magnetick body is governed, rotated, and
directed, in any arc of that orbe, both while the centre of the magnetick body ſtands ſtill, and alſo while it moves along.   And yet
we do not mean that the magnetick forms and orbes exiſt in air or
water or in any medium that is not magnetical ; as if the air or
the water were ſuſceptible of them, or were induced by them ; for
the forms are only effuſed and really ſubſiſt when magnetick ſubſtances are there ; whence a magnetick body is laid hold of within
the forces and limits of the orbes ; and within the orbes magneticks
                                                               diſpoſe

difpofe magneticks and incite them, as if the orbes of virtue were folid and material loadftones. For the magnetick force does not pafs through the whole medium or really exift as in a continuous body; fo the orbes are magnetick, and yet not real orbes nor exiftent by themfelves.

Diagram of motions in magnetick orbes.

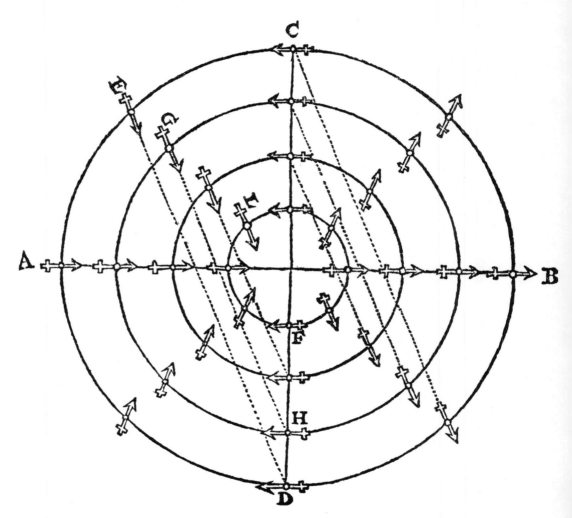

A B is the axis of the terrella and of the orbes, C D the æquator. On all the orbes, as on the terrella, at the æquator the verforium arranges itfelf along the plane of the horizon; on the axis it everywhere looks perpendicularly toward the centre; in the intermediate fpaces E looks toward D; and G looks toward H, not toward F, as the verforium L does on the furface of the terrella. But as is the relation of L to F on the furface of the terrella, fo is that of G to H on its orbe and of E to D on its orbe; alfo all the rotations on

the

the orbes toward the termini of the orbes are such as they are on the surface of the terrella, or toward the termini of its surface. But if in the more remote orbes this fails somewhat at times, it happens on account of the sluggishness of the stone, or on account of the feebler forces due to the too great distance of the orbes from the terrella.

Demonstration.

SET upon the instrumental diagram described farther back [chap. 3] a plate or stiff circle of brass or tin, on which may be described the magnetick orbes, as in the diagram above; and in the middle let a hole be made according to the size of the terrella, so that the plate may lie evenly on the wood about the middle of the terrella on a meridional circle. Then let a small verforium of the length of a barley-corn be placed on any orbe; upon which, when it is moved to various positions on the same circle, it will always pay regard to the dimensions of that orbe, not to those of the stone; as is shown in the diagram of the effused magnetick forms.

While some affign occult and hidden virtues of substances, others a property of matter, as the causes of the wonderful magnetical effects; we have discovered the primary substantive form of globes, not from a conjectural shadow of the truth of reasons variously controverted; but we have laid hold of the true efficient cause, as from many other demonstrations, so also from this most certain diagram of magnetick forces effused by the form. Though this (the form) has not been brought under any of our senses, and on that account is the less perceived by the intellect, it now appears manifest and conspicuous even to the eyes through this effential activity which proceeds from it as light from a lamp. And here it must be noted that a magnetick needle, moved on the top of the earth or of a terrella or of the effused orbes, makes two complete rotations in one circuit of its centre, like some epicycle about its orbit.

CHAP.

CHAP. XII.

Magnetick force is animate, or imitates life ; and in
many things furpaffes human life, while this is bound
up in the organick body.

LOADSTONE is a wonderful thing in very many experiments, and like a living creature.   And one of its remarkable virtues is that which the ancients confidered to be a living foul in the fky, in the globes and in the ftars, in the fun and in the moon. For they fufpected that fuch various motions could not arife without a divine and animate nature, immenfe bodies turned about in fixed times, and wonderful powers infufed into other bodies; whereby the whole univerfe flourifhes in moft beautiful variety, through this primary form of the globes themfelves.   The ancients, as Thales, Heraclitus, Anaxagoras, Archelaus, Pythagoras, Empedocles, Parmenides, Plato, and all the Platonifts, and not only the older Greeks, but the Egyptians and Chaldæans, feek for fome univerfal life in the univerfe, and affirm that the whole univerfe is endowed with life.   Ariftotle affirms that not the whole univerfe is animate, but only the fky ; but he maintains that its elements are inanimate ; whilft the ftars themfelves are animate.   We, however, find this life in globes only and in their homogenic parts; and though it is not the fame in all globes (for it is much more eminent in the fun and in certain ftars than in others of lefs nobility) yet in very many the lives of the globes agree in their powers.   For each feveral homogenic part draws to its own globe in a fimilar manner, and has an inclination to the common direction of the whole in the univerfe ; and the effufed forms extend outward in all, and are carried out into an orbe, and have bounds of their own ; hence the order and regularity of the motions and rotations of all the planets, and their courfes, not wandering away, but fixed and determined. Wherefore Ariftotle concedes life to the fphæres themfelves and to the orbes of the heavens (which he feigns), becaufe they are fuitable and fitted for a circular motion and actions, and are carried along in fixed and definite courfes.   It is furely wonderful, why the globe of the earth alone with its emanations is condemned by him and his followers and caft into exile (as fenfelefs and lifelefs), and driven out of all the perfection of the excellent univerfe.   It is treated as a fmall corpufcle in comparifon with the whole, and in the numerous con- courfe of many thoufands it is obfcure, difregarded, and unhonoured.
                                                                      With

With it alfo they connect the kindred elements, in a like unhappi-
nefs, wretched and neglected.   Let this therefore be looked upon
as a monftrofity in the Ariftotelian univerfe, in which everything
is perfect, vigorous, animated; whilft the earth alone, an unhappy
portion, is paltry, imperfect, dead, inanimate, and decadent.   But
on the other hand Hermes, Zoroafter, Orpheus, recognize a univerfal life.   We, however, confider that the whole univerfe is
animated, and that all the globes, all the ftars, and alfo the noble
earth have been governed fince the beginning by their own appointed
fouls and have the motives of felf-confervation.   Nor are there
wanting, either implanted in their homogenic nature or fcattered
through their homogenic fubftance, organs fuitable for organic
activity, although thefe are not fafhioned of flefh and blood as
animals, or compofed of regular limbs, which are alfo hardly perceptible in certain plants and vegetables; fince regular limbs are
not neceffary for all life.   Nor can any organs be difcerned or
imagined by us in any of the ftars, the fun, or the planets, which
are fpecially operative in the univerfe; yet they live and imbue
with life the fmall particles in the prominences on the earth.   If
there be anything of which men can boaft, it is in fact life, intelligence; for the other animals are ennobled by life; God alfo (by
whofe nod all things are ruled) is a living foul.   Who therefore
will demand organs for the divine intelligences, which rife fuperior
to every combination of organs and are not reftrained by materialized
organs?   But in the feveral bodies of the ftars the implanted force
acts otherwife than in thofe divine exiftences which are fuper-
naturally ordained; and in the ftars, the fources of things, otherwife than in animals; in animals again otherwife than in plants.
Miferable were the condition of the ftars, abject the lot of the
earth, if that wonderful dignity of life be denied to them, which is
conceded to worms, ants, moths, plants, and toadftools; for thus
worms, moths, grubs would be bodies more honoured and perfect
in nature; for without life no body is excellent, valuable, or diftinguifhed.   But fince living bodies arife and receive life from the
earth and the fun, and grafs grows on the earth apart from any
feeds thrown down (as when foil is dug up from deep down in the
earth, and put on fome very high place or on a very high tower,
in a funny fpot, not fo long after various graffes fpring up unbidden)
it is not likely that they can produce what is not in them; but
they awaken life, and therefore they are living.   Therefore the
bodies of the globes, as important parts of the univerfe, in order
that they might be independent and that they might continue in
that condition, had a need for fouls to be united with them, without
which there can be neither life, nor primary activity, nor motion,
nor coalition, nor controlling power, nor harmony, nor endeavour,
nor fympathy; and without which there would be no generation

E E   of

of anything, no alternations of the feafons, no propagation; but all things would be carried this way and that, and the whole univerfe would fall into wretchedeft Chaos, the earth in fhort would be vacant, dead, and ufelefs.　But it is only on the fuperficies of the globes that the concourfe of living and animated beings is clearly perceived, in the great and pleafing variety of which the great mafter-workman is well pleafed.　But thofe fouls which are reftrained within a kind of barrier and in prifon cells, as it were, do not emit immaterial effufed forms outfide the limits of their bodies; and bodies are not moved by them without labour and wafte. They are brought and carried away by a breath; and when this has calmed down or been fuppreffed by fome untoward influence, their bodies lie like the dregs of the univerfe and as the refufe of the globes.　But the globes themfelves remain and continue from year to year, move, and advance, and complete their courfes, without wafte or wearinefs.　The human foul ufes reafon, fees many things, inquires about many more; but even the beft inftructed receives by his external fenfes (as through a lattice) light and the beginnings of knowledge.　Hence come fo many errors and follies, by which our judgments and the actions of our lives are perverted; fo that few or none order their actions rightly and juftly.　But the magnetick force of the earth and the formate life or living form of the globes, without perception, without error, without injury from ills and difeafes, fo prefent with us, has an implanted activity, vigorous through the whole material mafs, fixed, conftant, directive, executive, governing, confentient; by which the generation and death of all things are carried on upon the furface.　For, without that motion, by which the daily revolution is performed, all earthly things around us would ever remain favage and neglected, and more than deferted and abfolutely idle.　But thofe motions in the fources of nature are not caufed by thinking, by petty fyllogifms, and theories, as human actions, which are wavering, imperfect, and undecided; but along with them reafon, inftruction, knowledge, difcrimination have their origin, from which definite and determined actions arife, from the very foundations that have been laid and the very beginnings of the univerfe; which we, on account of the infirmity of our minds, cannot comprehend.　Wherefore Thales, not without caufe (as Ariftotle relates in his book *De Anima*), held that the loadftone was animate, being a part and a choice offspring of its animate mother the earth.

BOOK

BOOK SIXTH.

*C*HAP. I.

ON THE GLOBE OF THE EARTH, THE
great magnet.

HITHERTO our fubject hath been the loadftone and things magnetical : how they confpire together, and are acted upon, how they conform themfelves to the terrella and to the earth.   Now muft we confider feparately the globe itfelf of the earth. Thofe experiments which have been proved by means of the terrella, how magnetick things conform themfelves to the terrella, are all or at leaft the principal and moft important of them, difplayed by means of the earth's Body : And to the earth things magnetical are in all refpects affociate.   Firft, as in the terrella the æquator, meridians, parallels, axis, poles are natural boundaries, as numerous experiments make plain : So alfo in the earth thefe boundaries are natural, not mathematical only (as all before us ufed to fuppofe).   Thefe boundaries the fame experiments difplay and eftablifh in both cafes alike, in the earth no lefs than in the terrella.   Juft as on the periphery of a terrella a loadftone or a magnetick piece of iron is directed to its proper pole : fo on the earth's furface are there turnings-about, peculiar, manifeft, and conftant on either fide of the æquator.   Iron is indued with verticity by being extended toward a pole of the earth, juft as toward a pole of the terrella :   By its being placed down alfo, and cooling toward the earth's pole after the priftine verticity has
been

been annulled by fire, it acquires new verticity, conformable to its position earthward. Iron rods also, when placed some considerable time toward the poles, acquire verticity merely by regarding the earth; just as the same rods, if placed toward the pole of a loadstone, even without touching it, receive polar virtue. There is no magnetick body that in any way runs to the terrella which does not also wait upon the earth. As a loadstone is stronger at one end on one side or other of its æquator: so is the same property displayed by a small terrella upon the surface of a larger terrella. According to the variety and artistick skill in the rubbing of the magnetick iron upon the terrella, so do the magnetick things perform their function more efficiently or more feebly. In motions toward the earth's body, as toward the terrella a variation is displayed due to the unlikeness, inequality, and imperfection of its eminences: So every variation of the verforium or mariners' compass, everywhere by land or by sea, which thing has so sorely disturbed men's minds, is discerned and recognized as due to the same causes. The magnetick dip (which is the wonderful turning of magnetick things to the body of the terrella) in systematick course, is seen in clearer light to be the same thing upon the earth. And that single experiment, by a wonderful indication, as with a finger, proclaims the grand magnetick nature of the earth to be innate and diffused through all her inward parts. A magnetick vigour exists then in the earth just as in the terrella, which is a part of the earth, homogenic in nature with it, but rounded by Art, so as to correspond with the earth's globous shape and in order that in the chief experiments it might accord with the globe of the earth.

CHAP. II.

The Magnetick axis of the Earth
persists invariable.

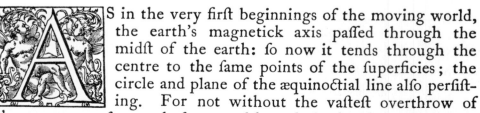A in the very first beginnings of the moving world, the earth's magnetick axis passed through the midst of the earth: so now it tends through the centre to the same points of the superficies; the circle and plane of the æquinoctial line also persisting. For not without the vastest overthrow of the terrene mass can these natural boundaries be changed, as it is easy to gather from magnetick demonstrations. Wherefore the opinion of Dominicus Maria of Ferrara, a most talented man, who was the teacher of Nicolas Copernicus, must be cancelled; a view which,

which, according to certain obfervations of his own, is as follows.
" I," he fays, " in former years while ftudying Ptolemy's *Geographia*
" difcovered that the elevations of the North pole placed by him in
" the feveral regions, fall fhort of what they are in our time by one
" degree and ten minutes : which divergence can by no means be
" afcribed to an error of the tables : For it is not credible that the
" whole feries in the book is equally wrong in the figures of the
" tables : Hence it is neceffary to allow that the North pole has been
" tilted toward the vertical point.   Accordingly a lengthy obferva-
" tion has already begun to difclofe to us things hidden from our fore-
" fathers ; not indeed through any floth of theirs, but becaufe they
" lacked the prolonged obfervation of their predeceffors : For before
" Ptolemy very few places were obferved with regard to the eleva-
" tions of the pole, as he himfelf alfo bears witnefs at the beginning
" of his *Cofmographia:* (For, fays he) Hipparchus alone hath handed
" down to us the latitudes of a few places, but a good many have noted
" thofe of diftances; efpecially thofe which lie toward funrife or fun-
" fet were received by some general tradition, not owing to any floth
" on the part of authors themfelves, but to the faſt that there was as
" yet no practice of more exaſt mathematicks.   'Tis accordingly no
" wonder, if our predeceffors did not mark this very flow motion :
" For in one thoufand and feventy years it fhows itfelf to be difplaced
" fcarce one degree toward the apex of dwellers upon the earth.
" The ftrait of Gibraltar fhows this, where in Ptolemy's time the
" North pole appears elevated 36 degrees and a quarter from the
" Horizon : whereas now it is 37 and two-fifths.   The like diver-
" gence is alfo fhown at Leucopetra in Calabria, and at particular
" fpots in Italy, namely thofe which have not changed from Ptolemy's
" time to our own.   And fo by reafon of this movement, places now
" inhabited will fome day become deferted, while thofe regions which
" are now parched at the torrid zone will, though long hence, be
" reduced to our temper of climate.   Thus, as in a courfe of three
" hundred and ninety five thoufands of years, is that very flow move-
" ment completed."   Thus, according to thefe obfervations of
Dominicus Maria, the North pole is at a higher elevation, and the
latitudes of places are greater than formerly ; whence he argues a
change of latitudes.   Now, however, Stadius, taking juft the contrary view, proves by obfervations that the latitudes have decreafed.
For he fays : " The latitude of Rome in Ptolemy's *Geographia* is 41
" degrees ⅔ : and that you may not fuppofe any error of reckoning to
" have crept in on the part of Ptolemy, on the day of the Æquinox
" in the city of Rome, the ninth part of the gnomon of the fun-dial
" is lacking in fhadow, as Pliny relates and Vitruvius witneffeth in
" his ninth book."   But the obfervation of moderns (according to
Erafmus Rheinholdus) gives the fame in our time as 41 degrees
with a fixth : fo that you are in doubt as to half of one degree in
the

the centre of the world, whether you fhow it to have decreafed
by the earth's obliquity of motion.   One may fee then how from
inexact obfervations men rafhly conceive new and contradictory
opinions and imagine abfurd motions of the mechanifm of the
earth.   For fince Ptolemy only received certain latitudes from
Hipparchus, and did not in very many places make the obfervations
himfelf; it is likely that he himfelf, knowing the pofition of the
places, formed his eftimate of the latitude of cities from probable
conjecture only, and then placed it in the maps.   Thus one may
fee, in the cafe of our own Britain, that the latitudes of cities are
wrong by two or three degrees, as experience teaches.   Wherefore all the lefs fhould we from thofe miftakes infer a new motion,
or let the noble magnetick nature of the earth be debafed for
an opinion fo lightly conceived.   Moreover, thofe miftakes crept
the more readily into geography, from the fact that the magnetick virtue was utterly unknown to thofe geographers.   Befides,
obfervations of latitudes cannot be made fufficiently exactly, except
by experts, ufing alfo finer inftruments, and taking into account the
refraction of the lights.

CHAP. III.

On the magnetick diurnal revolution of the Earth's
globe, as a probable affertion againft the time-honoured
opinion of a Primum Mobile.

AMONG the ancients Heraclides of Pontus and
Ecphantus, afterwards the Pythagoreans, as Nicetas
of Syracufe and Ariftarchus of Samos, and fome
others (as it feems), ufed to think that the earth
moves, and that the ftars fet by the interpofition
of the earth and rofe by her retirement.   In fact
they fet the earth moving and make her revolve around her axis
from weft to eaft, like a wheel turning on its axle.   Philolaus
the Pythagorean would have the earth to be one of the ftars, and
believed that it turned in an oblique circle around fire, juft as the
fun and moon have their own courfes.   He was a diftinguifhed
mathematician, and a moft able inveftigator of nature.   But after
Philofophy became a fubject treated of by very many and was
popularized, theories adapted to the vulgar intelligence or bafed
on fophiftical fubtility occupied the minds of moft men, and pre-
vailed like a torrent, the multitude confenting.   Thereupon
many valuable difcoveries of the ancients were rejected, and
were difmiffed to perifh in banifhment; or at leaft by not being
further cultivated and developed became obfolete.   So that Copernicus (among later difcoverers, a man moft deferving of literary
honour) is the firft who attempted to illuftrate the φαινόμενα of
moving

moving bodies by new hypothefes : and thefe demonftrations of reafons others either follow or obferve in order that they may more furely difcover the phænomenal harmony of the movements; being men of the higheft attainments in every kind of learning.   Thus the fuppofed and imaginary orbes of Ptolemy and others for finding the times and periods of the motions are not neceffarily to be admitted to the phyfical inquiries of philofophers.   It is then an ancient opinion and one that has come down from old times, but is now augmented by important confiderations that the whole earth rotates with a daily revolution in the fpace of 24 hours.   Well then, fince we fee the Sun and Moon and other planets and the glory of all the ftars approach and retire within the fpace of one natural day, either the Earth herfelf muft needs be fet in motion with a diurnal movement from Weft to Eaft, or the whole heaven and the reft of nature from Eaft to Weft.   But, in the firft place, it is not likely that the higheft heaven and all thofe vifible fplendours of the fixed ftars are impelled along that moft rapid and ufelefs courfe.   Befides, who is the Mafter who has ever made out that the ftars which we call fixed are in one and the fame fphere, or has eftablifhed by reafoning that there are any real and, as it were, adamantine fphæres ?   No one has ever proved this as a fact ; nor is there a doubt but that juft as the planets are at unequal diftances from the earth, fo are thofe vaft and multitudinous lights feparated from the Earth by varying and very remote altitudes ; they are not fet in any fphærick frame or firmament (as is feigned), nor in any vaulted body : accordingly the intervals of fome are from their un-fathomable diftance matter of opinion rather than of verification ; others do much exceed them and are very far remote, and thefe being located in the heaven at varying diftances, either in the thinneft æther or in that moft fubtile quinteffence, or in the void ; how are they to remain in their pofition during fuch a mighty fwirl of the vaft orbe of fuch uncertain fubftance.   There have been obferved by aftronomers 1022 ftars ; befides thefe, numberlefs others are vifible, fome indeed faint to our fenfes, in the cafe of others our fenfe is dim and they are hardly perceived and only by exception-ally keen eyes, and there is no one gifted with excellent fight who does not when the Moon is dark and the air at its rareft, difcern numbers and numbers dim and wavering with minute lights on account of the great diftance : hence it is credible both that thefe are many and that they are never all included in any range of vifion.   How immeafurable then muft be the fpace which ftretches to thofe remoteft of fixed ftars !   How vaft and immenfe the depth of that imaginary fphere !   How far removed from the Earth muft the moft widely feparated ftars be and at a diftance tranfcending all fight, all fkill and thought !   How monftrous then fuch a motion

would

would be! It is evident then that all the heavenly bodies set as if in deftined places are there formed into fphæres, that they tend to their own centres, and that round them there is a confluence of all their parts. And if they have motion, that motion will rather be that of each round its own centre, as that of the Earth is; or a forward movement of the centre in an orbit, as that of the Moon: there would not be circular motion in the cafe of a too numerous and fcattered flock. Of thefe ftars fome fituate near the Æquator would feem to be borne around at a very rapid rate, others nearer the pole to have a fomewhat gentler motion, others, apparently motionlefs, to have a flight rotation. Yet no differences in point of light, mafs or colours are apparent to us: for they are as brilliant, clear, glittering and dufkifh toward the poles, as they are near the Æquator and the Zodiack: thofe which remain fet in thofe pofitions do not hang, and are neither fixed, nor bound to anything of the nature of a vault. All the more infane were the circumvolution of that fictitious *Primum Mobile*, which is higher, deeper, and ftill more immeafurable. Moreover, this inconceivable *Primum Mobile* ought to be material and of enormous depth, far furpaffing all inferior nature in fize: for nohow elfe could it conduct from Eaft to Weft fo many and fuch vaft bodies of ftars, and the univerfe even down to the Earth: and it requires us to accept in the government of the ftars a univerfal power and a defpotifm perpetual and intenfely irkfome. That *Primum Mobile* bears no vifible body, is nohow recognizable, is a fiction believed in by thofe people, accepted by the weak-minded folk, who wonder more at our terreftrial mafs than at bodies fo vaft, fo inconceivable, and fo far feparated from us. But there can be no movement of infinity and of an infinite body, and therefore no diurnal revolution of that vafteft *Primum Mobile*. The Moon being neighbour to the Earth revolves in 27 days; Mercury and Venus have their own moderately flow motions; Mars finifhes a period in two years, Jupiter in twelve years, Saturn in thirty. And thofe alfo who afcribe a motion to the fixed ftars make out that it is completed in 36,000 years, according to Ptolemy, in 25,816 years, according to Copernicus' obfervations; fo that the motion and the completion of the journey always become flower in the cafe of the greater circles. And would there then be a diurnal motion of that *Primum Mobile* which is fo great and beyond them all immenfe and profound? 'Tis indeed a fuperftition and in the view of philofophy a fable now only to be believed by idiots, deferving more than ridicule from the learned: and yet in former ages, that motion, under the preffure of an importunate mob of philofophizers, was actually accepted as a bafis of computations and of motions, by mathematicians. The motions of the bodies (namely planets) feem all to take place eaftward and following the order of the figns.

The

The common run of mathematicians and philofophers alfo fuppofe
that the fixed ftars in the fame manner advance with a very flow
motion: and from ignorance of the truth they are forced to join
to them a ninth fphære.   Whereas now this firft and unthinkable
Primum Mobile, a fiction not comprehended by any judgment, not
evidenced by any vifible conftellation, but devifed of imagination
only and mathematical hypothefis, unfortunately accepted and
believed by philofophers, extended into the heaven and beyond all
the ftars, muft needs with a contrary impulfe turn about from
Eaft to Weft, in oppofition to the inclination of all the reft of the
Univerfe.   Whatfoever in nature is moved naturally, the fame is
fet in motion both by its own forces and by the confentient compact
of other bodies.   Such is the motion of parts to their whole, of all
interdependent fphæres and ftars in the univerfe: fuch is the circular
impulfe in the bodies of the planets, when they affect and incite
one another's courfes.   But with regard to the *Primum Mobile* and
its contrary and exceeding rapid movement, what are the bodies
which incite it or propel it?   What is the nature that confpires
with it?   Or what is that mad force beyond the *Primum Mobile?*
Since it is in bodies themfelves that acting force refides, not in
fpaces or intervals.   But he who thinks that thofe bodies are at
leifure and keeping holiday, while all the virtue of the univerfe
appertains to the very orbits and fphæres, is on this point not lefs
mad than he who, in fome one elfe's houfe, thinks that the walls
and floors and roof rule the family rather than the wife and
thoughtful paterfamilias.   Therefore not by the firmament are they
borne along, or are moved, or have their pofition; much lefs are
thofe confufed crowds of ftars whirled around by the *Primum
Mobile*, nor are they torn away and huddled along by a contrary
and extremely rapid movement.   Ptolemy of Alexandria feems to
be too timid and weak-minded in dreading the diffolution of this
nether world, were the Earth to be moved round in a circle.
Why does he not fear the ruin of the Univerfe, diffolution, confufion, conflagration, and infinite difafters celeftial and fuper-celeftial,
from a motion tranfcending all thoughts, dreams, fables, and poetic
licences, infurmountable, ineffable, and inconceivable?   Wherefore
we are carried along by a diurnal rotation of the earth (a motion
for fure more congruous), and as a boat moves above the waters, fo
do we turn about with the earth, and yet feem to ourfelves to be
ftationary, and at reft.   Great and incredible it feems to fome
philofophers, by reafon of inveterate prejudice, that the Earth's
vaft body fhould be fwirled wholly round in the fpace of 24 hours.
But it would be more incredible that the Moon fhould travel
through her orbit, or complete an entire courfe in a fpace of 24
hours; more fo the Sun or Mars; ftill more Jupiter and Saturn;
more than marvellous would be the velocity in the cafe of the
fixed

fixed ftars and the firmament; what in the world they would have to wonder at in the cafe of their ninth fphere, let them imagine as they like. But to feign a *Primum Mobile*, and to attribute to the thing thus feigned a motion to be completed in the fpace of 24 hours, and not to allow this motion to the Earth in the fame interval of time, is abfurd. For a great circle of the Earth is to the ambit of the *Primum Mobile* lefs than a furlong to the whole Earth. If the diurnal rotation of the Earth feem head-long, and not admiffible in nature by reafon of its rapidity, worfe than infane will be the movement of the *Primum Mobile* both for itfelf and the whole univerfe, agreeing as it does with no other motion in any proportion or likenefs. It feems to Ptolemy and the Peripateticks that nature muft be difordered, and the frame-work and ftructure of this globe of ours be diffolved, by reafon of fo fwift a terreftrial revolution. The Earth's diameter is 1718 German miles; the greateft elongation of the new Moon is 65, the leaft is 55 femi-diameters of the Earth: the greateft altitude of the half moon is 68, the leaft 52: yet it is probable that its fphære is ftill larger and deeper. The Sun in its greateft eccentricity has a diftance of 1142 femi-diameters of the Earth; Mars, Jupiter, Saturn, being flower in motion, are fo proportionately further remote from the Earth. The diftances of the firmament and of the fixed ftars feem to the beft mathematicians inconceivable. Leaving out the ninth fphære, if the convexity of the *Primum Mobile* be duly eftimated in proportion to the reft of the fphæres, the vault of the *Primum Mobile* muft in one hour run through as much fpace as is comprifed in 3000 great circles of the Earth, for in the vault of the firmament it would complete more than 1800; but what iron folidity can be imagined fo firm and tough as not to be difrupted and fhattered to fragments by a fury fo great and a velocity fo ineffable. The Chaldæans indeed would have it that the heaven confifts of light. In light, however, there is no fo-great firmnefs, neither is there in Plotinus' fiery firmament, nor in the fluid or aqueous or fupremely rare and tranfparent heaven of the divine Mofes, which does not cut off from our fight the lights of the ftars. We muft accordingly reject the fo deep-fet error about this fo mad and furious a celeftial velocity, and the forced retardation of the reft of the heavens. Let theologians difcard and wipe out with fponges thofe old women's tales of fo rapid a fpinning round of the heavens borrowed from certain inconfiderate philofophers. The Sun is not propelled by the fphære of Mars (if a fphære there be) and by his motion, nor Mars by Jupiter, nor Jupiter by Saturn. The fphære, too, of the fixed ftars, feems well enough regulated except fo far as motions which are in the Earth are afcribed to the heavens, and bring about a certain change of phænomena. The fuperiors do not exercife a defpotifm over the inferiors; for the heaven of philo-

fophers

fophers, as of theologians, muft be gentle, happy, and tranquil, and not at all fubject to changes: nor fhall the force, fury, fwiftnefs, and hurry of a *Primum Mobile* have dominion over it.   That fury defcends through all the celeftial fphæres, and celeftial bodies, invades the elements of our philofophers, fweeps fire along, rolls along the air, or at leaft draws the chief part of it, conducts the univerfal æther, and turns about fiery impreffions (as if it were a folid and firm body, when in fact it is a moft refined effence, neither refifting nor drawing), leads captive the fuperior.   O marvellous conftancy of the terreftrial globe, the only one unconquered; and yet one that is holden faft, or ftationary, in its place by no bonds, no heavinefs, by no contiguity with a groffer or firmer body, by no weights.   The fubftance of the terreftrial globe withftands and fets itfelf againft univerfal nature.   Ariftotle feigns for himfelf a fyftem of philofophy founded on motions fimple and compound, that the heavens revolve in a fimple circle, its elements moving with a right motion, the parts of the earth feeking the earth in ftraight lines, falling on its furface at right angles, and tending together toward its centre, always, however, at reft therein; accordingly alfo the whole Earth remains immovable in its place, united and compacted together by its own weight.   That cohæfion of parts and aggregation of matter exift in the Sun, in the Moon, in the planets, in the fixed ftars, in fine in all thofe round bodies whofe parts cohære together and tend each to their own centres; otherwife the heaven would fall, and that fublime ordering would be loft: yet thefe cœleftial bodies have a circular motion.   Whence the Earth too may equally have her own motion: and this motion is not (as fome deem it) unfuitable for the affembling or adverfe to the generation of things.   For fince it is innate in the terreftrial globe, and natural to it; and fince there is nothing external that can fhock it, or hinder it by adverfe motions, it goes round without any ill or danger, it advances without being forced, there is nothing that refifts, nothing that by retiring gives way, but all is open.   For while it revolves in a fpace void of bodies, or in the incorporeal æther, all the air, the exhalations of land and water, the clouds and pendent meteors, are impelled along with the globe circularly: that which is above the exhalations is void of bodies: the fineft bodies and thofe which are leaft cohærent almoft void are not impeded, are not diffolved, while paffing through it.   Wherefore alfo the whole terreftrial globe, with all its adjuncts, moves bodily along, calmly, meeting no refiftance.   Wherefore empty and fuperftitious is the fear that fome weak minds have of a fhock of bodies (like Lucius Lactantius, who, in the fafhion of the unlettered rabble and of the moft unreafonable men fcoffs at an Antipodes and at the fphærick ordering of the Earth all round).   So for thefe reafons, not only probable but manifeft, does the diurnal rotation of the earth feem,

fince

fince nature always acts through a few rather than through many; and it is more agreeable to reafon that the Earth's one fmall body fhould make a diurnal rotation, than that the whole univerfe fhould be whirled around. I pafs over the reafons of the Earth's remaining motions, for at prefent the only queftion is concerning its diurnal movement, according to which it moves round with refpect to the Sun, and creates a natural day (which we call a nycthemeron). And indeed Nature may be thought to have granted a motion very fuit-able to the Earth's fhape, which (being fphærical) is revolved about the poles affigned it by Nature much more eafily and fittingly than that the whole univerfe, whofe limit is unknown and unknowable, fhould be whirled round; and than there could be imagined an orbit of the *Primum Mobile*, a thing not accepted by the ancients, which Ariftotle even did not devife or accept as in any fhape or form exifting beyond the fphære of the fixed ftars; which finally the facred fcriptures do not recognize any more than they do the revolution of the firmament.

CHAP. IIII.

That the Earth moves circularly.

IF then the philofophers of the common fort, with an unfpeakable abfurdity, imagine the whole heaven and the vaft extent of the univerfe to rotate in a whirl, it yet remains that the earth performs a diurnal change. For in no third way can the apparent revolutions be explained. This day, then, which is called natural, is a revolution of fome meridian of the Earth from Sun to Sun. It revolves indeed in an entire courfe, from a fixed ftar round to that ftar again. Thofe bodies which in nature are moved with a circular, æquable and conftant motion, are furnifhed, in their parts, with various boundaries. But the Earth is not a Chaos nor difordered mafs; but by reafon of its aftral virtue, it has boundaries which fubferve the circular motion, poles not mathematical, an æquator not devifed by imagination, meridians alfo and parallels; all of which we find permanent, certain and natural in the Earth: which by numerous experiments the whole magnetick philofophy fets forth. For in the earth there are poles fet in fixed bounds, and at them the verticity mounts up on either fide from the plane of the Earth's æquator, with forces which are mightier and præpotent from the common action of the whole; and with thefe poles the diurnal revolution is in agreement. But in no turnings-about of bodies, in none of the motions of the planets are there to be recognized, beheld, or affured to us by any reafoning any fenfible or natural poles in the firmament, or in any *Primum Mobile;*

Mobile; but thofe are the conception of an unfettled imagination. Wherefore we, following an evident, fenfible and tefted caufe, do know that the earth moves on its own poles, which are apparent to us by many magnetick demonftrations.   For not only on the ground of its conftancy, and its fure and permanent pofition, is the Earth endowed with poles and verticity: for it might be directed toward other parts of the univerfe, toward Eaft or Weft or fome other region.   By the wondrous wifdom then of the Builder forces, primarily animate, have been implanted in the Earth, that with determinate conftancy the Earth may take its direction, and the poles have been placed truly oppofite, that about them as the termini, as it were, of fome axis, the motion of diurnal turning might be performed.   But the conftancy of the poles is regulated by the primary foul.   Wherefore, for the Earth's good, the collimations of her verticities do not continually regard a definite point of the firmament and of the vifible heaven.   For changes of the æquinoxes take place from a certain deflection of the Earth's axis; yet in regard to that deflection, the Earth has a conftancy of motion derived from her own forces.   The Earth, that fhe may turn herfelf about in a diurnal revolution, leans on her poles.   For fince at A and B there is conftant verticity, and the axis is ftraight; at C and D (the æquinoctial line) the parts are free, the whole forces on either fide being fpread out from the plane of the æquator to-

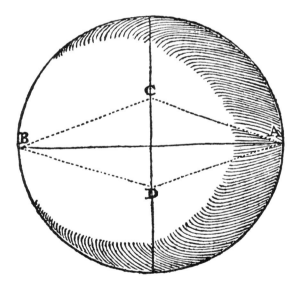

ward the poles, in æther which is free from renitency, or elfe in a void; and A and B remaining conftant, C revolves toward D both from innate conformity and aptitude, and for neceffary good, and the avoidance of evil; but being chiefly moved forward by the diffufion of the folar orbes of virtues, and by their lights.   And 'tis borne around, not upon a new and ftrange courfe, but (with the
tendency

tendency common to the reft of the planets) it tends from Weft to Eaft.   For all planets have a like motion Eaftward according to the fucceffion of the figns, whether Mercury and Venus revolve beneath the Sun, or around the Sun.   That the Earth is capable of and fitted for moving circularly its parts fhow, which when feparated from the whole are not only borne along with the ftraight movement taught by the Peripateticks, but rotate alfo.   A loadftone fixed in a wooden veffel is placed on water fo as to fwim freely, turn itfelf, and float about.   If the pole B of the loadftone

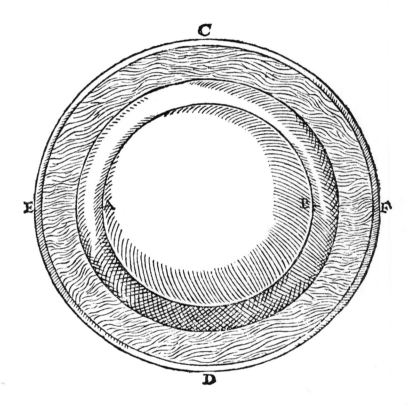

be fet contrary to nature toward the South, F, the Terrella is turned about its own centre with a circular motion in the plane of the Horizon, toward the North, E, where it refts, not at C or D. So does a fmall ftone if only of four ounces; it has the fame motion alfo and juft as quick, if it were a ftrong magnet of one hundred pounds.   The largeft magnetical mountain will poffefs the fame turning-power alfo, if launched in a wide river or deep fea : and yet a magnetick body is much more hindered by water than the whole Earth is by the æther.   The whole Earth would do the fame, if the Boreal pole were to be diverted from its true direction ; for the Boreal pole would run back with the circular motion of the whole around the centre toward the Cynofure.   But this motion by which the parts naturally fettle themfelves in their own refting-

places

places is no other than circular. The whole Earth regards the
Cynofure with her pole according to a fteadfaft law of her nature:
and thus each true part of it feeks a like refting-place in the world,
and is moved circularly toward that pofition. The natural movements of the whole and of the parts are alike: wherefore when
the parts are moved in a circle, the whole alfo has the potency of
moving circularly. A fphærical loadftone placed in a veffel on
water moves circularly around its centre (as is manifeft) in the
plane of the Horizon, into conformity with the earth.

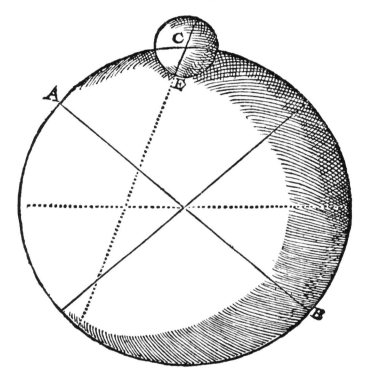

So alfo it would move in any other great circle if it could be
free; as in the declination inftrument, a circular motion takes
place in the meridian (if there were no variation), or, if there
fhould be fome variation, in a great circle drawn from the Zenith
through the point of variation on the horizon. And that circular
motion of the magnet to its own juft and natural pofition fhows
that the whole Earth is fitted and adapted, and is fufficiently furnifhed with peculiar forces for diurnal circular motion. I omit what
Peter Peregrinus conftantly affirms, that a terrella fufpended above
its poles on a meridian moves circularly, making an entire revolution in 24 hours: which, however, it has not happened to ourfelves as yet to fee; and we even doubt this motion on account of
the weight of the ftone itfelf, as well as becaufe the whole Earth,
as fhe is moved of herfelf, fo alfo is fhe propelled by other ftars:
and this does not happen in proportion (as it does in the terrella)

in

in every part.   The Earth is moved by her own primary form and natural defire, for the confervation, perfection, and ordering of its parts, toward things more excellent: and this is more likely than that the fixed ftars, thofe luminous globes, as well as the Wanderers, and the moft glorious and divine Sun, which are in no way aided by the Earth, or renewed, or urged by any virtue therein, fhould circulate aimleffly around the Earth, and that the whole heavenly hoft fhould repeat around the Earth courfes never ending and of no profit whatever to the ftars.   The Earth, then, which by fome great neceffity, even by a virtue innate, evident, and confpicuous, is turned circularly about the Sun, revolves; and by this motion it rejoices in the folar virtues and influences, and is ftrengthened by its own fure verticity, that it fhould not rovingly revolve over every region of the heavens.   The Sun (the chief agent in nature) as he forwards the courfes of the Wanderers, fo does he prompt this turning about of the Earth by the diffufion of the virtues of his orbes, and of light.   And if the Earth were not made to fpin with a diurnal revolution, the Sun would ever hang over fome determinate part with conftant beams, and by long tarriance would fcorch it, and pulverize it, and diffipate it, and the Earth would fuftain the deepeft wounds; and nothing good would iffue forth; it would not vegetate, it would not allow life to animals, and mankind would perifh.   In other parts, all things would verily be frightful and ftark with extreme cold; whence all high places would be very rough, unfruitful, inacceffible, covered with a pall of perpetual fhades and eternal night.   Since the Earth herfelf would not choofe to endure this fo miferable and horrid appearance on both her faces, fhe, by her magnetick aftral genius, revolves in an orbit, that by a perpetual change of light, there may be a perpetual alternation of things, heat and cold, rifings and fettings, day and night, morn and eve, noon and midnight.   Thus the Earth feeks and re-feeks the Sun, turns away from him and purfues him, by her own wondrous magnetick virtue.   Befides, it is not only from the Sun that evil would impend, if the Earth were to ftay ftill and be deprived of folar benefit; but from the Moon alfo ferious dangers would threaten.   For we fee how the ocean rifes and fwells beneath certain known pofitions of the Moon: And if there were not through the daily rotation of Earth a fpeedy tranfit of the Moon, the flowing fea would be driven above its level into certain regions, and many fhores would be overwhelmed with huge waves. In order then that Earth may not perifh in various ways, and be brought to confufion, fhe turns herfelf about by magnetick and primary virtue: and the like motions exift alfo in the reft of the Wanderers, urged fpecially by the movement and light of other bodies.   For the Moon alfo turns herfelf about in a monthly courfe, to receive in fucceffion the Sun's beams in which fhe, like the Earth,

rejoices

rejoices, and is refreshed : nor could she endure them for ever on one particular side without great harm and sure destruction. Thus each one of the moving globes is for its own safety borne in an orbit either in some wider circle, or only by a rotation of its body, or by both together. But it is ridiculous for a man a philosopher to suppose that all the fixed stars and the planets and the still higher heavens revolve to no other purpose, save the advantage of the Earth. It is the Earth, then, that revolves, not the whole heaven, and this motion gives opportunity for the growth and decrease of things, and for the generating of things animate, and awakens internal heat for the bringing of them to birth. Whence matter is quickened for receiving forms ; and from the primary rotation of the Earth natural bodies have their primary impetus and original activity. The motion then of the whole Earth is primary, astral, circular, around its own poles, whose verticity arises on both sides from the plane of the æquator, and whose vigour is infused into opposite termini, in order that the Earth may be moved by a sure rotation for its good, the Sun also and the stars helping its motion. But the simple straight motion downwards of the Peripateticks is a motion of weight, a motion of the aggregation of disjoined parts, in the ratio of their matter, along straight lines toward the body of the Earth : which lines tend the shortest way toward the centre. The motions of disjoined magnetical parts of the Earth, besides the motion of aggregation, are coition, revolution, and the direction of the parts to the whole, for harmony of form, and concordancy.

CHAP. V.

Arguments of those denying the Earth's motion, and
their confutation.

NOW it will not be superfluous to weigh well the arguments of those who say the Earth does not move ; that we may be better able to satisfy the crowd of philosophizers who assert that this constancy and stability of the Earth is confirmed by the most convincing arguments. Aristotle does not allow that the Earth moves circularly, on the ground that each several part of it would be affected by this particular motion ; that whereas now all the separate parts of the Earth are borne toward the middle in straight lines, that circular motion would be violent, and strange to nature, and not enduring. But it has been before proved that all actual portions of the Earth move in a circle, and that all magnetick bodies (fitly disposed) are borne around in an orbe. They are borne, however, toward the centre of the Earth in a

straight

ftraight line (if the way be open) by a motion of aggregation as though to their own origin : they move by various motions agreeably to the conformation of the whole : a terrella is moved circularly by its innate forces. " Befides " (fays he), " all things which " are borne in an orbe, afterwards would feem to be abandoned by " the firft motion, and to be borne by feveral motions befides the " firft.   The Earth muft alfo be borne on by two forts of motion, " whether it be fituate around a mid-point, or in the middle fite of " the univerfe : and if this were fo, there muft needs be at one time " an advance, at another time a retrogreffion of the fixed ftars : This, " however, does not feem to be the cafe, but they rife and fet always " the fame in the fame places."   But it by no means follows that a double motion muft be affigned to the Earth.   But if there be but one diurnal motion of the Earth around its poles, who does not fee that the ftars muft always in the fame manner rife and fet at the fame points of the horizon, even although there be another motion about which we are not difputing : fince the mutations in the fmaller orbit caufe no variation of afpect in the fixed ftars owing to their great diftance, unlefs the axis of the Earth have varied its pofition, concerning which we raife a queftion when fpeaking of the caufe of the præceffion of the æquinoxes.   In this argument are many flaws.   For if the Earth revolve, that we afferted muft needs occur not by reafon of the firft fphære, but of its innate forces.   But if it were fet in motion by the firft fphære, there would be no fucceffions of days and nights, for it would continue its courfe along with the *Primum Mobile*.   But that the Earth is affected by a double movement at the time when it rotates around its own centre, becaufe the reft of the ftars move with a double motion, does not follow. Befides, he does not well confider the argument, nor do his interpreters underftand the fame.   τούτου δὲ συμβαίνοντος, ἀναγκαῖον γίγνεσθαι παρόδους καὶ τροπὰς τῶν ἐνδεδεμένων ἄστρων. (Arift. *de Cælo*, ii. chap. 14.) That is, " If this be fo, there muft needs be changes, and retro" greffions of the fixed ftars."   What fome interpret as retrogreffions or regreffions, and changes of the fixed ftars, others explain as diverfions : which terms can in no way be underftood of axial motion, unlefs he meant that the Earth moved by the *Primum Mobile* is borne and turned over other poles diverfe even from thofe which correfpond to the firft fphære, which is altogether abfurd.   Other later theorifts fuppofe that the eaftern ocean ought to be impelled fo into weftern regions by that motion, that thofe parts of the Earth which are dry and free from water would be daily flooded by the eaftern ocean.   But the ocean is not acted upon by that movement, fince nothing oppofes it ; and even the whole atmofphere is carried round : And for that reafon in the Earth's fwift courfe all the things in the air are not left behind by us nor do they feem to move toward the Weft : Wherefore alfo the clouds

are

are at reft in the air, unlefs the force of the winds drive them ; and objects which are projected into the air fall again into their own place. But thofe foolifh folk who think that towers, temples, and buildings muft neceffarily be fhaken and overthrown by the Earth's motion, may fear left men at the Antipodes fhould flip off into an oppofite orbe, or that fhips when failing round the entire globe fhould (as foon as they have dipped under the plane of our horizon) fall into the oppofite region of the fky. But thofe follies are old wives' goffip, and the rubbifh of certain philofophizers, men who, when they effay to treat of the higheft truths and the fabrick of the univerfe, and hazard anything, can fcarce underftand aught *ultra crepidam*. They would have the Earth to be the centre of a circle ; and therefore to reft motionlefs amid the rotation. But neither the ftars nor the wandering globes move about the Earth's centre : the high heaven alfo does not move circularly round the Earth's centre ; nor if the Earth were in the centre, is it a centre itfelf, but a body around a centre. Nor is it confiftent with reafon that the heavenly bodies of the Peripateticks fhould attend on a centre fo decadent and perifhable as that of the Earth. They think that Nature feeks reft for the generation of things, and for promoting their increafe while growing ; and that accordingly the whole Earth is at reft. And yet all generation takes place from motion, without which the univerfal nature of things would become torpid. The motion of the Sun, the motion of the Moon, caufe changes ; the motion of the Earth awakens the internal breath of the globe ; animals themfelves do not live without motion, and the ceafelefs activity of the heart and arteries. For of no moment are the arguments for a fimple ftraight motion toward the centre, that this is the only kind in the Earth, and that in a fimple body there is one motion only and that a fimple one. For that ftraight motion is only a tendency toward their own origin, not of the parts of the Earth only, but of thofe of the Sun alfo, of the Moon, and of the reft of the fphæres which alfo move in an orbit. Joannes Coftæus, who raifes doubts concerning the caufe of the Earth's motion, looking for it externally and internally, underftands magnetick vigour to be internal, active, and difponent ; alfo that the Sun is an external promotive caufe, and that the Earth is not fo vile and abject a body as it is generally confidered. Accordingly there is a diurnal movement on the part of the Earth for its own fake and for its advantage. Thofe who make out that that terreftrial motion (if fuch there be) takes place not only in longitude, but alfo in latitude, talk nonfenfe. For Nature has fet in the Earth determinate poles, and definite unconfufed revolutions. Thus the Moon revolves with refpect to the Sun in a monthly courfe ; yet having her own definite poles, facing determinate parts of the heaven. To fuppofe that the air moves the Earth would be ridicul-

ous

ous. For air is only exhalation, and is an enveloping effluvium from
the Earth itfelf; the winds alfo are only a rufh of the exhalations
in fome part near the Earth's furface; the height of its motion is
flight, and in all regions there are various winds unlike and contrary.
Some writers, not finding in the matter of the Earth the caufe (for
they fay that they find nothing except folidity and confiftency), deny
it to be in its form; and they only admit as qualities of the Earth cold
and drynefs, which are unable to move the Earth. The Stoicks attribute a foul to the Earth, whence they pronounce (amid the laughter
of the learned) the Earth to be an animal. This magnetick form,
whether vigour or foul, is aftral. Let the learned lament and bewail
the fact that none of thofe old Peripateticks, nor even thofe common
philofophizers heretofore, nor Joannes Coftæus, who mocks at fuch
things, were able to apprehend this grand and important natural
fact. But as to the notion that furface inequality of mountains and
valleys would prevent the Earth's diurnal revolution, there is nothing
in it: for they do not mar the Earth's roundnefs, being but flight
excrefcences compared with the whole Earth; nor does the Earth
revolve alone without its emanations. Beyond the emanations, there
is no renitency. There is no more labour exerted in the Earth's
motion than in the march of the reft of the Stars: nor is it excelled
in dignity by fome ftars. To fay that it is frivolous to fuppofe that
the Earth rather feeks a view of the Sun, than the Sun of the Earth,
is a mark of great obftinacy and unwifdom. Of the theory of the
rotation we have often fpoken. If anyone feek the caufe of the
revolution, or of other tendency of the Earth, from the fea furrounding it, or from the motion of the air, or from the Earth's gravity,
he would be no lefs filly as a theorift than thofe who ftubbornly
ground their opinions on the fentiments of the ancients. Ptolemy's
reafonings are of no weight; for when our true principles are laid
down, the truth comes to light, and it is fuperfluous to refute them.
Let Coftæus recognize and philofophers fee how unfruitful and vain
a thing it becomes then to take one's ftand on the principles and
unproved opinions of certain ancients. Some raife a doubt how it
can be that, if the Earth move round its own axis, a globe of iron
or of lead dropped from the higheft point of a tower falls exactly
perpendicularly to a fpot of the Earth below itfelf. Alfo how it is
that cannon balls from a large culverin, fired with the fame quantity
and ftrength of powder, in the fame direction and at a like elevation
through the fame air, would be caft at a like diftance from a given
fpot both Eaftward and Weftward, fuppofing the Earth to move
Eaftward. But thofe who bring forward this kind of argument are
being mifled: not attending to the nature of primary globes, and
the combination of parts with their globes, even though they be
not adjoined by folid parts. Whereas the motion of the Earth in
the diurnal revolution does not involve the feparation of her more
                                                                    folid

folid circumference from the furrounding bodies; but all her effluvia furround her, and in them heavy bodies projected in any way by force, move on uniformly along with the Earth in general cohær-ence. And this alfo takes place in all primary bodies, the Sun, the Moon, the Earth, the parts betaking themfelves to their firft origins and fources, with which they connect themfelves with the fame appetence as terrene things, which we call heavy, with the Earth. So lunar things tend to the Moon, folar things to the Sun, within the orbes of their own effluvia. The emanations hold together by continuity of fubftance, and heavy bodies are alfo united with the Earth by their own gravity, and move on together in the general motion: efpecially when there is no renitency of bodies in the way. And for this caufe, on account of the Earth's diurnal revolution, bodies are neither fet in motion, nor retarded; they do not overtake it, nor do they fall fhort behind it when violently projected toward Eaft or Weft.

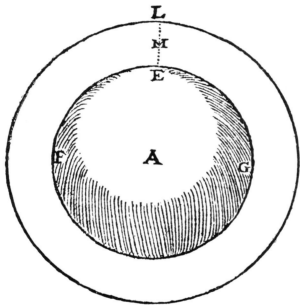

Let E F G be the Earth's globe, A its centre, L E the afcending effluvia: Juft as the orbe of the effluvia progreffes with the Earth, fo alfo does the unmoved part of the circle at the ftraight line L E progrefs along with the general revolution. At L and E, a heavy body, M, falls perpendicularly toward E, taking the fhorteft way to the centre, nor is that right movement of weight, or of aggrega-tion compounded with a circular movement, but is a fimple right motion, never leaving the line L E. But when thrown with an equal force from E toward F, and from E toward G, it completes an equal diftance on either fide, even though the daily rotation of the Earth is in procefs: juft as twenty paces of a man mark an equal fpace whether toward Eaft or Weft: fo the Earth's diurnal motion

is

is by no means refuted by the illuſtrious Tycho Brahe, through arguments ſuch as theſe.

The tendency toward its origin (which, in the caſe of the Earth, is called by Philoſophers weight) cauſes no reſiſtance to the diurnal revolution, nor does it direct the Earth, nor does it retain the parts of the Earth in place, for in regard to the Earth's ſolidity they are imponderous, nor do they incline further, but are at reſt in the maſs. If there be a flaw in the maſs, ſuch as a deep cavity (ſay 1000 fathoms), a homogenic portion of the Earth, or compacted terreſtrial matter, deſcends through that ſpace (whether filled with water or air) toward an origin more aſſured than air or water, ſeeking a ſolid globe. But the centre of the Earth, as alſo the Earth as a whole, is imponderous; the ſeparated parts tend toward their own origin, but that tendency we call weight; the parts united are at reſt; and even if they were ponderable, they would introduce no hindrance to the diurnal revolution. For if around

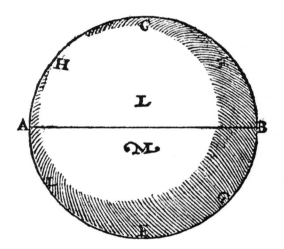

the axis A B, there be a weight at C, it is balanced from E; if at F, from G; if at H, from I. So internally at L, they are balanced from M: the whole globe, then, having a natural axis, is balanced in æquilibrio, and is eaſily ſet in motion by the ſlighteſt cauſe, but eſpecially becauſe the Earth in her own place is nowiſe heavy nor lacking in balance. Therefore weight neither hinders the diurnal revolution, nor influences either the direction or continuance in poſition. Wherefore it is manifeſt that no ſufficiently ſtrong reaſon has yet been found out by Philoſophers againſt the motion of the Earth.

CHAP.

CHAP. VI.

On the caufe of the definite time, of an entire ro-
tation of the Earth.

IURNAL motion is due to caufes which have now to be fought, arifing from magnetick vigour and from the confederated bodies; that is to fay, why the diurnal rotation of the Earth is completed in the fpace of twenty-four hours. For no curious art, whether of Clepfydras or of fand-clocks, or thofe con-trivances of little toothed wheels which are fet in motion by weights, or by the force of a bent fteel band, can difcover any degree of difference in the time. But as foon as the diurnal rotation has been gone through, it at once begins over again. But we would take as the day the abfolute turning of a meridian of the Earth, from fun to fun. This is fomewhat greater than one whole revolution of it; in this way the yearly courfe is completed in 365 and nearly $\frac{1}{4}$ turnings with refpect to the fun. From this fure and regular motion of the Earth, the number and time of 365 days, 5 hours, 55 minutes, in folar tropical years is always certain and definite, except that there are fome flight differences due to other caufes. The Earth therefore revolves not fortuitoufly, or by chance, or precipitately; but with a rather high intelligence, equably, and with a wondrous regularity, in no other way than all the reft of the movable ftars, which have definite periods belonging to their motions. For the Sun himfelf being the agent and incitor of the univerfe in motion, other wander-ing globes fet within the range of his forces, when acted on and ftirred, alfo regulate each its own proper courfes by its own forces; and they are turned about in periods correfponding to the extent of their greater rotation, and the differences of their effufed forces, and their intelligence for higher good. And for that caufe Saturn, having a wider orbit, is borne round it in a longer time, Jupiter a fhorter, and Mars ftill lefs; while Venus takes nine months, Mercury 80 days, on the hypothefes of Copernicus; the Moon going round the Earth with refpect to the Sun in 29 days, 12 hours, 44 minutes. We have afferted that the Earth moves circularly about its centre, com-pleting a day by an entire revolution with refpect to the Sun. The Moon revolves in a monthly courfe around the Earth, and, repeating a conjunction with the Sun after a former fynodic conjunction, con-ftitutes the month or Lunar day. The Moon's mean concentrick orbit, according to numerous obfervations of Copernicus and later aftronomers, is found to be diftant 29 and about $\frac{5}{8}$ diameters of the Earth from the Earth's centre. The Moon's revolution with refpect to the Sun takes place in $29\frac{1}{2}$ days and 44 minutes of time. We reckon the motion with refpect to the fun, not the periodic motion,

juft

juft as a day is one entire revolution of the Earth with refpeſt to the Sun, not one periodick revolution; becaufe the Sun is the caufe of lunar as of terreftrial motion: alfo, becaufe (on the hypothefes of later obfervers) the fynodical month is truly periodic, on account of the Earth's motion in a great orbit. The proportion of diameters to circumferences is the fame. And the concentrick orbit of the Moon contains twice over 29 and ½ great circles of the Earth & a little more. The Moon & the Earth, then, agree together in a double proportion of motion; & the Earth moves in the fpace of twenty-four hours, in its diurnal motion; becaufe the Moon has a motion proportional to the Earth, but the Earth a motion agreeing with the lunar motion in a nearly double proportion. There is fome difference in details, becaufe the diftances of the ftars in details have not been examined fufficiently exaſtly, nor are mathematicians as yet agreed about them. The Earth therefore revolves in a fpace of 24 hours, as the Moon in her monthly courfe, by a magnetick confederation of both ftars, the globes being forwarded in their movement by the Sun, according to the proportion of their orbits, as Ariſtotle allows, *de Cœlo*, bk. ii., chap. 10. "It happens" (he fays) "that the motions are performed "through a proportion exiſting between them feverally, namely, at the "fame intervals in which fome are fwifter, others flower." But it is more agreeable to the relation between the Moon and the Earth, that that harmony of motion fhould be due to the faſt that they are bodies rather near together, and very like each other in nature and fubftance, and that the Moon has more evident effeſts upon the Earth than the reft of the ftars, the Sun excepted; alfo becaufe the Moon alone of all the planets conduſts her revolutions, direſtly (however diverfe even), with reference to the Earth's centre, and is efpecially akin to the Earth, and bound to it as with chains. This, then, is the true fymmetry and harmony between the motions of the Earth and the Moon; not that old oft-befung harmony of cœleftial motions, which affumes that the nearer any fphære is to the *Primum Mobile*, and that fiſtitious and pretended rapideft Prime Motion, the lefs does it offer refiftance thereto, and the flower it is borne by its own motion from weft to eaft: but that the more remote it is, the greater is its velocity, and the more freely does it complete its own movement; and therefore that the Moon (being at the greateft diftance from the *Primum Mobile*) revolves the moft fwiftly. Thofe vain tales have been conceded in order that the *Primum Mobile* may be accepted, and be thought to have certain effeſts in retarding the motions of the lower heavens; as though the motion of the ftars arofe from retardation, and were not inhærent and natural; and as though a furious force were perpetually driving the reft of the heaven (except only the *Primum Mobile*) with frenzied incitations. Much more likely is it that the ftars are borne around fymmetrically by their own forces, with a certain mutual concert and harmony.

CHAP.

CHAP. VII.

On the primary magnetick nature of the Earth,
whereby its poles are parted from the poles
of the Ecliptick.

RIMARILY having fhown the manner and caufes of the diurnal revolution of the Earth, which is partly brought about from the vigour of the magnetick virtue, partly effected by the præ-eminence and light of the Sun; there now follows an account of the diftance of its poles from the poles of the Ecliptick—a fupremely neceffary fact. For if the poles of the univerfe or of the Earth remained faft at the poles of the Zodiack, then the Æquator of the Earth would lie exactly beneath the line of the Ecliptick, and there would be no variation in the feafons of the year, no Winter, no Summer, nor Spring, nor Autumn: but one and the fame invariable afpect of things would continue. The direction of the axis of the Earth has receded therefore from the pole of the Zodiack (for lafting good) juft fo far as is fufficient for the generation and variety of things. Accordingly the declination of the tropicks and the inclination of the Earth's pole remain perpetually in the twenty-fourth degree; though now only 23 degrees 28 minutes are counted; or, as others make out, 29 minutes: But once it was 23 degrees 52 minutes, which are the extreme limits of the declinations hitherto obferved. And that has been prudently ordained by nature, and is arranged by the primary excellence of the Earth. For if thofe poles (of the Earth and the Ecliptick) were to be parted by a much greater diftance, then when the Sun approached the tropick, all things in the other deferted part of the globe, in fome higher latitude, would be defolate and (by reafon of the too prolonged abfence of the Sun) brought to deftruction. As it is, however, all is fo proportioned that the whole terreftrial globe has its own varying feafons in fucceffion, and alternations of condition, appropriate and needful: either from the more direct and vertical radiation of light, or from its increafed tarriance above the horizon.

Around thefe poles of the Ecliptick the direction of the poles of the Earth is borne: and by this motion the præceffion of the æquinoxes is apparent to us.

CHAP.

CHAP. VIII.

On the Præceffion of the Æquinoxes, from the mag-
netick motion of the poles of the Earth, in the Arctick
and Antarctick circle of the Zodiack.

RIMITIVE mathematicians, fince they did not pay attention to the inæqualities of the years, made no diftinction between the æquinoctial, or folftitial revolving year, and that which is taken from fome one of the fixed ftars. Even the Olympick years, which they ufed to reckon from the rifing of the dogftar, they thought to be the fame as thofe counted from the folftice. Hipparchus of Rhodes was the firft to call attention to the fact that thefe differ from each other, and difcovered that the year was longer when meafured by the fixed ftars than by the æquinox or folftice : whence he fuppofed that there was in the fixed ftars alfo fome motion in a common fequence ; but very flow, and not at once perceptible. After him Menelaus, a Roman geometer, then Ptolemy, and long afterward Mahometes Aractenfis, and feveral more, in all their literary memoirs, perceived that the fixed ftars and the whole firmament proceeded in an orderly fequence, regarding as they did the heaven, not the earth, and not underftanding the magnetical inclinations. But we fhall demonftrate that it proceeds rather from a certain rotatory motion of the Earth's axis, than that that eighth fphære (fo called) the firmament, or non-moving empyrean, revolves ftudded with innumerable globes and ftars, whofe diftances from the Earth have never been proved by anyone, nor can be proved (the whole univerfe gliding, as it were). And furely it fhould feem much more likely that the appearances in the heavens fhould be clearly accounted for by a certain inflection and inclination of the comparatively fmall body of the Earth, than by the fetting in motion of the whole fyftem of the univerfe ; efpecially if this motion is to be regarded as ordained folely for the Earth's advantage : While for the fixed ftars, or for the planets, it is of no ufe at all. For by this motion the rifings and fettings of ftars in every Horizon, as well as their culminations at the height of the heavens, are fhifted fo much that the ftars which once were vertical are now fome degrees diftant from the zenith. For Nature has taken care, through the Earth's foul or magnetick vigour, that, juft as it was needful in tempering, receiving, and warding off the fun's rays and light, by fuitable feafons, that the points toward which the Earth's pole is directed fhould be 23 degrees and more

from

from the poles of the Ecliptick: fo now for moderating and for
receiving the luminous rays of the fixed ftars in due turn and fucceffion, the Earth's poles fhould revolve at the fame diftance from
the Ecliptick at the Ecliptick's arctick circle ; or rather that they
fhould creep at a gentle pace, that the actions of the ftars fhould not
always remain at the fame parallel circles, but fhould have a rather
flow mutation.   For the influences of the ftars are not fo forceful as
that a fwifter courfe fhould be defired.   Slowly, then, is the Earth's
axis inflected ; and the ftars' rays, falling upon the face of the
Earth, fhift only in fo long a time as a diameter of the arctick or
polar circle is extended : whence the ftar at the extremity of the tail
of the Cynofure, which once was 12 degrees 24 minutes (namely,
in the time of Hipparchus) diftant from the pole of the univerfe,
or from that point which the pole of the Earth ufed to face, is now
only 2 degrees and 52 minutes diftant from the fame point ;
whence from its nearnefs it is called by the moderns *Polaris*.   Some
time it will be only $\frac{1}{2}$ degree away from the pole : afterward it
will begin to recede from the pole until it will be 48 degrees diftant; and this, according to the Prutenical tables, will be in Anno
Domini 15000.   Thus *Lucida Lyræ* (which to us fouthern Britons
now almoft culminates) will fome time approach to the pole of the
world, to about the fifth degree.   So all the ftars fhift their rays of
light at the furface of the Earth, through this wonderful magnetical inflection of the Earth's axis.   Hence come new varieties of the
feafons of the year, and lands become more fruitful or more barren ;
hence the characters and manners of nations are changed ; kingdoms
and laws are altered, in accordance with the virtue of the fixed
ftars as they culminate, and the ftrength thence received or loft in
accordance with the fingular and fpecifick nature of each ; or on
account of new configurations with the planets in other places of the
Zodiack ; on account alfo of rifings and fettings, and of new con-
currences at the meridian.   The præceffion of the æquinoxes arifing
from the æquable motion of the Earth's pole in the arctick circle of
the Zodiack is here demonftrated.   Let A B C D be the Ecliptick
line ; I E G the arctic circle of the Zodiack.   Then if the Earth's
pole look to E, the æquinoxes are at D, C.   Let this be at the
time of Metho, when the horns of Aries were in the æquinoctial
colure.   Now if the Earth's pole have advanced to I ; then the
æquinoxes will be at K, L; and the ftars in the ecliptick C will
feem to have progreffed, in the order of the figns, along the whole
arc K C : L will be moved on by the præceffion, againft the order
of the figns, along the arc D L.   But this would occur in the contrary order, if the point G were to face the poles of the earth,
and the motion were from E to G : for then the æquinoxes would
be M N, and the fixed ftars would anticipate the fame at C and D,
counter to the order of the figns.

CHAP.

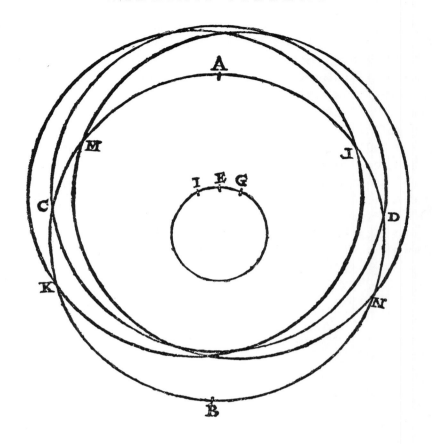

CHAP. IX.

On the anomaly of the Præceffion of the Æquinoxes,
and of the obliquity of the Zodiack.

T one time the fhifting of the æquinoxes is quicker, at another flower, being not always equal : becaufe the poles of the earth travel unequally in the arctick and antarctick circle of the Zodiack ; and decline on both fides from the middle path : whence the obliquity of the Zodiack to the Æquator feems to change. And as this has become known by means of long obfervations, fo alfo has it been perceived, that the true æquinoctial points have been elongated from the mean æquinoctial points, on this fide and on that, by 70 minutes (when the proftaphærefis is greateft) : but that the folftices either approach the æquator unequally 12 minutes nearer, or recede as far behind ; fo that the neareft approach is 23 degrees 28 minutes, and the greateft elongation 23 degrees 52 minutes. Aftronomers have given various explanations to account for this inæquality of the præceffion and alfo of the obliquity of the tropicks. Thebit, with the view of

laying

laying down a rule for fuch confiderable inæqualities in the motion of the ftars, explained that the eighth fphære does not move with a continuous motion from weft to eaft; but is fhaken with a certain motion of trepidation, by which the firft points of Aries and Libra in the eighth heaven defcribe certain fmall circles with diameters equal to about nine degrees, around the firft points of Aries and Libra in the ninth fphære.   But fince many things abfurd and impoffible as to motion follow from this motion of trepidation, that theory of motion is therefore long fince obfolete.   Others there-fore are compelled to attribute the motion to the eighth fphære, and to erect above it a ninth heaven alfo, yea, and to pile up yet a tenth and an eleventh : In the cafe of mathematicians, indeed, the fault may be condoned; for it is permiffible for them, in the cafe of difficult motions, to lay down fome rule and law of equality by any hypothefes.   But by no means can fuch enormous and monftrous celeftial ftructures be accepted by philofophers.   And yet here one may fee how hard to pleafe are thofe who do not allow any motion to one very fmall body, the Earth; and notwithftand-ing they drive and rotate the heavens, which are huge and immenfe above all conception and imagination: I declare that they feign the heavens to be three (the moft monftrous of all things in Nature) in order that fome obfcure motions forfooth may be accounted for. Ptolemy, who compares with his own the obfervations of Timocharis and Hipparchus, one of whom flourifhed 260 years, the other 460 years before him, thought that there was this motion of the eighth fphære, and of the whole firmament; and proved by help of nu-merous phænomena that it took place over the poles of the Zodiack, and, fuppofing its motion to be fo far æquable, that the non-planetary ftars in the fpace of 100 years completed juft one degree beneath the *Primum Mobile.*   After him 750 years Albategnius difcovered that one degree was completed in a fpace of 66 years, fo that a whole period would be 23,760 years.   Alphonfus made out that this motion was ftill flower, completing one degree and 28 minutes only in 200 years; and that thus the courfe of the fixed ftars went on, though unequally.   At length Copernicus, by means of the obfervations of Timocharis, Ariftarchus of Samos, Hipparchus, Menelaus, Ptolemy, Mahometes Aractenfis, Alphonfus, and of his own, detected the anomalies of the motion of the Earth's axis: though I doubt not that other anomalies alfo will come to light fome ages hence.   So difficult is it to obferve motion fo flow, unlefs extending over a period of many centuries; on which account we ftill fail to underftand the intent of Nature, what fhe is ftriving after through fuch inæquality of motion.   Let A be the pole of the Ecliptick, B C the Ecliptick, D the Æquator; when the pole of the Earth near the arctick circle of the Zodiack faces the point M, then there is an anomaly of the præceffion of the æquinox at F;

but

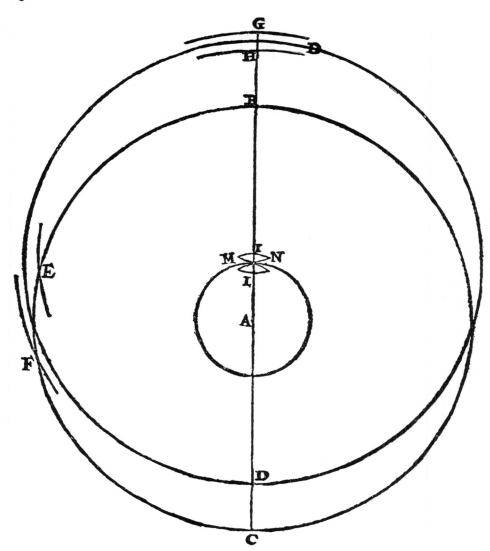

but when it faces N, there is an anomaly of the præceſſion at E. But when it faces I directly, then the maximum obliquity G is obſerved at the ſolſtitial colure; but when it faces L, there is the minimum obliquity H at the ſolſtitial colure.

Copernicus' contorted circlet in the Arctick circle of the Zodiack.

LET F B G be the half of the Arctick circle deſcribed round the pole of the Zodiack : A B C the ſolſtitial colure : A the pole of the Zodiack; D E the anomaly of longitude 140 minutes at either ſide on both ends : B C the anomaly of obliquity 24 minutes : B the greater obliquity of 23 degrees 52 minutes : D the mean obliquity of 23 degrees 40 minutes : C the minimum obliquity of 23 degrees 28 minutes.

The

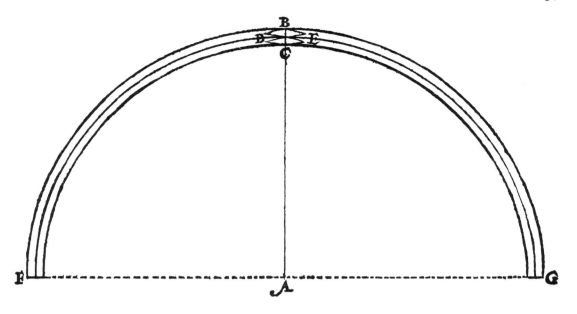

The true and natural motion of the axis or pole of the
Earth directed to the Arctick circle of the Zodiack.

A I is part of the Arctick circle of the Zodiack, in which one period of obliquity is performed; from A to E is the period of the anomaly of the præceſſion of the æquinoxes; A I is the ſhape of the curved line which the pole of the Earth deſcribes by a true motion compounded of the three motions, that is to ſay, of the æquable motion præceſſional, of that of the anomaly of the præceſ-ſions, and that of obliquity.

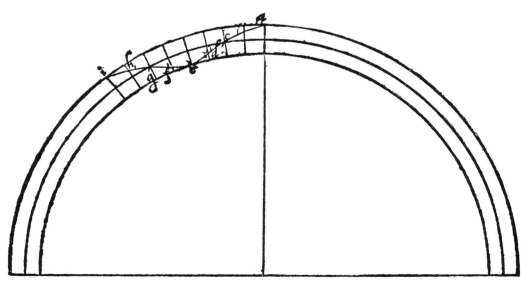

The

The period of motion of the præceſſion of the æquinoxes is 25,816 Ægyptian years; the period of the obliquity of the Zodiack is 3434 years, and a little more. The period of the anomaly of the præceſſion of the æquinoxes is 1717 years, and a little more. If the whole time of the motion A I were divided into eight equal parts: in the firſt eighth the pole is borne ſomewhat ſwiftly from A to B; in the ſecond eighth, more ſlowly from B to C; in the third, with the ſame ſlowneſs from C to D; in the fourth, more ſwiftly again from D to E; in the fifth, with the ſame ſwiftneſs from E to F; again-more ſlowly from F to G; and with the ſame ſlowneſs from G to H; in the laſt eighth, ſomewhat ſwiftly again from H to I. And this is the contorted circlet of Copernicus, fuſed with the mean motion into the curved line which is the path of the true motion. And thus the pole attains the period of the anomaly of the præceſſion of the æquinoxes twice; and that of the declination or obliquity once only. It is thus that by later aſtronomers, but eſpecially by Copernicus (the Reſtorer of Aſtronomy), the anomalies of the motion of the Earth's axis are deſcribed, ſo far as the obſervations of the ancients down to our own times admit; but there are ſtill needed more and exact obſervations for anyone to eſtabliſh aught certain about the anomaly of the motion of the præceſſions, and at the ſame time that alſo of the obliquity of the Zodiack. For ever ſince the time at which, by means of various obſervations, this anomaly was firſt obſerved, we have only arrived at half a period of the obliquity. So that all the more all theſe matters about the unequal motion both of the præceſſion and of the obliquity are uncertain and not well known: wherefore neither can we ourſelves aſſign any natural cauſes for it, and eſtabliſh it for certain. Wherefore alſo do we to our reaſonings and experiments magnetical here ſet an end and period.

FINIS.

INDEX.

ABOT, Sebaftian, 4.
Cælius Calcagninus, 7.
Cæfare, or Cefare, Giulio, 141.
Calaber, Hannibal Rofetius, 3.
calamita, or *kalamita*, 11.
Calcagninus, Cælius, 7.
Camillus Leonhardus, 3.
Candifh, or Cavendifh, Thomas, *iij, 117.
cap of iron for a loadftone, 86, 89, 90, 95.
carabe, or *karabe*, 47.
carbuncle, electrick properties of, 48, 111.
Cardan, Hieronymo, 2.
  De Proportionibus:
    on iron and earth, 43, 62, 67.
    on diftance of centre of cofmos, 169.
  De Rerum Varietate:
    on fall of meteorick iron, 26.
    on attraction of amber, 49.
    on a perpetual motion engine, 107.
  De Subtilitate:
    alleges magnet to feed on iron, 37, 63, 92.
    on magnet that draws filver, 110.
    on magnetick influence of ftar in tail of
      Urfa Minor, 5, 116, 153.
carnelian, the, 51, 55.
catoblepas, the antelope called, 63.
Cefare, Giulio, 141.
chalybs, 18, 25, 33.
chatochitis, 111.
chemifts, the, 19, 20, 21, 24, 37, 66.
China, 4, 8, 9, 11, 17, 32, 119.
Chinocrates, 2.
circumpulfion, doctrine of, 3, 61.
clamps (open kilns), 26.
clay when burnt is magnetick, 26, 43, 97.
clepfydra, 231.
Coimbra, College of, 5.
coition (mutual attraction), 45, 46, 60, 65,
  67, 68, 81, 98, 99, 103, 109, 131.
    definition of, *vj, 68.
    orbe of, *vj.
colours of loadftones, 9, 10, 27.
Como, 23.
compafs, alleged invention of, by Amalfians, 4.
    origin of the compafs-card, 4, 165.
    the mariners' (*pyxis*), 3, 115, 147, 165, 172.
    the little (*pyxidula*), 4, 181, 202.
    different forms of, Italian, Baltic, Portuguefe,
      Englifh, 165, 166, 177, 181.
conduction, magnetick, 85, 104, 125.
confequent poles, 129, 142.
Copernican fyftem, 231.
Copernicus, Nicolas, 212, 214, 216, 231,
  237, 238, 240.
Cordus, Valerius, 10.
Cornelius Agrippa, 3.
Cornelius Gemma, 63.
Cornelius Tacitus, 25.
corolla intorta, or contorted circlet, 238,
  240.
Cortes, Martin, 5, 116, 152.

Corvo, Ifland of, 167.
Cofta, Filippo (of Mantua), 141.
Coftæus, Joannes, 3, 62, 227, 228.
creagus, the, or flefh-magnet, 110.
cryftal, rock, 48, 52, 59, 111.
Curtius, Nicolaus, 35.
Cufan (Michael Khrypffs), Cardinal de
  Cufa, 3, 64, 108.
Cynofure, the, or Pole-ftar, 14, 81, 117,
  222, 235.

EAN, Foreft of, loadftone found
  in the, 11.
    decay of the magnetick virtue,
      18, 37, 124, 138, 149.
    declination, the, or dip, 184.
denarius of Antony, 110.
diamond, an electrick, 48, 50, 59, 111.
    alleged power to attract iron, 109, 112.
    alleged antipathy to magnet, 2, 7, 109, 143.
    experiments upon, 143.
Diego Alfonfo, 178.
Differences between electricks and magneticks, 47, 60, 65.
Diofcorides, 1, 2, 9, 32.
dip, the, alfo called declination, 8, 46, 184-
  204.
dipping-needle, or declination inftrument,
  185, 203.
direction, or directive force, 41, 46, 115,
  119.
dividing a loadftone, 16, 72, 100, 121, 122,
  127, 130, 136, 145, 146.
Dominicus Maria Ferrarienfis, 212, 213.
Doria, Andrea (Admiral), 4.
Drake, Sir Francis, *iij *bis*, 117.
Du Puys (alfo called Puteanus), 3, 63.

ARTH, the, a great magnet,
  38, 39, 40, 41, 44, 119, 211.
    echeneis (the fucking fifh), 7,
      63, 110.
    Ecphantus, 214.
effluvia, electrical, 52, 53, 59, 66.
    magnetical, 61.
electrical attraction, 50, 51, 111.
electrick force, definition of, 52.
electricks, *vj, 46-60.
electrum (ἤλεκτρον), 47.
emerald is non-electrick, 51.
emery, 22, 51.
Empedocles, 208.
Encelius (or Entzelt, Chriftoph.), 3, 111.
Epicurus, 61, 62.
Erafmus Rheinholdus, 213.
Eraftus, Thomas, 3, 22.
errors in navigation, 166, 177.
Evax, King of Arabia, 111.
Euripides, 9, 11, 18.

THIS TREATISE BY WILLIAM GILBERT, OF COLCHESTER,
PHYSICIAN OF LONDON, ON THE MAGNET, WAS FIRST
PUBLISHT IN THE LATIN TONGUE IN LONDON IN THE
YEAR OF OUR LORD M.D.C.; THIS ENGLISH TRANSLA-
TION, WHICH WAS COMPLETED IN THE YEAR M.C.M.,
IS PRINTED FOR THE GILBERT CLUB, TO THE NUMBER
OF TWO HUNDRED AND FIFTY COPIES, BY CHARLES
WHITTINGHAM AND COMPANY, AT THE CHISWICK
PRESS, TOOKS COURT, CHANCERY LANE, LONDON.

NOTES

ON THE

DE MAGNETE

OF

DR. WILLIAM GILBERT

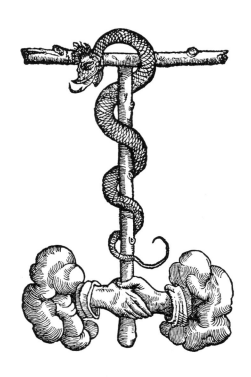

PRIVATELY PRINTED
LONDON MCMI

"For out of olde feldes, as men feith,
Cometh al this newe corn fro yeer to yere;
And out of olde bokes, in good feith,
Cometh al this newe fcience that men lere."
—*Chaucer.*

"I finde that you have vfed in this your trãflation greate art, knowledge, and difcretion. For walking as it were in golden fetters (as al Tranflators doe) you notwithftanding fo warilie follow your Auctor, that where he trippeth you hold him vp, and where he goeth out of the way, you better direct his foote. You haue not only with the Bee fucked out the beft iuyce from fo fweete a flower, but with the Silke-worme as it were wouen out of your owne bowels, the fineft filke; & that which is more, not rude & raw filke, but finely died with the frefh colour of your owne Art, Invention, and Practife. If thefe Adamantes draw you not to effect this which you haue fo happilie begunne: then let thefe fpurres driue you forward: viz. Your owne promife, the expectation of your friends, the loffe of fome credit if you fhould fteppe backe, the profit which your labours may yeeld to many, the earneft defire which you yourfelfe haue to reviue this Arte, and the vndoubted acceptation of your paines, if you performe the fame."—(Prefatory epiftle of John Cafe, D. of Phyficke, printed in R. Haydocke's tranflation of *The Artes of Curious Painting*, of Lomatius, Oxford, 1598.)

"This booke is not for every rude and unconnynge man to fee, but for clerkys and very gentylmen that underftand gentylnefs and fcyence."—*Caxton.*

CHISWICK PRESS: CHARLES WHITTINGHAM AND CO.
TOOKS COURT, CHANCERY LANE, LONDON.

BIBLIOGRAPHY OF *DE MAGNETE*.

I. (**The London Folio of 1600**.) *Fol. ✳j. title* GVILIELMI GIL | berti colceſtren | fis, medici londi- | nenfis, | DE MAGNETE, MAGNETI- | cifqve corporibvs, et de mag- | no magnete tellure ; Phyſiologia noua, | plurimis & argumentis, & expe- | rimentis demonſtrata. | *Printer's Mark* | Londini | excudebat Petrvs Short anno | MDC. || *✳j verſo* Gilbert's coat of arms. || *✳ij* Ad Lectorem || *✳iij verſo* Ad graviſſimvm doctiſſimvmqve . . . || *✳vj* Verborum quorundam interpretatio. || *✳vj verſo* Index capitum. || p. 1. GVILIELMI GILBERTI | DE MAGNETE, LIB. I. || p. 240. FINIS. | Errata. Without any colophon, printer's Mark, or date at end. *Folio. 8 ll. of preliminary matter.* ABCDEFGHIKLMNOPQRSTV, *all ternions, making* 120 *numbered leaves. One blank leaf at front and one at end. Page* 114 *at end of Liber II. blank. A folded woodcut plate inſerted between p.* 200 *and p.* 201. *Woodcut initials, headlines and diagrams. All known copies except one have ink corrections in ſeveral pages, particularly pp.* 11, 22, 47.

II. (**The Stettin Quarto of 1628**.) *Four preliminary unnumbered leaves, viz.* (1) *Baſtard title* GULIELMI GILBERTI | Tractatus | DE MAGNETE || *verſo* blank ; (2) *Engraved title.* TRACTATVS | Siue | PHYSIOLOGIA NOVA | DE MAGNETE, | MAGNETICISQVE CORPO- | RIBVS ET MAGNO MAGNETE | tellure Sex libris comprehenfus | ã | Guilielmo Gilberto Colceſtrenfi, | Medico Londinenfi | . . . Omnia nunc diligenter recognita & emen- | datius quam ante in lucem edita, aucta & figu- | ris illuſtrata operâ & ſtudio | Wolfgangi 𝔏𝔬𝔠𝔥𝔪𝔞𝔫𝔰 I.U.D. | & Mathemati : | Ad calcem libri adjunctus eſt Index Capi- | tum Rerum et Verborum locupletiſſimus | EXCVSVS SEDINI | Typis Götzianis Sumptibus | *Ioh: Hallervordij.* | Anno MDC.XXVIII || *verſo* blank ; (3) Præfatio ; (4) Amicorum Acclamationes (verſes) || *verſo* blank. *Sig.* A Ad Lectorem Candidum. *Sig.* A2 *verſo* Ad Graviſſimum Doctiſſimumq̄ Virum. *Sig.* B2 Verborum quorundam interpretatio. *Verſo* blank, followed by twelve engraved plates numbered I. to XII. *Sig.* B3 is numbered as p. 1, and begins GVILIELMI GILBERTI | DE MAGNETE. | LIBER I. *Sig.* C *begins as p.* 5 ; *Sig.* D *as p.* 13 ; *and ſo forth. The collation therefore is :* 4 *ll. unnumbered,* ABCDEFGHIKLMNOPQRSTVXYZAaBbCcDdEe FfGgHhIiKkLlMm, *all fours. Pagination ends on p.* 232, *which has Sig.* H3 *in error for* Hh3, *being the end of the text. Verſo of* Hh3 *blank. Index capitum begins fol.* [Hh4] *and with Index Verborum continues to verſo of* Mm3. *Laſt leaf* [Mm4] *contains Errata, and inſtructions to binder to place plates : verſo blank. Quarto. Woodcut initials and diagrams. Without any colophon, printer's Mark, or date at end.* In ſome copies the engraved title differs, having the words *Ioh: Hallervordij.* replaced by the word *Authoris.*

✳ij

III. (**The Stettin Quarto of 1633.**) *Four preliminary unnumbered leaves,* viz., (1) *title.* Tractatus, five Phyfiologia Nova | de | MAGNETE, | Magneticifq; corporibus & magno | Magnete tellure, fex libris comprehenfus, | a GUILIELMO GILBERTO Colce- | ftrenfi, Medico Londinenfi. | . . . Omnia nunc diligenter recognita, & emendatius quam ante | in lucem edita, aucta & figuris illuftrata, opera & ftudio D. | WOLFGANGI LOCHMANS, I.U.D. | & Mathematici. | Ad calcem libri adiunctus eft Index capitum, Rerum & Verborum | locupletiffimus, qui in priore æditione defiderabatur | SEDINI, | Typis GOTZIANIS. | ANNO M.DC. XXXIII. | | *verfo* blank; (2) Præfatio; (3) Amicorum acclamationes (verfes) | | *verfo* Claudianus de Magnete (verfes); (4) *ibid. Sig.* A Ad Lectorem Candidum. *Sig.* A2 *verfo* Ad Graviffimum Doctiffimumq. Virum. *Sig.* B2 Verborum quorundam interpretatio; *verfo* blank. *Sig.* B3 is numbered as p. 1, and begins GVILIELMI GILBERTI | DE MAGNETE. | LIBER I. *Sig.* C begins as p. 5; *Sig.* D as p. 13; and fo forth. The Collation therefore is: 4 *ll.* unnumbered, A *to* Mm, *all fours.* Pagination *ends on p. 232, which bears Sig.* H3 *in error for* Hh3. *Verfo of Sig.* Hh3. Errata. Index capitum *begins* Hh4, *and with* Index Verborum *extends to verfo of* Mm3. *The laft leaf* [Mm4] *bears the Inftructions to binder, with verfo blank. There is no colophon, printer's Mark, or date at end. Quarto. Woodcut initials, and diagrams. Twelve etched plates of various fizes inferted.*

With the exception of the preliminary matter and the Inftructions to binder, the pagination is the fame as in the edition of 1628, the pages in the body of the work being reprinted word for word; though with exceptions. For example, p. 18 in Ed. 1633 is one line fhorter than in Ed. 1628. The etched plates are entirely different. It has been thought from the pagination being alike that thefe two editions were really the fame with different plates, titles, and preliminary matter. But they are really different. The fpacing of the words, letters and lines is different throughout, and there are different mifprints. The watermarks of the paper alfo differ.

IV. (**The Berlin "facsimile" Folio of 1892**.) This is a photo-zincograph reproduction of the London folio of 1600. It lacks the ink emendations on pages 11, 22, 47, &c., found in the original, and is wanting alfo in fome of the afterifks in the margins.

V. (**The American translation of 1893.**) Frontifpiece portrait | | *p. i. title* WILLIAM GILBERT | OF COLCHESTER, | phyfician of London, | on the | Loadftone and Magnetic Bodies, | and on | the great magnet the earth. | A new Phyfiology, | demonftrated with many arguments and experiments. | A tranflation by | P. Fleury Mottelay, | . . . | New York : | John Wiley & Sons, | 53 Eaft Tenth Street | 1893. | | *p. ii* bears imprint of Ferris Bros. *Printers*, 326 Pearl Street, New York. | | *p. iii.* reduced reproduction of title of 1600 edition | | *verfo* the Gilbert arms | | *p. v.* Tranflator's Preface | | *p. ix.* Biographical Memoir | | *p. xxxi.* Contents | | *p. xxxvii.* Addrefs of Edward Wright | | *p. xlvii.* Author's Preface. | | *p. liii.* Explanation of fome terms. |¶ pp. 1-358 text of the work. | | p. 359 reduced reproduction of title of 1628 edition. | | p. 360 *ditto* of 1633 edition. | | p. 361 *ditto* of Gilbert's *De Mundo Noftro* of 1651. | | pp. 363 to 368 General Index. | | Pages *xxx, xlvi, lii,* and 362 are blanks. There are no fignatures. Octavo. Diagrams reduced from woodcuts of the folio of 1600. Some copies bear on title the imprint | London : | Bernard Quaritch, | 15 Piccadilly. | |

NOTES ON THE *DE MAGNETE* OF
DR. WILLIAM GILBERT.

URING the work of revifing and editing the Englifh tranf-
lation of *De Magnete*, many points came up for difcuffion,
requiring critical confideration, and the examination of the
writings of contemporary or earlier authorities. Difcrep-
ancies between the texts of the three known editions—the
London folio of 1600, and the two Stettin quartos of 1628
and 1633 refpectively—demanded inveftigation. Paffages relating to aftrology,
to pharmacy, to alchemy, to geography, and to navigation, required to be
referred to perfons acquainted with the early literature of thofe branches.
Phrafes of non-claffical Latin, prefenting fome obfcurity, needed explanation
by fcholars of mediæval writings. Defcriptions of magnetical experiments
needed to be interpreted by perfons whofe knowledge of magnetifm enabled
them to infer the correct meaning to be affigned to the words in the text.
In this wife a large amount of mifcellaneous criticifm has been brought to
bear, and forms the bafis for the following notes. To make them available
to all ftudents of Gilbert, the references are given to page and line both of
the Latin folio of 1600 and of the Englifh edition of 1900. S. P. T.

THE GLOSSARY:

Gilbert's gloffary is practically an apology for the introduction into the
Latin language of certain new words, fuch as the nouns *terrella*, *verforium*,
and *verticitas*, and the adjectival noun *magneticum*, which either did not exift
in claffical Latin or had not the technical meaning which he now affigns to
them. His *terrella*, or μικρόγη, as he explains in detail on p. 13, is a little
magnetic model of the earth, but in the gloffary he fimply defines it as
magnes globofus. Neither *terrella* nor *verforium* appears in any Latin dictionary.
No older writer had ufed either word, though Peter Peregrinus (*De Magnete*,
Augfburg, 1558) had defcribed experiments with globular loadftones, and
pivotted magnetic needles fuitable for ufe in a compafs had been known for
nearly three centuries. Yet the pivotted needle was not denominated *verforium.* Blondo (*De Ventis*, Venice, 1546) does not ufe the term. Norman
(*The Newe Attractiue*, London, 1581) fpeaks of the "needle or compaffe," and
of the " wyre." Barlowe (*The Navigators Supply*, London, 1597) fpeaks of

A

the "flie," or the "wier." The term *verforium* (literally, the *turn-about*) is Gilbert's own invention. It was at once adopted into the fcience, and appears in the treatifes of Cabeus, *Philofophia Magnetica* (Ferrara, 1629), and of Kircher, *Magnes five de Arte Magnetica* (Coloniæ, 1643), and other writers of the feventeenth century. Curioufly enough, its adoption to denote the pivotted magnetic needle led to the growth of an erroneous fuggeftion that the mariners' compafs was known to the ancients becaufe of the occurrence in the writings of Plautus of the term *verforiam*, or *vorforiam*. This appears twice as the accufative cafe of a feminine noun *verforia*, or *vorforia*, which was ufed to denote part of the gear of a fhip ufed in tacking-about. Forcellini defines *verforia* as "funiculus quo extremus veli angulus religatur"; while *verforiam capere* is equivalent to "reverti," or (metaphorically) "fententiam mutare." The two paffages in Plautus are:

EUT. Si huc item properes, ut iftuc properas, facias rectius,
      Huc fecundus ventus nunc eft; cape modo vorforiam;
      Hic Favonius ferenu'ft, iftic Aufter imbricus:
      Hic facit tranquillitatem, ifte omnes fluctus conciet.
                              (in *Mercat.* Act. V., sc. 2.)

CHARM. Stafime, fac te propere celerem recipe te ad dominum domum;
        . . . .
        . . . .
        . . . . Cape vorforiam
        Recipe te ad herum.
                              (in *Trinum.* Act. IV., sc. 3.)

The word *magneticum* is alfo of Gilbert's own coinage, as a noun; as an adjective it had been certainly ufed before, at leaft in its Englifh form, *magneticall*, which appears on the title-page of William Borough's *Difcourfe of the Variation of the Compaffe* (London, 1596). Gilbert does not ufe anywhere the noun *magnetifmus*, *magnetifm*. The firft ufe of that noun occurs in William Barlowe's *Magneticall Aduertifements* (1616), in the *Epiftle Dedicatorie*, wherein, when fpeaking of Dr. Gilbert, he fays "vnto whom I communicated what I had obferued of my felfe, and what I had built vpon his foundation of the *Magnetifme* of the earth." Gilbert fpeaks of the *virtus magnetica*, or *vis magnetica;* indeed, he has a rich vocabulary of terms, ufing, befide *virtus* and *vis*, *vires*, *robur*, *poteftas*, *potentia*, *efficientia*, and *vigor* for that which we fhould now call *magnetifm* or *the magnetic forces*. Nor does he ufe the verb *magnetifare*, or its participle, *magnetifatus:* he fpeaks of *ferrum tactum*, or of *ferrum excitatum a magnete*. In fpite of certain obfcurities which occur in places in his work, he certainly fhows a nice appreciation of words and their ufe, and a knowledge of ftyle. One finds occafionally direct quotations from, and overt references to, the claffic authors, as in the references to Plato and Ariftotle on page 1, and in the paffage from the Georgics of Vergil on p. 21. But here and there one finds other traces of unmiftakable fcholarfhip, as in the reference to goat's wool on p. 35, or in the ufe, on p. 210, of the word *perplacet*, which occurs in the letter of Cicero *ad Atticum*, or in that of *commonftrabit*, occurring on p. 203, and found only in Cicero, Terence and Plautus; whilft the phrafe on p. 3, in which Gilbert rallies the fmatterers on having loft both their oil and their pains, has a delightfully claffical echo.

The term *orbis virtutis*, defined by Gilbert in the gloffary, and illuftrated by the cuts on pages 76, 77, and 96, might be effectively tranflated by *fphere of influence*, or *orbit within which there is fenfible attraction*. It has been preferred, however, to tranflate it literally as the *orbe of virtue*, or *orbe of magnetick virtue*. This choice has been determined by the defire to adopt fuch an Englifh phrafe as Gilbert would himfelf have ufed had he been writing Englifh. T. Hood, writing in 1592 in his book *The Vfe of both the Globes*, in ufing the word *orbe*, fays that the word *globe* fignifies a folid body, while a *fphere* is hollow, like two "difhes joyned by the brimme"; " The Latines properly call *Orbis* an Orbe"; "Moreouer the word *Sphaera* fignifieth that inftrument made of brafen hoopes (wee call it commonly a ringed Sphere) wherewith the Aftronomers deliuer unto the nouices of that Science the vnderftanding of things which they imagine in the heauen." Further, Dr. Marke Ridley in his *Treatife of Magneticall Bodies and Motions* (1613), has a chapter (XIIII) " Of the diftance and Orbe of the Magnets vertue," throughout which the term Orbe is retained. Sir Thomas Browne alfo writes of " the orb of their activities."

The word *Coitio*, ufed by Gilbert for the mutual force between magnet and iron, has been retained in its Englifh form, *coition*. Gilbert evidently adopted this term after much thought. The Newtonian conception of action and reaction being neceffarily equal had not dawned upon the mediæval philofophers. The term *attraction* had been ufed in a limited fenfe to connote an action in which a force was conceived of as being exerted on one fide only. Diogenes of Apollonia, Alexander Aphrodifeus, Democritus, and others, conceived the magnet to draw at the iron without the iron in any way contributing to that action. Saint Bafil fpecially affirms that the magnet is not drawn by iron. On the other hand, Albertus Magnus had conceived the idea that the iron fought the magnet by a one-fided effort in which the magnet took no part. Gilbert had the wit to difcern that the action was mutual, and to mark the new conception he adopted the new term, and defined it as it ftands in his gloffary. It is " a concourfe or concordancy of both," and to emphafize his meaning he adds, "not as if there were an ἑλκτικὴ δύναμις, but a συνδρομή "—not a tractile power, but a running together. The adjective ἑλκτικὴ is obvioufly related to the verb ἕλκω, I draw : but its meaning puzzled the fubfequent editors of the text, for in the two Stettin editions of 1628 and 1633, the phrafe appears in the refpective forms of ἑλητικὴ δύναμις and ἑλκυστικὴ δύναμις. In Creech's Englifh verfion of Lucretius (edition of 1722, p. 72*a*, in the footnote) is the commentary " Galen, dif-puting againft Epicurus, ufes the term ἑλκεῖν, which feems likewife too violent." It may be noted that the fame verb occurs in the paffage from the *Io* of Plato quoted below. The term συνδρομή applied by Gilbert to explain his term *Coitio* is ufed by Diodorus for the mutual onfet of two hoftile forces.

A picturefque fentence from Sir Thomas Browne's *Pfeudodoxia Epidem-ica* (London, 1650, p. 51) fets the matter fuccinctly forth. " If in two fkiffs of cork, a Loadftone and Steel be placed within the orb of their activities, the one doth not move the other ftanding ftill, but both hoift fayle and fteer unto each other ; fo that if the Loadftone attract, the Steel hath alfo its attraction ; for in this action the Alliency is reciprocall, which jointly felt, they mutually approach and run into each others arms."

The page and line references given in thefe notes are in all cafes firſt to the Latin edition of 1600, and fecondly to the Engliſh edition of 1900.

Page 1, line 28. Page 1, line 28. *Plato in Ione.*—The paſſage in the *Io* of Plato is in chap. v. Socrates addreſſing the poet Io tells him that his facility in reciting Homer is not really an art: θεία δὲ δύναμις, ἥ σε κινεῖ ὥσπερ ἐν τῇ λίθῳ, ἥν Εὐριπίδης μὲν Μαγνῆτιν ὠνόμασεν, οἱ δὲ πολλοὶ Ἡράκλειαν. καὶ γὰρ αὕτη ἡ λίθος οὐ μόνον αὐτοὺς τοὺς δακτυλίους ἄγει τοὺς σιδηροῦς, ἀλλὰ καὶ δύναμιν ἐντίθησι τοῖς δακτυλίοις, ὥστ᾽ αὖ δύνασθαι ταὐτὸν τοῦτο ποιεῖν, ὅπερ ἡ λίθος, ἄλλους ἄγειν δακτυλίους, ὥστ᾽ ἐνίοθ᾽ ὁρμαθὸς μακρὸς πάνυ σιδηρίων καὶ δακτυλίων ἐξ ἀλλήλων ἤρτηται· πᾶσι δὲ τούτοις ἐξ ἐκείνης τῆς λίθου ἡ δύναμις ἀνήρτηται. The idea is that as the loadſtone in attraċting an iron ring will make it into a magnet, which can in turn aċt magnetically on another ring, and this on yet another, ſo the inſpiration of the Muſe is transferred to the poet, who in turn hands on the inſpiration through the reciter to the liſtener. After further expanding the ſame idea of the transference of influence, Socrates again mentions the magnet (chap. vii.): Οἶσθ᾽ οὖν ὅτι οὗτός ἐστιν ὁ θεατὴς τῶν δακτυλίων ὁ ἔσχατος, ὧν ἐγὼ ἔλεγον ὑπὸ τῆς Ἡρακλειώτιδος λίθου ἀπ᾽ ἀλλήλων τ᾽ν δύναμιν λαμβάνειν, ὁ δὲ μέσος σὺ ὁ ῥαψῳδὸς καὶ ὑποκριτής, ὁ δὲ πρῶτος αὐτὸς ὁ ποιητής; ὁ δὲ θεὸς διὰ πάντων τούτων ἕλκει τὴν ψυχὴν ὅποι ἂν βούληται τῶν ἀνθρώπων, κ.τ.λ. (Edition Didot of 1856, vol. i., p. 391; or Stephanus, p. 533 D).

There is another reference in Plato to the magnet, namely, in the *Timæus* (p. 240, vol. ii., Edit. citat.). See the Note to p. **61.**

The reference by Euripides to the magnet occurs in the loſt play of Œneus, in a fragment preſerved by Suidas. See *Fragmenta Euripidis* (Ed. Didot, 1846, p. 757, or Nauck's edition, No. 567).

ὡς Εὐριπίδης ἐν Οἰνεῖ· τὰς βροτῶν γνώμας σκοπῶν, ὥστε Μαγνῆτις λίθος τὴν δόξαν ἕλκει καὶ μεθίστησιν πάλιν.

Page 1, line 28. Page 1, line 29. The brief paſſage from Ariſtotle's *De Anima* referring to Thales is quoted by Gilbert himſelf at the bottom of p. **11.**

Page 2, line 1. Page 1, line 29. The edition of 1628 inſerts commas between Theophraſtus and Leſbius, and between Julius and Solinus, as though theſe were four perſons inſtead of two.

Page 2, line 8. Page 2, line 5. *si allio magnes illitus fuerit, aut ſi adamas fuerit.* An excellent verſion of this myth is to be found in Julius Solinus, *Polyhiſtor, De Memorabilibus,* chap. lxiv., of which the Engliſh verſion of 1587, by A. Golding, runs thus: "The Diamonde will not ſuffer the Lodeſtone to drawe yron unto him: or if yᵉ Lodeſtone haue alreadie drawne a peece of yron to it, the Diamond ſnatcheth and pulleth away as hys bootye whatſoever the Lodeſtone hath taken hold of." Saint Auguſtine repeats the diamond myth in his *De Civitate Dei,* lib. xxi. Baptiſta Porta ſays (p. 211 of the Engliſh verſion of 1658): "It is a common Opinion amongſt Sea-men, That Onyons and Garlick are at odds with the Loadſtone: and Steers-men, and ſuch as tend the Mariners Card are forbid to eat Onyons or Garlick, left they make the Index of the Poles drunk. But when I tried all theſe things, I found them to be falſe: for not onely breathing and belching upon the Loadſtone after eating of Garlick, did not ſtop its vertues: but when it was all anoynted over with the juice of Garlick, it did perform its office as well as if it had never been touched with it: and I could obſerve almoſt not the leaſt difference, left I ſhould make void the endeavours of the Ancients.

And again, When I enquired of Marines, whether it were fo, that they were forbid to eat Onyons and Garlick for that reafon ; they faid, They were old Wives fables, and things ridiculous; and that Sea-men would fooner lofe their lives, then abftain from eating Onyons and Garlick."

The fables refpecting the antipathy of garlick and of the diamond to the operation of the magnet, although already difcredited by Ruellius and by Porta, died hard. In fpite of the expofure and denunciations of Gilbert—compare p. **32**—thefe tales were oft repeated during the fucceeding century. In the appendix to Sir Hugh Plat's *Jewel Houfe of Art and Nature*, in the edition of 1653, by D. B. Gent, it is ftated there (p. 218): "The Loadftone which . . . hath an admirable vertue not onely to draw Iron to it felf, but alfo to make any Iron upon which it is rubbed to draw iron alfo, it is written notwithftanding, that being rubbed with the juyce of Garlick, it lofeth that vertue, and cannot then draw iron, as likewife if a Diamond be layed clofe unto it."

Pliny wrote of the alleged antipathy between diamond and goat's blood. The paffage as quoted from the Englifh verfion of Pliny's *Natural Hiftorie of the World*, tranflated by Philemon Holland (London, 1601, p. 610, chap. iv.), runs: "But I would gladly know whofe invention this might be to foake the Diamond in Goats bloud, whofe head devifed it firft, or rather by what chance was it found out and knowne? What conjecture fhould lead a man to make an experiment of fuch a fingular and admirable fecret, efpecially in a goat, the filthieft beaft . . . in the whole world? Certes I muft afcribe both this invention and all fuch like to the might and beneficence together of the divine powers: neither are we to argue and reafon how and why Nature hath done this or that? Sufficient is it that her will was fo, and thus fhe would have it."

Page 2, line 22. Page 2, line 22. *Machometis facellum.* Gilbert credits Matthiolus (the well-known herbalift and commentator on Diofcorides) with producing the fable as to Mahomet's coffin being fufpended in the air by a magnet. Sir Richard Burton, in his famous pilgrimage to El Medïnah in 1855, effectually difpofed of this myth. The reputed farcophagus refts fimply on bricks on the floor. But it had long been known that aerial fufpenfion, even of the lighteft iron object, in the air, without contact above or below, was impoffible by any magnetic agency.

In Barlowe's *Magneticall Aduertifements* (London, 1616, p. 45) is the following : "As for the Turkes *Mahomet*, hanging in the ayer with his yron cheft it is a moft groffe vntruth, and vtterly impoffible it is for any thing to hange in the ayer by any *magneticall* power, but that either it muft touch the ftone it felfe, or elfe fome intermediate body, that hindreth it from comming to the ftone (like as before I haue fhewed) or elfe fome ftay below to keepe it from afcending, as fome fmall wier that may fcantly bee feene or perceiued."

Page 2, line 26. Page 2, line 26. *Arfinoes templum.*—The account in Pliny of the magnetic fufpenfion of the ftatue of Arfinoe in the temple built by Chinocrates is given as follows in the Englifh verfion (London, 1601) of Philemon Holland (p. 515): "And here I cannot chufe but acquaint you with the fingular invention of that great architect and mafter devifer, of Alexandria in Ægypt *Dinocrates*, who began to make the arched roufe of the temple of *Arfinoe* all of Magnet or this Loadftone, to the end, that within that temple the ftatue of the faid princeffe made of yron, might feeme to hang in the aire by nothing. But prevented he was by death before hee could finifh his worke, like as king *Ptolomæe* alfo, who ordained that temple to be built in the honour of the faid *Arfinoe* his fifter."

There are a number of fimilar myths in Aufonius, Claudian, and Caffiodorus, and in the writings of later ecclefiaftical hiftorians, fuch as Rufinus and Profper Aquitanus. The very meagre accounts they have left, and the fcattered references to the reputed magical powers of the loadftone, fuggeft that there exifted amongft the primitive religions of mankind a *magnet-worfhip*, of which thefe records are traces.

Page 2, line 37. Page 2, line 41. *Brafevolus* [or *Brafavola*].—The lift of authorities here cited confifts moftly of well-known mediæval writers on *materia medica* or on minerals: the laft on the lift, *Hannibal Rofetius Calaber*, has not been identified.

The following are the references in the order named by Gilbert:

Antonio Mufa Brafavola. *Examen omnium fimplicium medicamentorum*, Section 447 (Lugdun., 1537).

Joannes Baptifta Montanus. *Metaphrafis fummaria eorum quæ ad medicamentorum doctrinā attinet* (Auguftæ Rheticæ, 1551).

Amatus Lufitanus. *Amati Lufitani in Diofcoridis Anazarbei de materia medica libros quinque* (Venet., 1557, p. 507).

Oribafius. *Oribafii Sardiani ad Eunapium libri 4 quibus . . . facultates fimplicium . . . continentur* (Venet., 1558).

Aetius Amidenus. *Aetii Amideni Librorum medicinalium . . . libri octo nunc primum in lucem editi* (Greek text, Aldine edition, Venet., 1534). A Latin edition appeared in Bafel, 1535. See alfo his *tetrabiblos ex veteribus medicinæ* (Bafil., 1542).

Avicenna (Ibn Sinâ). *Canona Medicinæ* (Venice, 1486), liber ii., cap. 474.

Serapio Mauritanus (Yuhanná Ibn Sarapion). *In hoc volumine continentur . . . Ioan. Sarapionis Arabis de Simplicibus Medicinis opus præclarum et ingens . . .* (edited by Brunfels, Argentorati, 1531, p. 260).

Hali Abbas ('Alí Ibn Al 'Abbās). *Liber totius medicinæ neceffaria cōtinens . . . quem Haly filius Abbas edidit . . . et a Stephano ex arabica lingua reductus* (Lugd., 1523, p. 176 *verfo*).

Santes de Ardoniis (or Ardoynis). *Incipit liber de venenis quem magifter fantes de ardoynis . . . edere cepit venetiis die octauo nouēbris*, 1424 (Venet., 1492).

Petrus Apponenfis (or Petrus de Abano). The loadftone is referred to in two works by this author.

(1) *Conciliator differentiarum philofophorum: et precipue medicorum clariffimi viri Petri de Abano Patauini feliciter incipit* (Venet., 1496, p. 72, *verfo*, Quæftio LI.).

(2) *Tractatus de Venenis* (Roma, 1490, cap. xi.).

Marcellus (called Marcellus Empiricus). *De Medicamentis*, in the volume *Medici antiqui omnes* (Venet., 1547, p. 89).

Arnaldus (Arnaldus de Villa Nova). *Incipit Tractatus de virtutibus herbarum* (Venet., 1499). See alfo *Arnaldi Villanovani Opera omnia* (Bafil., 1585).

Marbodeus Gallus. *Marbodei Galli poetae vetuftiffimi de lapidibus pretiofis Enchiridion* (Friburgi, 1530 [1531], p. 41).

Albertus Magnus. *De Mineralibus et rebus metallicis* (Venet., 1542, lib. ii., *de lapidibus preciofis*, p. 192). There is a reference to the loadftone alſo in a work attributed falſely to Albertus, but now aſcribed to Henricus de Saxonia, *De virtutibus herbarum, de virtutibus lapidum*, etc. (Rouen, 1500, and ſubſequent editions). An Engliſh verſion, *The Secrets of Albertus Magnus of the vertues of hearbs ſtones and certaine beaſts* was publiſht in London in 1617.

Matthæus Silvaticus. *Pandeĉtæ Medicinæ* (Lugduni, 1541, cap. 446).

Hermolaus Barbarus. His work, *Hermolai Barbari Patritii Veneti et Aqvileienſis patriarchæ Corollarii Libri quinque* . . . Venet., 1516, is an early herbal. On p. 103 are to be found deſcriptions of *lapis gagatis* and *lapis magnes*. The latter is moſtly taken from Pliny, and mentions the alleged theamedes, and the myth of the floating ſtatue.

Camillus Leonardus. *Speculum Lapidum* (Venet., 1502, fol. xxxviii.). An Engliſh tranſlation, *The Mirror of Stones*, appeared in London in 1750.

Cornelius Agrippa. *Henrici Cor. Agrippæ ab Netteſheym* . . . *De Occulta Philoſophia Libri Tres* (Antv., 1531). The Engliſh verſion *Of the Vanitie and uncertaintie of Artes* was publiſht in London, 1569, and again later.

Fallopius (Gabriellus). *G. F. de ſimplicibus medicamentis purgantibus traĉtatus* (Venet., 1566). See alſo his *Traĉtatus de compoſitione medicamentorum* (Venet., 1570).

Johannes Langius. *Epiſtolarum medicinalium volumen tripartitum* (Paris, 1589, p. 792).

Cardinalis Cuſanus (Nicolas Khrypffs, Cardinal de Cuſa). *Nicolai Cuſani de ſtaticis experimentis dialogus* (Argentorati, 1550). The Engliſh edition, entitled *The Idiot in four books*, is dated London, 1650.

Page 3, line 1. Page 2, line 42. *Marcellus.*—"Marcellus Empiricus, médecin de Théodoſe-le-Grand, dit que l'aimant, appelé *antiphyſon*, attire et repouſſe le fer." (Klaproth, *Sur l'invention de la bouſſole*, 1834, p. 12.) The paſſage from Marcellus runs: "Magnetes lapis, qui antiphyſon dicitur, qui ferrum trahit et abjicit, et magnetes lapis qui ſanguinem emittit et ferrum ad ſe trahit, collo alligati aut circa caput dolori capitis medentur." (Marcellus, *de Medicamentis*: in the volume *Medici antiqui omnes, qui latinis literis morborum genera perſecuti ſunt.* Venet., 1547, p. 89.)

Page 3, line 11. Page 3, line 9. *Thomas Eraſtus.*—The work in queſtion is *Diſpvtationvm de Medicina nova Philippi Paracelſi, Pars Prima: in qua quæ de remediis ſvperſtitioſis & Magicis curationibus ille prodidit, præcipuè examinantur à Thoma Eraſto in Schola Heydebergenſi, profeſſore.* (Baſiliæ, 1572. Parts 2 and 3 appeared the ſame year, and Part 4 in 1573.)

Gilbert had no more love for Paracelſus than for Albertus Magnus or others of the magic-mongers. Indeed the few paſſages in Paracelſus on the magnet are ſorry ſtuff. They will moſtly be found in the ſeventh volume of his collecĉted works (*Opera omnia*, Frankfurt, 1603). A ſample may be taken from the Engliſh work publiſht in London, 1650, with the title : *Of the Nature of Things, Nine Books ; written by Philipp Theophraſtus of Hohenheim, called Paracelſvs.*

" For any Loadſtone that Mercury hath but touched, or which hath been ſmeered with Mercuriall oyle, or only put into Mercury will never draw Iron more " (p. 23).

" The life of the Loadſtone is the ſpirit of Iron; which may bee extracĉted, and taken away with ſpirit of Wine" (p. 32).

Page 3, line 13. Page 3, line 11. *Encelius* (or *Entzelt*, Chriſtoph) wrote a work publisht in 1551 at Frankfurt, with the title *De re metallica, hoc est, de origine, varietate, et natura corporum metallicorum, lapidum, gemmarum, atque aliarum quæ ex fodinis eruuntur, rerum, ad medicinæ usum deservientium, libri iii.* This is written in a singular medley of Latin and German. Gilbert undoubtedly took from it many of his ideas about the properties of metals. See the note to p. **27** on *plumbum album*.

Page 3, line 20. Page 3, line 21. *Thomas Aquinas.*—The reference is to his commentaries upon the *Physica* of Aristotle. The passage will be found on p. 96 *bis* of the Giunta edition (Venet., 1539). The essential part is quoted by Gilbert himself on p. **64**.

Page 3, line 39. Page 3, line 45. *pyxidem.*—The word *pyxis*, which occurs here, and in the next sentence as *pyxidem nauticam*, is translated *compass*. Eleven lines lower occurs the term *nautica pyxidula*. This latter word, literally the "little compass," certainly refers to the portable compass used at sea. Compare several passages in Book IV. where a contrasting use is made of these terms; for example, on pp. **177** and **202**. Calcagninus, *De re nautica*, uses the term *pyxidecula* for an instrument which he describes as "vitro intecta." On p. **152**, line **9**, Gilbert uses the non-classical noun *compassus*, "boreale lilium compassi (quod Boream respicit)," and again on p. **178**, line **3**.

Page 4, line 2. Page 4, line 2. *Melphitani.*—The inhabitants of Amalfi in the kingdom of Naples. The claim of the discovery or invention of the mariners' compass in the year 1302 by one Joannes Goia, or Gioia, also named as Flavio Goia, has been much disputed. In Guthrie's *New System of Modern Geography* (London, 1792, p. 1036), in the Chronology, is set down for the year 1302:

"The mariner's compass invented, or improved by Givia, of Naples. The flower de luce, the arms of the Duke of Anjou, then King of Naples, was placed by him at the point of the needle, in compliment to that prince."

In 1808 an elaborate treatise was printed at Naples, by Flaminius Venanson with the title, *De l'invention de la Boussole Nautique.* Venanson, who cites many authorities, endeavours to prove that if Gioia did not discover magnetic polarity he at least invented the compass, that is to say, he pivotted the magnetic needle and placed it in a box, with a card affixed above it divided into sixteen parts bearing the names of the sixteen principal winds. He alleges in proof that the compass-card is emblazoned in the armorial bearings of the city of Amalfi. This view was combatted in the famous letter of Klaproth to Humboldt publisht in Paris in 1834. He shows that the use of the magnetized needle was known in Europe toward the end of the twelfth century; that the Chinese knew of it and used it for finding the way on land still earlier; that there is no compass-card in the arms of the city of Amalfi; but he concedes that Gioia may have improved the compass in 1302 by adding the wind-rose card. The most recent contributions to the question are a pamphlet by Signorelli, *Sull' invenzione della Bussola nautica, ragionamento di Pietro Napoli Signorelli, segretario perpetuo della Società Pontaniana; letto nella seduta del 30 settembre* 1860; Matteo Camera's *Memorie Storico-diplomatiche dell' antica città e ducato di Amalfi* (Salerno, 1876); and Admiral Luigi Fincati's work *Il Magnete, la Calamita, e la Bussola* (Roma, 1878). An older mention of Gioia is to be found in Blundevile's *Exercises* (3rd edition, 1606, pp. 257-258). See also Crescentio *della Nautica Mediterranea*, (Roma, 1607, p. 253), and Azuni, *Dissertazione sull' origine della bussola nautica* (Venezia, 1797).

There appears to be a flip in Gilbert's reference to Andrea Doria, as he has confounded the town of Amalfi in Principato Citra with Melfi in Bafilicata.

One of the fources relied upon by hiftorians for afcribing this origin of the compafs is the *Compendio dell' Iftoria del Regno di Napoli*, of Collenuccio (Venet., MDXCI.), p. 5.

" Nè in quefto tacerò Amalfi, picciola terra, & capo della cofta di Picentia, alla quale tutti quelli, che'l mar caualcano, vfficiofamente eterno gratie debono referire, effendo prima in quella terra trovato l'vfo, & l'artificio della calamita, & del buffolo, col quale i nauiganti, la ftella Tramontana infallibilmente mirando, direzzano il lor corfo, fi come è publica fama, & gli Amalfitani fi gloriano, nè fenza ragione dalli piu fi crede, effendo cofa certa, che gli antichi tale inftromento non hebbero; nè effendo mai in tutto falfo quello, che in molto tempo è da molti fi diuolga."

Another account is to be found in the *Hiftoriarum fui temporis*, etc., of Paulus Jovius (Florent., 1552), tom. ii., cap. 25, p. 42.

" Quum effem apud Philippum fuperuenit Ioachinus Leuantius Ligur a Lotrechio miffus, qui depofceret captiuos; fed ille negauit fe daturum, quando eos ad ipfum Andream Auriam ammirantem deducendos effe iudicaret. Vgonis uerò cadauer, ut illudentium Barbarorum contumeliis eriperetur, ad Amalphim urbem delatum eft, in ædeque Andreæ apoftoli, tumultuariis exequiis tumulatum. In hac urbe citriorum & medicorum odoratis nemoribus æquè peramœna & celebri, Magnetis ufum nauigantibus hodie familiarem & neceffarium, adinuentum fuiffe incolæ afferunt."

Flavius Blondus, whom Gilbert cites, gives the following reference, in which Gioia's name is not mentioned, in the fection upon Campania Felix of his Italy (*Blondi Flavii Forlinenfis . . . Italia Illuftrata*, Bafiliæ, 1531, p. 420).

" Sed fama eft qua Amalphitanos audiuimus gloriari, magnetis ufum, cuius adminiculo nauigantes ad arcton diriguntur, Amalphi fuiffe inuentum, quicquid uero habeat in ea re ueritas, certũ eft id noctu nauigandi auxilium prifcis omnino fuiffe incognitum."

There is a further reference to the alleged Amalphian in Caelius Calcagninus *De re nautica commentatio*. (*See Thefaurus Græcarum Antiquitatum*, 1697, vol. xi., p. 761.) On the other hand Baptifta Porta, who wrote in Naples in 1558 (*Magia Naturalis*) diftinctly fets afide the claim as bafelefs.

William Barlowe, in *The Navigators Supply* (1597, p. A3), fays: " Who was the firft inuentor of this Inftrument miraculous, and endued, as it were, with life, can hardly be found. The lame tale of one *Flauius* at *Amelphis*, in the kingdome of *Naples*, for to haue deuifed it, is of very flender prob-abilitie. *Pandulph Collenutius* writing the Neapolitane hiftorie telleth vs, that they of *Amelphis* fay, it is a common opinion there, that it was firft found out among them. But *Polidore Virgil*, who fearched moft diligently for the Inuentors of things, could neuer heare of this opinion (yet himfelfe being an Italian) and as he confeffeth in the later ende of his third booke *de inventoribus rerum*, could neuer vnderftand anything concerning the firft inuention of this inftrument."

According to Park Benjamin (*Intellectual Rife in Electricity*, p. 146) the ufe of the pivotted compafs arofe and fpread not from Amalfi at the hands of Italians in the fourteenth century, but from Wifbuy, at the hands of the Finns, in the middle of the twelfth century.

Hakewill (*An Apologie or Declaration of the Power and Providence of God*, London, 1673, pp. 284-285) fays:

"But *Blondus*, who is therein followed by *Pancirollus*, both *Italians*, will not haue *Italy* loofe the praife thereof, telling vs that about 300 yeares agoe it was found out at Malphis or Melphis, a Citty in the Kingdome of *Naples* in the *Province* of *Campania*, now called *Terra di Lovorador*.   But for the Author of it, the one names him not, and the other affures vs, he is not knowne: yet *Salmuth* out of *Ciezus* & *Gomara* confidently chriftens him with the name of *Flavius*, and fo doth *Du Bartas* in thofe excellent verfes of his touching this fubject.

> "'W' are not to *Ceres* fo much bound for bread,
> Neither to *Bacchus* for his clufters red,
> As Signior *Flavio* to thy witty tryall,
> For firft inventing of the Sea-mans dyall,
> Th' vfe of the needle turning in the fame,
> Divine device, O admirable frame!'

"It may well be then that *Flavius* the *Melvitan* was the firft inventor of guiding the fhip by the turning of the needle to the *North:* but fome *German* afterwards added to the *Compaffe* the 32 points of the winde in his owne language, whence other Nations haue fince borrowed it."

Page 4, line 14.   Page 4, line 14.   *Paulum Venetum.*—The reference is to Marco Polo. He returned in 1295 from his famous voyage to Cathay. But the oft-repeated tale that he firft introduced the knowledge of the compafs into Europe on his return is difpofed of by feveral well-eftablifhed facts.   Klaproth (*op. citat.*, p. 57) adduces a mention of its ufe in 1240 in the Eaftern Mediterranean, recorded in a work written in 1242 by Bailak of Kibdjak.   And the paffages in the Iceland Chronicle, and in Alexander of Neckham are ftill earlier.

Page 4, line 17.   Page. 4, line 17.   *Goropius.*   See *Hifpanica Ioannis Goropii Becani* (Plantin edition, Antv., 1580), p. 29.   This is a difcuffion of the etymologies of the names of the points of the compafs : but is quite unauthoritative.

Page 4, line 23.   Page 4, line 26.   *Paruaim.*—Refpecting this reference, Sir Philip Magnus has kindly furnifht the following note. A clue to the meaning of *Parvaim*, which fhould be written in Englifh letters with a *v*, not a *u*, will be found in 2 *Chronicles*, iii. 6.   In the verfe quoted the author fpeaks of gold as the gold of Parvaim, וְהַזָּהָב זְהַב פַּרְוָיִם, and פרוים Parvaim is taken as a gold-producing region.   It is regarded by fome as the fame as Ophir.   The word is fuppofed to be cognate with a Sanfkrit word *pûrva* fignifying "prior, anterior, oriental."   There is nothing in the root indicating gold.   A form fimilar to Parvaim, and alfo a proper name, is Sepharvaim, found in 2 *Kings*, xix. 13, and in *Ifaiah*, xxxvii. 13, and fuppofed to be the name of a city in Affyria.

Page 4, line 35.   Page 4, line 41.   Cabot's obfervation of the variation of the compafs is narrated in the *Geografia* of Livio Sanuto (Vinegia, 1588, lib. i., fol. 2).   See alfo Fournier's *Hydrographie*, lib. xi., cap. 10.

Page 4, line 36.   Page 4, line 42.   *Gonzalus Oviedus.*—The reference is to Gonzalo Fernandez de Oviedo y Valdès.   *Summario de la Hiftoria general y natural de las Indias occidentales*, 1525, p. 48, where the author fpeaks of the croffing of "la linea del Diametro, donde las Agujas hacen la

diferencia del Nordeftear, ò Noroeftear, que es el parage de las Iflas de los
Açores."

Page 5, line 8. Page 5, line 11. *Petri cujufdam Peregrini.*—This
opufculum is the famous letter of Peter Peregrinus written in 1269, of which
fome twenty manufcript copies exift in various libraries in Oxford, Rome,
Paris, etc., and of which the oldeft printed edition is that of 1558 (Augfburg).
See alfo Libri, *Hiftoire des Sciences Mathématiques* (1838); Bertelli in
Boncompagni's *Bull. d. Bibliogr.* T. I. and T. IV. (1868 and 1871), and
Hellmann's *Rara Magnetica* (1898). A fummary of the contents of
Peregrinus's book will be found in Park Benjamin's *Intellectual Rife in
Electricity* (1895), pp. 164-185.

Page 5, line 12. Page 5, line 15. *Johannes Taifner Hannonius.*—
Taifnier, or Tayfnier, of Hainault, was a plagiarift who took moft of the
treatife of Peregrinus and publifht it in his *Opufculum . . . de Natura
Magnetis* (Coloniæ, 1562), of which an Englifh tranflation by Richard
Eden was printed by R. Jugge in 1579.

Page 5, line 18. Page 5, line 23. *Collegium Conimbricenfe.*—This is
a reference to the commentaries on Ariftotle by the Jefuits of Coimbra.
The work is *Colegio de Coimbra da Companhia de Jefu, Curfus Conimbricenfis
in Octo libros Phyficorum* (Coloniæ, fumptibus Lazari Ratzneri, 1599).
Other editions: Lugd. 1594; and Colon., 1596. The later edition of 1609,
in the Britifh Mufeum, has the title *Commentariorum Collegii Conimbricenfis in
octo libros phyficorum.*

Page 5, line 25. Page 5, line 31. *Martinus Cortefius.*—His *Arte de
Navegar* (Sevilla, 1556) went through various editions in Spanifh, Italian,
and Englifh. Eden's tranflation was publifht 1561, and again in 1609.

Page 5, line 26. Page 5, line 33. *Beffardus.*—Touffainéte de Beffard
wrote a treatife, *Dialogue de la Longitude* (Rouen, 1574), which gives fome
ufeful notes of nautical practice, and of the French conftruction of the
compafs. Speaking of the needle he fays: "Elle ne tire pas au pole du
monde: ains regarde, au Pole du Zodiaque, comme il fera difcourfu, cy
apres" (p. 34). On p. 50 he fpeaks of "l'aiguille Aymantine." On p. 108
he refers to Mercator's *Carte Générale*, and denies the exiftence of the alleged
loadftone rock. On p. 15 he gives the moft naïve etymologies for the terms
ufed: thus he affigns as the derivation of *Sud* the Latin *fudor*, becaufe the
fouth is hot, and as that of *Oueft* that it comes from *Ou* and *Eft*. "Coñe,
qui diroit, Ou eft-il? à fcauoir le Soleil, qui eftoit nagueres fur la terre."

Page 5, line 28. Page 5, line 35. *Jacobus Severtius.*—Jacques Severt,
whofe work, *De Orbis Catoptrici feu mapparvm mvndi principiis defcriptione
ac ufu libri tres* (Paris, 1598), would have probably lapfed into obfcurity,
but being juft newly publifht was mentioned by Gilbert for its follies.

Page 5, line 30. Page 5, line 38. *Robertus Norman.*—Author of the
rare volume *The Newe Attractiue*, publifht in London, 1581, and feveral
times reprinted. This work contains an account of Norman's difcovery of
the Dip of the magnetic needle, and of his inveftigation of it by means of
the Dipping-needle, which he invented. He was a compaffmaker of the
port of London, and lived at Limehoufe.

Page 5, line 32. Page 5, line 40. *Francifcus Maurolycus.*—The work
to which the myth of the magnetic mountains is thus credited is, *D. Francifci
Abbatis Meffanenfis Opufcula Mathematica*, etc. (Venet., MDLXXV, p. 122a).
"Sed cur fagitta, vel obelus à vero Septentrione, quandoque ad dextram,

quandoque ad finiftram declinat? An quia fagitta, ficut magnes (cuius eft fimia) non verum Septentrionem, fed infulam quandam (quam Olaus Magnus Gothus in fua geographia vocat infulam magnetum) femper ex natura infpicere cogitur?"

Page 5, line 35. Page 5, line 43. *Olaus Magnus.*—The famous Archbifhop of Upfala, who wrote the hiftory of the northern nations (*Hiftoria de Gentibus Septentrionalibus*), of which the beft edition, illuftrated with many woodcuts, appeared in Rome in 1555. An Englifh edition entitled *A Compendious Hiftory of the Goths, Swedes, and Vandals, and Other Northern Nations* was printed in London in 1658; but it is much abbreviated and has none of the quaint woodcuts. The reference on p. **5** appears to be to the following paffage on p. 409 (ed. 1555). "Demum in fuppolaribus infulis magnetum montes reperiuntur, quorum fragmentis ligna fagina certo tempore applicata, in faxeam duritiem, et vim attractivam convertuntur," or the following on p. 89 : "Magnetes enim in extremo Septentrionis veluti montes, unde nautica directio conftat, reperiuntur : quorum etiam magnetum tam vehemens eft operatio, ut certis lignis fagineis conjuncti, ea vertunt in fui duritiem, & naturam attractivam." On p. 343 is a woodcut depicting the penalties inflicted by the naval laws upon any one who fhould malicioufly tamper with the compafs or the loadftone, "qui malitiofe nauticum gnomonem, aut compaffum, & præcipuè portionem magnetis, unde omnium directio dependet, falfaverit." He was to be pinned to the maft by a dagger thruft through his hand. It will be noted that the fhips carried both a compafs, and a piece of loadftone wherewith to ftroke the needle.

There is in the Bafel edition of this work, 1567, a note *ad lectorem*, on the margin of Carta 16a, as follows:

"Infula 30 milliarium in longitud. & latitud. Polo arctico fubjecta.

"Vltra quam directorium nauticum boffolo dicũ uires amittit: propterea quòd illa infula plena eft magnetum."

This myth of the magnetic mountains, probably originating with Nicander, appears, poffibly from an independent fource, in the Eaft, in China, and in the tales of the Arabian Nights.

Ptolemy gives the following account in his *Geographia* (lib. vii., cap. 2):

Φέρονται δὲ καὶ ἄλλαι συνεχεῖς δέκα νῆσοι καλούμεναι Μανίολαι ἐν αἷς φάσι τὰ σιδήρους ἔχοντα ἥλους πλοῖα κατέχεσθαι, μήποτε τῆς Ἡρακλείας λίθου περὶ αὐτὰς γενομένης, καὶ διὰ τοῦτο ἐπιούροις ναυπηγεῖσθαι. Some editions omit the name of the Manioles from the paffage.

No two authorities agree as to the place of thefe alleged magnetic mountains. Some place them in the Red Sea. Fracaftorio, *De Sympathia et Antipathia*, cap. 7 (*Opera omnia*, Giunta edition, 1574, p. 63), gives the following reafon for the variation of the compafs:

"Nos igitur diligentius rem confiderãtes dicimus caufam, q̃ perpendiculum illud ad polum vertatur, effe montes ferri, & magnetis, qui fub polo funt, vt negociatores affirmant, quorum fpecies per incredibilem diftantiam vfque ad maria noftra propagata ad perpendiculum vfq;, vbi eft magnes, confuetam attractionem facit : propter diftantiam autem quum debilis fit, non moueret quidem magnetem, nifi effet in perpendiculo : quare & fi non trahit vfq; ac principium, vnde effluxit, at mouet tamẽ, & propinquiorem facit, quo poteft. Quod fi naues forte vllæ propinquiores fint illis montibus, ferrum omne earũ euellitur, propter quod nauigijs incolæ vtuntur clauis ligneis aftrictis."

In the laft chapter of his *De Sympathia*, Fracaftorio returns to the fubject in confequence of fome doubts expreffed by Giambattifta Rhamnufio, feeing that the loadftones in the Ifland of Elba do not fenfibly deflect the magnet. Fracaftorio replies thus (p. 76, *op. citat.*):

"Primum igitur vtrum fub Polo fint. Magnetis mõtes, nec ne, fub ambiguo relinquamus, fcimus enim effe, qui fcribãt planas magis effe eas regiones, de quo Paulus Iouius Epus Nucerinus Luculẽtus hiftoriarũ noftri tẽporis fcriptor, circa eã Sarmatiæ partem, quæ Mofcouia nũc dicitur, diligentẽ inquifitionem ab incolis fecit, qui ne eos etiã inueniri montes retulere, qui Rhyphei ab antiquis dicti funt: meminimus tamẽ nos quafdam chartas vidiffe earum, quas mundi mappas appellãt, in quibus fub polo montes notati erant (qui Magnetis montes infcripti fuerant). Siue igitur fint, fiue non fint ij montes, nihil ad nos in præfentiarum attinet, quando per montes polo fubiectos cathenam illam montium intelligimus, qui ad feptentrionem fpectant tanti, & tam vafti, ac Ferri & Magnetis feraces: qui, & fi magis diftant à noftro mari, q̃ Iluæ infulæ montes, potentiores tamen funt ad mouendum perpendiculum propter abundantiam & copiã Ferri, & Magnetis. Fortaffe autem, & qui in Ilua eft Magnes, non multæ actionis eft in ea minera: multi enim dũ in minera funt, minus valent, q̃ extracti, q̃ fpirituales fpecies fua habeant impedimenta: fignum autem parum valere in fua minera Iluæ infulæ Magnetem, q̃ tam propinquus quum fit nauigijs illac prætereuntibus, perpendiculum tamen non ad fe cõuertit."

Aldrovandi in the *Mufæum Metallicum* (Bonon., 1648, p. 554) gives another verfion of the fable:

"Nonnulli, animadverfa hac Magnetis natura, fcripferunt naves, quibus in Calecutanam regionem navigatur, clavis ferreis non figi, ob magneticorum frequentiam fcopulorum, quoniam facilè diffoluerentur. Sed Garzias in Hiftoria Aromatum id fabulofum effe tradidit: quandoquidem plures naues Calecutanæ regionis, & illius tractus, ferreis clauis iunctas obferuauit: immò addidit naues in infulis Maldiuis ligneis quidem clauis copulari, non quia à Magnete fibi metuant, fed quoniam ferri inopia laborant."

According to Aldrovandi (p. 563, *op. citat.*) the magnetic mountains are ftated by Sir John Mandeville to be in the region of Pontus.

Lipenius in his *Navigatio Salomonis Ophritica illuftrata* (Witteb., 1660), which is a mine of curious learning, in difcuffing the magnetic mountains quotes the reply of Socrates to the inquirer who afked him as to what went on in the infernal regions, faying that he had never been there nor had he ever met any one who had returned thence.

The loadftone rock figures in feveral early charts. In Nordenfkiöld's *Facfimile Atlas* (Stockholm, 1889) is given a copy of the Map of Johan Ruyfch from an edition of Ptolemy, publifht in Rome in 1508, which fhows four iflands within the ice-bound Arctic regions. South of thefe iflands and at the eaft of the coaft of Greenland is the infcription: *Hic compaffus navium non tenet, nec naves quæ ferrum tenent revertere valent.* To which (on p. 63) Nordenfkiöld adds the comment: *Sagan om magnetberg, fom fkulle draga till fig fartyg förande jern, är gamal.* And he recalls the reference of Ptolemy to the magnetic rocks in the Manioles. A fecond infcription is added to Ruyfch's map in the ornamental margin that borders the Arctic iflands. *Legere eft in libro de inventione fortunati fub polo arctico rupem effe excelfam ex lapide magnete 33 miliarium germanorum ambitu.* This refers to a matter recorded in Hakluyt's *Principall Navigations* (Lond., 1589, p. 249), namely: "A Teftimonie of the learned Mathematician, maifter John Dee, touching the forefaid voyage of Nicholas de Linna. Anno 1360 a frier of Oxford, being a good Aftronomer, went in companie with others to the moft Northren iflands of the world, and there leaving his company together, he travelled alone, and purpofely defcribed all the Northern iflands, with the indrawing feas: and the record thereof at his return he delivered to the king of England. The name of which booke is *Inventio Fortunata (aliter fortunæ) qui liber incipit a gradu 54 ufq. ad polum.*"

The fituation of the alleged loadftone rock is thus defcribed by T. Blundevile in his *Exercifes* in the chapter entitled *A plaine and full defcription of Peter Plancius his vniuerfall Map, feruing both for fea and land, and by him lately put foorth in the yeare of our Lord*, 1592. . . . Written in our mother tongue by M. Blundeuill, Anno Domini 1594. The paffage is quoted from p. 253 of the third edition (1606):

"Now betwixt the 72. and 86. degrees of North latitude he fetteth downe two long Ilands extending from the Weft towardes the Eaft fomewhat beyond the firft Meridian, and from the faide Meridian more Eaftward he fetteth downe other two long Ilandes . . . and hee faith further that right under the North pole there is a certaine blacke and moft high rocke which hath in circuite thirtie and three leagues, which is nintie and nine miles, and that the long Iland next to the Pole on the Weft is the beft and moft healthfull of all the North parts. Next to the forefaide Ilandes more Southward hee fetteth downe the Ilandes of Crocklande and Groynelande, making them to haue a farre longer and more flender fhape then all other mappes doe. . . . Moreouer at the Eaft end of the laft Ilande fomewhat to the Southwarde, he placeth the Pole of the Lodeftone which is called in Latine Magnes, euen as Mercator doth in his Mappe who fuppofing the firft Meridian to paffe through Saint Marie or Saint Michael, which are two of the outermoft Ilandes of the Azores Eaftwarde, placeth the Pole of the ftone in the feuentie fiue degree of Latitude, but fuppofing the firft Meridian to paffe through the Ile Coruo, which is the furtheft Ile of the Azores Weftwarde, he placeth the Pole of the Lodeftone in the feuentie feuen degree of Latitude."

Further, in the chapter on *The Arte of Nauigation* in the fame work. (p. 332, *ed. citat.*), Blundevile fays:

"But whereas Mercator affirmeth that there fhould bee a mine or great rocke of Adamant, wherunto all other leffer rockes or Needles touched with the Lodeftone doe incline as to their chiefe fountaine, that opinion feemeth to mee verie ftraunge, for truely I rather beleeue with Robert Norman that the properties of the Stone, as well in drawing fteele, as in fhewing the North Pole, are fecret vertues given of GOD to that ftone for mans neceffarie vfe and behoofe, of which fecrete vertues no man is able to fhewe the true caufe."

The following is one of the infcriptions in the compartments of the great Chart of Mercator entitled *Ad Ufum Navigantium*, publifhed in 1569:

"Teftatur Francifcus Diepanus peritiffimus nauarchus volubiles libellas, magnetis virtute infectas recta mundi polum refpicere in infulis C. Viridis, Solis, Bonauifta, et Maio, cui proxime aftipulantur qui in Tercera, aut S. Maria (infulæ funt inter Açores) id fieri dicunt, pauci in earundem occidentaliffima Corvi nomine id contingere opinantur. Quia vero locorum longitudinis a communi magnetis et mundi meridiano iuftis de caufis initium fumere oportet, plurium teftimonium fequuutus primum meridianum per dictas C. Viridis infulas protraxi, et quum alibi plus minufque a polo deuiante magnete polum aliquum peculiarem effe oporteat quo magnetes ex omni mundi parte defpiciant, euum hoc quo affignaui loco exiftere adhibita declinatione magnetis Ratifbonæ obferuata didici. Supputaui autem eius poli fitum etiam refpectu infulæ Corui, ut iuxta extremo primi meridiani pofitus extremi etiam termini, intra quos polum hunc inueniri neceffe eft, confpicui fierent, donec certius aliquod nauclerorum obferuatio attulerit."

Not all the map-makers were as frank as Paulus Merula, the author of a *Cofmographia Generalis*, printed by Plantin in 1605, at Leyden. For in the defcription of his *tabula univerfalis* (*op. citat.* lib. iii., cap. 9) he fays that he does not believe in the magnetic iflands; but that he has put them into his chart left unfkilful folk fhould think that he had been fo carelefs as to leave them out!

In the well-known myth of Ogier the Dane, immortalized by William Morris in the *Earthly Paradife* (London, 1869, vol. i., p. 625), the loadftone rock is an ifland in the far North. But this ftory is not one of the Scandinavian fagas, and belongs to the Carlovingian cycle of heroic poems, of which the chief is the *Chanfon de Roland*; and Ogier le Danois is really not a Dane but an *Ardennois*.

In the Middle-High German epic of Kudrun, the adventures of the fleet of Queen Hilda when attracted by the loadftone mountain at Givers, in the North Sea, are narrated at fome length. (See *Kudrun, heraufgegeben und erklärt von Ernst Martin.* Halle, 1872.) One ftanza will ferve as a fample:

> 1126. Ze Givers vor dem berge | lac daz Hilden her.
> fwie guot ir anker wæren, | an daz vinfter mer.
> magnêten die fteine | heten fi gezogen.
> ir guote fegelboume | ftuonden alle gebogen.

which may be rendered :

> 1126. At Givers before the mountain | lay Hilda's fhips by.
> Though good their anchors were, | upon the murky fea.
> Magnets the ftones were | had drawn them thither.
> Their good failing mafts | ftood all bent together.

Recent magnetic refearch has fhown that while there are no magnetic mountains that would account for the declination of the compafs in general, yet there are minor local variations that can only be accounted for by the prefence of magnetic reefs or rocks. The reader is referred to the account of the magnetic furvey of Great Britain in the *Philofophical Tranfactions* (1890) by Profeffors Rücker and Thorpe. The well-known rocky peak the Riffelhorn above Zermatt, in Switzerland, produces diftinct perturbations in the direction of the compafs within half a mile of its bafe. Such local perturbations are regularly ufed in Sweden for tracing out the pofition of underground lodes of iron ore. See Thalén, *Sur la Recherche des Mines de Fer à l'aide de Mefures magnétiques* (Soc. Royale des Sciences d'Upfal, 1877); or B. R. Brough, *The Ufe of the Magnetic Needle in exploring for Iron Ore* (*Scientific American*, Suppl. No. 608, p. 9708, Aug. 27, 1887).

Quite recently Dr. Henry Wilde, F.R.S., has endeavoured to elucidate the deviations of the compafs as the refult of the configurations of land and fea on the globe, by means of a model globe in which the ocean areas are covered with thin fheet iron. This apparatus Dr. Wilde calls a *Magnetarium*. See *Proc. Roy. Soc.*, June, 1890, Jan., 1891, and June, 1891.

An actual magnetic rock exifts in Scandinavia, the following account of it being given in the *Electrical Review* of New York, May 3, 1899 :

"The ifland of Bornholm in the Baltic, which confifts of a mafs of magnetic iron ore, is much feared by mariners. On being fighted they difcontinue fteering by compafs, and go inftead by lighthoufes. Between Bornholm and the mainland there is alfo a dangerous bank of rock under water. It is faid that the magnetic influence of this ore bank is fo powerful that a balanced magnetic needle fufpended freely in a boat over the bank will take a vertical pofition."

Page 5, line 35. Page 5, line 43. *Jofephus Cofta.*—This is unqueftionably a mifprint for *Acofta* (Jofeph de), the Jefuit, whofe work *Hiftoria natural y moral de las Indias* was publifht at Seville in 1590. An Italian edition appeared at Venice in 1596. The Englifh edition, tranflated by E. Grimeftone, *The Naturall and Morall Hiftorie of the Eaft and Weft Indies*, was publifht in London in 1604 and 1878. There are in Gilbert's book references to two writers of the name of Cofta or Coftæus, Joannes Cofta of Lodi, who edited Galen and Avicenna (fee pp. **3** and **62**), and Filippo Cofta of Mantua, who wrote on antidotes and medicaments (fee p. **141**). The paffage to which Gilbert refers is in Acofta's *Hiftoria* (ed. 1590, p. 64).

"Deziame a mi vn piloto muy dieftro Portugues q̃ eran quatro puntos en todo el orbe, donde fe afixaua el aguja con el Norte, y contaualas por fus nombres, de que no me acuerdo bien. Vno deftos es el paraje de la Ifla del Cueruo, en las Terceras, o Iflas de Açores, como es cofa y a muy fabida. Paffando di alli a mas altura, Norueftea, que es dezir, q̃ declina al Poniente . . . que me digã la caufa defta efecto ? . . . Porque vn poco de hierro de fregarfe cõ la piedra Iman . . .

"Mejor es, como dize Gregorio Theologo, que a la Fe fe fujete la razon, pues aun en fu cafa no fabe bien entenderfe. . . ."

Page 5, line 36. Page 5, line 45. *Livius Sanutus.*—Livio Sanuto publifht at Venice in 1588 a folio work, *Geografia diftinta in xii Libri; ne' quali, oltre l'efplicatione di noftri luoghi di Tolomeo, della Buffola e dell' Aguglia, fi dichiarono le provincie . . . dell' Africa.* In this work all Liber i. (pages 1-13) deals with obfervations of the compafs, mentioning Sebaftian Cabot, and other navigators. He gives a map of Africa, fhowing the central lakes out of which flow the *Zaires fluvius* and the *Zanberes fluvius.*

Page 6, line 2. Page 6, line 5. *Fortunius Affaitatus.*—The work of Affaytatus, *Phyficæ ac aftronomiæ confiderationes*, was publifht in Venice in 1549.

Page 6, line 3. Page 6, line 6. *Baptifta Porta.*—The reference is to his celebrated *Magia naturalis*, the firft edition of which came out in 1558 at Naples. An Englifh edition, *Natural Magick by John Baptifta Porta, a Neapolitaine*, was printed in London, 1658. Book feven of this volume treats "Of the wonders of the Load-ftone." In the proem to this book Porta fays: "I knew at Venice R. M. Paulus, the Venetian, that was bufied in the fame ftudy: he was Provincial of the Order of fervants, but now a moft worthy Advocate, from whom I not only confefs, that I gained fomething, but I glory in it, becaufe of all the men I ever faw, I never faw any man more learned, or more ingenious, having obtained the whole body of learning; and is not only the Splendor and Ornament of Venice or Italy, but of the whole world." The reference is to Fra Paolo Sarpi, better known as the hiftorian of the Council of Trent. Sarpi was himfelf known to Gilbert.

His relations with Gilbert are fet forth in the memoir prefixt to the edition of his works, *Opere di Fra Paolo Sarpi, Servita* . . . in Helmftat, MDCCLXI, p. 83. " Fino a quefti giorni continuava il Sarpi a raccorre offervazioni fulla declinazione dell' Ago Calamitato; e poi ch' egli, attefo il variare di tal declinazione, affurdità alcuna non trovava riguardo al penfamento dell' Inglefe Guglielmo Gilberto, cioè, che l'interno del noftro Globo foffe gran Calamita. . . ." Here follows a quotation from a letter of Sarpi to Lefcafferio :

" . . . Unde cufpidem trahi a tanta mole terrena, quæ fupereminet non abfurde putavit Gulliemus Gilbertus, et in eo meridiano refpicere recta polum, cave putes obfervatorem erraffe. Eft Vir accuratiffimus, et interfuit omnibus obfervationibus, quas plures olim fecimus, et aliquas in fui gratiam, et cum arcubus vertici cupreo innitentibus, et cum innatantibus aquæ, et cum brevibus, et cum longis, quibus modis omnibus et Hierapoli ufus fuit."

Sarpi had correfpondence with Gilbert, Bacon, Grotius, and Cafaubon. He alfo wrote on magnetifm and other topics *in materia di Fifica*, but thefe writings have perifht. He appears to have been the firft to recognize that fire deftroyed the magnetic properties. (See *Fra Paolo Sarpi, the greateft of the Venetians* by the Rev. Alexander Robertfon, London, 1894; fee alfo the notice of Sarpi in Park Benjamin's *Intellectual Rife in Electricity*.)

Page 6, line 7. Page 6, line 11. *R. M. Paulus Venetus*. See preceding note.

Page 6, line 21. Page 6, line 28. *Francifcus Rueus.*—François de la Rue, author of *De Gemmis Aliquot* . . . (Paris, 1547). Amongft other fables narrated by Rueus is that if a magnet is hung on a balance, when a piece of iron is attracted and adheres to the magnet, it adds nothing to the weight !

Page 6, line 25. Page 6, line 33. *Serapio.*—This account of the magnetic mountains will be found in an early pharmacology printed in 1531 (Argentorati, G. Ulricher Andlenus), with the title " In hoc volumine continetur infignium medicorum Joan. Serapionis Arabis de Simplicibus Medicinis opus præclarum et ingens, Averrois Arabis de eifdem liber eximius, Rafis filius Zachariæ de eifdem opufculum perutile." It was edited by Otho Brunfels. Achilles P. Gaffer, in his Appendix to the Augfburg edition of Peregrinus, gives a reference to Serapio Mauritanus, parte 2, cap. 394, libri *de medicinis compofitis*.

Page 6, line 30. Page 6, line 39. *Olaus Magnus*. See note to p. **5**.

Page 6, line 34. Page 6, line 44. *Hali Abas.*—A reference is given in Gaffer's (1558) edition of Peregrinus to Haliabbas Arabs, lib. 2, *practicæ* cap. 45, *Regalis Difpofitionis Medicinæ*. The paffage to which Gilbert refers is found in the volume *Liber totius medicinæ neceffaria cōtinens* . . . *quem Haly filius Abbas* . . . *edidit* . . . *et a Stephano ex arabica lingua reductus*. (Lugd., 1523, 4to.) Liber Primus. Practice, Cap xlv. *de fpeciebus lapidum*, § 466. " Lapis magnetes fīlis ē v̄tute fadenego: & aiunt qm̄ fi teneatʳ in manu mitigat q̄ funt in pedibˢ ipis dolores ac fpafmū."

Mr. A. G. Ellis identifies the noun *fadenegum* as a Latin corruption of the Arabic name of hæmatite, *fhâdanaj*.

Page 6, line 36. Page 6, line 46. *Pictorius.*—His poem was publifht at Bafel, 1567. See alfo note on Marbodæus, p. **7**, line **20**, below.

Page 6, line 36. Page 7, line 1. *Albertus Magnus.*—Albertus, the celebrated Archbifhop of Ratifbon, is refponfible for propagating fundry of the myths of the magnet; and Gilbert never lofes a chance of girding at him.

The following examples are taken from the treatife *De mineralibus et rebus metallicis* (Liber II. *de lapidibus preciofis*), Venet., 1542.

p. 171. "Et quod mirabile videtur multis hic lapis [adamas] quando Magneti fupponitur ligat Magnetem et non permittit ipfum ferrum trahere."

p. 193. "Vnctus autĕ lapis alleo non trahit, fi fuperponitur ei Adamas iterum non attrahit, ita quod paruus Adamas magnŭ ligat Magnetĕ. Inventus autĕ eft noftris tĕporibus Magnes qui ab uno angulo traxit ferrŭ et ab alio fugavit, et hunc Ariftot. ponit aliud genus effe Magnetis. Narrauit mihi quidam ex noftris fociis experimĕtator quod uidit Federicum Imperatorem habere Magnetem qui non traxit ferrum, fed ferrum uiceuerfa traxit lapidem."

The firft edition of this work *de mineralibus* appears to have been publifht in Venice as a folio in 1495.

Page 7, line 9. Page 7, line 15. *Gaudentius Merula.*—This obfcure paffage is from Liber IIII., cap. xxi., *Lapides*, of the work *Memorabilium Gaudentii Merulæ* . . . (Lugd., 1556), where we find :

"Qui magneti vrfæ fculpferit imaginem, quãdo Luna melius illuc afpiciat, & filo ferreo fufpĕderit, compos fiet vrfæ cæleftis virtutis : verùm cum Saturni radiis vegetetur, fatius fuerit eam imaginem non habere : fcribunt enim Platonici malos dæmones feptentrionales effe " (p. 287).

"Trahit autem magnes ferrum ad fe, quod ferro fit ordine fuperior apud vrfum " (p. 287).

The almoft equally obfcure paffage in the *De triplici vita* of Marfiglio Ficino (Bafil., 1532) runs :

"Videmus in fpecula nautarum indice poli libratum acum affectum in extremitate Magnete moueri ad Vrfam, illuc uidelicet trahente Magnete : quoniam & in lapide hoc præualet uirtus Vrfæ, & hinc transfertur in ferrum, & ad Vrfam trahit utrunq;. Virtus autem eiufmodi tum ab initio infufa eft, tum continue Vrfæ radijs uegetatur, Forfitan ita fe habet Succinum ad polum alterum & ad paleas. Sed dic interea, Cur Magnes trahit ubiq; ferrum? non quia fimile, alioquin & Magnetem Magnes traheret multo magis, ferrumq; ferrŭ : non quia fuperior in ordine corporum, imò fuperius eft lapillo metallum. . . . Ego autem quum hæc explorata hactenus habuiffem admodum gratulabar, cogitabamq; iuuenis adhuc Magneti pro uiribus infcluperet (*fic*) coeleftis Vrfæ figuram, quando Luna melius illuc afpiciat, & ferro tŭc filo collo fufpendere. Sperabam equidem ita demum uirtutis me fideris illius compotem fore," &c. (p. 172).

Page 7, line 14. Page 7, line 20. *Ruellius.*—Joannes Ruellius wrote a herbal *De Natura Stirpium*, Paris, 1536, which contains a very full account of amber, and a notice of the magnet (p. 125) and of the fable about garlic. But on p. 530 of the fame work he ridicules Plutarch for recording this very matter.

Page 7, line 20. Page 7, line 27. *Marbodæus Gallus.*—This rare little book is entitled *Marbodei Galli Poetæ vetuftiffimi de lapidibus pretiofis Enchiridion*. It was printed at Paris in 1531. The Freiburg edition, alfo of 1531, has the commentaries of Pictorius. The poem is in Latin hexameters. After a preface of twenty-one lines the virtues of ftones are dealt with, the paragraph beginning with a ftatement that Evax, king of the Arabs, is faid to have written to Nero an account of the fpecies, names and colours of ftones, their place of origin and their potencies ; and that this work formed the bafis of the poem. The alleged magical powers of the magnet are recited in Caput I., *Adamas*. Caput XLIII., *Magnes*, gives further myths.

The commentary of Pictorius gives references to earlier writers, Pliny, Dioscorides, Bartholomæus Anglicus, Solinus, Serapio, and to the book *de lapidibus* erroneously ascribed to Aristotle.

The following is a specimen of the poem of Marbodeus:

Magnetes lapis eft inuentus apud Trogloditas,
Quē lapidū genetrix nihilominus India mittit.
Hic ferruginei cognofcitur effe coloris,
Et ui naturæ uicinum tollere ferrum.
Ededon magus hoc primum ferè dicitur ufus,
Confcius in magica nihil effe potentius arte.
Poft illum fertur famofa uenefica Circe
Hoc in præftigijs magicis fpecialiter ufa.

This poem was reprinted (1854) in Migne's *Patrologia*. In 1799 Johann Beckmann issued an annotated variorum edition of Marbodeus (*Marbodi Liber Lapidvm fev de Gemmis . . .*, Göttingæ, 1799), in which there is a bibliography of the poem, the first edition of which appears to have been publisht in 1511, at Vienna, thirteen other editions being described. Beckmann adds many illustrative notes, and a notice of the Arabian Evax, who is supposed to have written the treatise *de lapidibus*. Not the least curious part is a French translation alleged to have been written in 1096, of which Chap. XIX. on the Magnet begins thus:

Magnete trovent Trogodite,
En Inde e precieus eft ditte.
Fer refemble e fi le trait,
Altrefi cum laimant fait.
Dendor lama mult durement.
Qi lufoit a enchantement.
Circe lus a dot mult chere,
Cele merveillofe forciere, &c.

Page 7, line 21. Page 7, line 28. *echeneidis.*—The *echeneis*, or fucking-fifh, reputed to have magical or magnetic powers, is mentioned by many writers. As an example, fee Fracaftorio, *De Sympathia et Antipathia*, lib. i., cap. 8, *De Echineide, quomodo firmare nauigia poffit* (Giunta edition, Venet., 1574, p. 63). For other references to the *Echeneis* fee Gaudentius Merula (*op. citat.*), p. 209. Alfo Dr. Walter Charleton, *Phyfiologia Epicuro Gaffendo-Charltoniana* (Lond., 1654), p. 375. Compare p. **63**, line **3**.

Page 7, line 33. Page 7, line 43. *Thomas Hariotus*, etc.—The four Englifhmen named were learned men who had contributed to navigation by magnetic obfervations. Harriot's account of his voyage to Virginia is printed in Hakluyt's *Voyages*. Robert Hues (or Hood) wrote a treatife *on Globes*, the Latin edition of which appeared in 1593 (dedicated to Sir Walter Raleigh), and the Englifh edition in 1638. It was republifht by the Hakluyt Society, 1889. Edward Wright, the mathematician and writer on navigation, alfo wrote the preface to Gilbert's own book. Abraham Kendall, or Abram Kendal was " Portulano," or failing-mafter of Sir Robert Dudley's fhip the *Bear*, and is mentioned in Dudley's *Arcano del Mare*. On the return of Dudley's expedition in 1595, he joined Drake's laft expedition, which failed that year, and died on the fame day as Drake himfelf, 28 January, 1596. (See *Hakluyt*, ed. 1809, iv., p. 73.)

Page 7, line 36. Page 8, line 1. *Guilielmus Borough.*—Borough's book has the title: *A Difcours of the Variation of the Cumpas, or magneticall*

Needle. Wherein is Mathematically ſhewed, the manner of the obſeruation, effeɛtes, and application thereof, made by W. B. And is to be annexed to *The Newe Attraɛtive* of R. N., 1581 (London).

Page 7, line 37. Page 8, line 2. · *Guilielmus Barlo.*—Archdeacon William Barlowe (author, in 1616, of the *Magneticall Aduertiſements*) wrote in 1597 a little work called *The Navigators Supply.* It gives a deſcription of the ordinary compaſs, and alſo one of a ſpecial form of meridian compaſs provided with ſights for taking the bearings by the ſun.

Page 7, line 37. Page 8, line 3. *Robertus Normannus.* See Note to p. 5.

Page 8, line 14. Page 8, line 21. *illo fabuloſo Plinij bubulco.*—The following is Pliny's account from Philemon Holland's Engliſh verſion of 1601 (p. 586): "As for the name Magnes that it hath, it tooke it (as *Nicander* ſaith) of the firſt inventor and deviſer thereof, who found it (by his ſaying) upon the mountaine Ida (for now it is to be had in all other countries, like as in Spaine alſo;) and (by report) a Neat-heard he was: who, as he kept his beaſts upon the aforeſaid mountaine, might perceive as he went up and downe, both the hob-nailes which were on his ſhoes, and alſo the yron picke or graine of his ſtaffe, to ſticke unto the ſaid ſtone."

Page 9, line 22. Page 9, line 30. *Differentiæ priſcis ex colore.*—Pliny's account of the loadſtones of different colours which came from different regions is mainly taken from Sotacus. The white magnet, which was friable, like pumice, and which did not draw iron, was probably ſimply magneſia. The blue loadſtones were the beſt. See p. 587 of Holland's tranſlation of Pliny, London, 1601. St. Iſidore (*Originum ſeu Etymologiarum*, lib. xvi., cap. 4) ſays: "Omnis autem magnes tanta melior eſt, quanto [magis] cæruleus eſt."

Page 10, line 29. Page 10, line 42. *Suarcebergo . . . Snebergum &* *Annæbergum.*—In the Stettin editions of 1628 and 1633 theſe are ſpelled *Swarcebergs . . . Schnebergum & Annebergum.* The Cordus given as authority for theſe localities is Valerius Cordus, the commentator on Dioſcorides.

Page 11, line 3. Page 11, line 12. *Adriani Gilberti viri nobilis.*— "Adrian Gylbert of Sandridge in the Countie of Devon, Gentleman" is the deſcription of the perſon to whom Queen Elizabeth granted a patent for the diſcovery of a North-Weſt paſſage to China. See Hakluyt's *Voyages,* vol. iii., p. 96.

Page 11, line 17. Page 11, line 28. *Dicitur a Græcis* ἡράκλιος.—The diſcuſſion of the names of the magnet in different languages by Gilbert in this place is far from complete. He gives little more than is to be found in Pliny. For more complete diſcuſſions the reader is referred to Buttmann, *Bemerkungen über die Benennungen einiger Mineralien bei den Alten, vorzüglich des Magnetes und des Baſaltes* (Muſæum der Alterthumſwiſſenſchaft, Bd. II., pp. 5-52, and 102-104, 1808); G. Fournier, *Hydrographie* (livre xi., chap. 1, 1643); Uliſſe Aldrovandi, *Muſæum Metallicum* (Bononiæ, 1648, lib. iv., cap. 2, p. 554); Klaproth, *Lettre à M. le Baron A. de Humboldt, ſur l'invention de la Bouſſole,* Paris, 1834; T. S. Davies, *The Hiſtory of Magnetical Diſcovery* (Thomſon's *Britiſh Annual,* 1837, pp. 250-257); Th. Henri Martin, *De l'Aimant, de ſes noms divers et de ſes variétés ſuivant les Anciens* (Mémoires préſentés par divers ſavants à l'Académie des Inſcriptions et Belles-lettres, 1ʳᵉ ſérie, t. vi., 1ʳᵉ partie, 1861); G. A. Palm, *Der Magnet in Alterthum* (Programm des k. württembergiſchen Seminars Maulbronn, Stuttgart,

1867). Of thefe works, thofe of Klaproth and of Martin are by far the moft important. Klaproth ftates that in modern Greek, in addition to the name μαγνῆτις, the magnet alfo has the names ἀδάμας and καλαμίτα. The former of thefe, in various forms, *adamas*, *adamant*, *aimant*, *yman*, and *piedramon*, has gone into many languages. Originally the word ἀδάμας (the unconquered) was applied by the Greeks to the hardeft of the metals with which they were acquainted, that is to fay, to hard-tempered iron or fteel, and it was fub-fequently becaufe of its root-fignification alfo given by them to the diamond for the fame reafon; it was even given to the henbane becaufe of the deadly properties of that plant. In the writings of the middle ages, in St. Auguftine, St. Ifidore, Marbodeus, and even in Pliny, we find fome confufion between the two ufes of *adamas* to denote the loadftone as well as the diamond. Certainly the word *adamas*, without ceafing to be applied to the diamond, alfo defignated the loadftone. At the fame time (fays Martin) the word *magnes* was preferved, as Pliny records, to defignate a loadftone of leffer ftrength than the *adamas*. On the other hand, the word *diamas*, or *deamans*, had already in the thirteenth century been introduced into Latin to fignify the diamond as diftinguifht from the magnet. *Adamas* was rendered *aymant* in the romance verfion of the poem of Marbodeus on ftones (fee Beckmann's variorum edition of 1799, p. 102), and in this form it was for a time ufed to denote both the magnet and the diamond. Then it gradually became reftricted in ufe to the ftone that attracts iron.

Some confufion has alfo arifen with refpect to the Hebrew name of the magnet. Sir W. Snow Harris makes the following ftatement (*Magnetifm*, p. 5): "In the Talmud it [the loadftone] is termed *achzhàb'th*, the ftone which attracts; and in their ancient prayers it has the European name *magnēs*." On this point Dr. A. Löwy has furnifht the following notes. The loadftone is termed in one of the Talmudical fections and in the Midrafh, *Eben Shoebeth* (lapis attrahens). This would of courfe be written אבן שואבת. Omitting the ו which marks the participial conftruction, the words would ftand thus: אבנשאבת. A perfon referring to Buxtorf's *Lexicon* Tal-mudicum would in the index look out for "Lapis magnefius," or for "magnes." He would then, in the firft inftance, be referred to the two words already quoted. Not knowing the value of the letters of the Hebrew alphabet, he reads אבן שאבת thus: אַבְןשאאבת achzhab'th. It is true that Buxtorf has inferted in his *Lexicon* the vocable מַגְנִיסֶם, "corruptum ex gr. μάγνης, μαγνήτης, μαγνῆτις, named after the Afiatic city Magnefia." He goes on to fay, "Inde Achilles Statius iftum lapidem vocavit μαγνήσιαν λίθον. Hinc אבן המגניסם חמשוך הברזל. Lapis Magnefius trahit ferrum." Here he quotes from (Sepher) Ikkarem IV., cap. 35.

Kircher, in his *Magnes, five de Arte magnetica* (Coloniæ, 1643), gives feveral other references to Hebrew literature. Others have fuppofed that the word חלמיש, *khallamifh*, which fignifies pebble, rock, or hard rock, to be ufed for the magnet.

As to the other Greek name, σιδηρῖτις, or λίθος σιδηρῖτις, this was given not only to the loadftone but alfo to non-magnetic iron. In the *Etymologicum magnum* (under the word μαγνῆτις), and in Photius (*Quæft. amphiloch.*, q. 131), it is ftated that the name *fideritis* was given to the loadftone either becaufe of its action on iron, or of its refemblance in afpect to iron, *or rather*, they fay, *becaufe the loadftone was originally found in the mines of this metal.* Alexander of Aphrodifias expreffly fays (*Quæftiones Phyficæ*, II. 23) that the loadftone appears to be nothing elfe than γῆ σιδηρῖτις, the earth which yields iron, or the earth of iron.

Page 11, line 19. Page 11, line 29. *ab Orpheo.*—The reference is to v. 301-328 of the Λιθικά. The paffage, as given in Abel's edition (Berol., 1881), begins:

> Τόλμα δ᾽ ἀθανάτους καὶ ἐνηέι μειλίσσεθαι
> μαγνήσσῃ, τὴν δ᾽ ἔξοχ᾽ ἐφίλατο θούσιος Ἄρης,
> οὕνεκεν, ὁππότε κεν πελάσῃ πολιοῖο σιδήρου,
> ἠΰτε παρθενικὴ τερενόχροα χερσὶν ἑλοῦσα
> ἠΐθεον στέρνῳ προσπτύσσεται ἱμεροέντι,
> ὣς ἥγ᾽ ἁρπάζουσα ποτὶ σφετερὸν δέμας αἰεὶ
> ἂψ πάλιν οὐκ ἐθέλει μεθέμεν πολεμιστὰ σίδηρον.

Page 11, line 20. Page 11, line 31. *Gallis aimant.*—The French word *aimant*, or *aymant*, is generally fuppofed to be derived from *adamas*. Neverthelefs Klaproth (*op. citat.*, p. 19) fuggefts that the word *aimant* is a mere literal tranflation into French of the Chinefe word *thfu chy*, which is the common name of the magnet, and which means *loving ftone*, or *ftone that loves*. All through the eaft the names of the magnet have moftly the fame fignification, for example, in Sanfkrit it is *thoumbaka* (the kiffer), in Hinduftani *tchambak*.

Page 11, line 20. Page 11, line 32. *Italis calamita.*—The name *calamita*, univerfal in Italian for the magnet, is alfo ufed in Roumanian, Croatian, Bofnian, and Wendifh. Its fuppofed derivation from the Hebrew *khallamifh* is repudiated by Klaproth, who alfo points out that the ufe of καλαμίτα in Greek is quite modern. He adds that the only reafonable explanation of the word *calamita* is that given by Father Fournier (*op. citat.*), who fays:

"Ils (les marins français) la nomment auffi *calamite*, qui proprement en français fignifie une *grenouille verte*, parce qu'avant qu'on ait trouvé l'invention de fufpendre et de balancer fur un pivot l'aiguille aimantée, nos ancêtres l'enfermaient dans une fiole de verre demi-remplie d'eau, et la faifaient flotter, par le moyen de deux petits fétus, fur l'eau comme une grenouille." Klaproth adds that he entirely agrees with the learned Jefuit, but maintains that the word *calamite*, to defignate the little green frog, called to-day *le graiffet*, *la raine*, or *la rainette*, is effentially Greek. For we read in Pliny (*Hift. Nat.*, lib. xxxii., ch. x.): "Ea rana quam Græci *calamiten* vocant, quoniam inter arundines, fruticefque vivat, minima omnium eft et viridiffima."

Page 11, line 20. Page 11, line 32. *Anglis* loadftone & adamant ftone.

The Englifh term *loadftone* is clearly connected with the Anglo-Saxon verb *lædan*, to lead, and with the Icelandic *leider-ftein*. There is no doubt that the fpelling *lodeftone* would be etymologically more correct, fince it means *ftone that leads*, not *ftone that carries a load*. The correct form is preferved in the word *lode-ftar*.

The word *adamant*, from *adamas*, the mediæval word for both loadftone and diamond, alfo occurs in Englifh for the loadftone, as witnefs Shakefpeare:

> "You draw me, you hard-hearted adamant
> But yet you draw not iron; for my heart
> Is true as fteel."
>
> *Midfummer Night's Dream*, Act II., Scene 1.

Page 11, line 21. Page 11, line 33. *Germanis magnefs, & fiegelftein.*
The Stettin edition of 1628 reads *Germanis* 𝔐agnetſtein, *Belgis* Seylſteen;
while that of 1633 reads *Germanis* 𝔐agnetſtein, *Belgis* Sylſteen.

Page 11, line 26. Page 11, line 39. In this line the Greek fentence
is, in every known copy of the folio of 1600, corrected in ink upon the text,
Θαλῆς being thus altered into Θαλῆς, and ἀπομνεμονύσσι into ἀπομνεμονεύσσι.
Four lines lower, brackets have been inſerted around the words (lapidum
ſpecularium modo). Theſe ink corrections muſt have been made at the
printers', poffibly by Gilbert's own hand. They have been carried out as
errata in the editions of 1628 and 1633. The "facſimile" Berlin reprint of
1892 has deleted them, however. Other ink corrections on pp. **14, 22, 38,
39, 47, 130,** and **200** of the folio edition of 1600 are noted in due courſe.

Page 11, line 29. Page 11, line 45. *lapis ſpecularis.* This is the
mediæval name for *mica*, but in Elizabethan times known as talc or muſcovy
ſtone. Cardan, *De Rerum Varietate* (Baſil., 1557, p. 418), lib. xiiii., cap.
lxxii., mentions the uſe of *lapis ſpecularis* for windows.

Page 11, line 31. Page 11, line 46. *Germanis Katzenſilbar & Talke.*
—In the editions of 1628 and 1633 this is corrected to *Germanis* 𝔎atzenſilber
(£ 𝔗alcfe. Goethe, in *Wilhelm Meiſter's Travels*, calls mica "cat-gold."

Page 12, line 30. Page 12, line 35. *integtum* appears to be a miſprint
for *integrum*, which is the reading of editions 1628 and 1633.

Page 13, line 4. Page 13, line 3. μικρόγη ſeu *Terrella.* Although
rounded loadſtones had been uſed before Gilbert's time (ſee Peregrinus, p. 3
of Augſburg edition of 1558, or Baptiſta Porta, p. 194, of Engliſh edition
of 1658), Gilbert's uſe of the ſpherical loadſtone as a model of the globe of
the earth is diſtinctive. The name *Terrella* remained in the language. In
Pepys's Diary we read how on October 2, 1663, he "received a letter from
Mr. Barlow with a terella." John Evelyn, in his *Diary*, July, 1655, mentions
a "pretty terella with the circles and ſhowing the magnetic deviations."

A Terrella, 4½ inches in diameter, was preſented in 1662 by King
Charles I. to the Royal Society, and is ſtill in its poffeffion. It was examined
in 1687 (ſee *Phil. Tranſactions* for that year) by the Society to ſee whether
the poſitions of its poles had changed.

In Grew's *Catalogue and Deſcription of the Rarities belonging to the Royal
Society and preſerved at Greſham College* (London, 1681, p. 364) is mentioned
a Terrella contrived by Sir Chriſtopher Wren, with one half immerſed in the
centre of a plane horizontal table, ſo as to be like a Globe with the poles in
the horizon, having thirty-two magnet needles mounted in the margin of
the table to ſhow "the different reſpect of the *Needle* to the ſeveral *Points* of
the *Loadſtone.*"

In Sir John Pettus's *Fleta Minor*, London, 1683, in the *Dictionary of
Metallick Words* at the end, under the word *Loadſtone* occurs the following
paſſage :

"Another piece of Curioſity I ſaw in the Hands of Sir *William Perſal*
(ſince Deceaſed alſo) *viz.*, a *Terrella* or *Load-ſtone*, of little more than 6 *Inches
Diameter*, turned into a *Globular Form*, and all the *Imaginery Lines* of our
Terreſtrial Globe, exactly drawn upon it : *viz.*, the *Artick* and *Antartick
Circles*, the *two Tropicks*, the *two Colures*, the *Zodiack* and *Meridian*; and
theſe *Lines*, and the ſeveral *Countryes*, artificially *Painted* on it, and all of
them with their true *Diſtances*, from the two *Polar Points*, and to find the
truth of thoſe *Points*, he took two *little pieces* of a *Needle*, each of about half

an Inch in length, and thofe he laid on the *Meridian line*, and then with *Brafs Compaffes*, moved one of them towards the *Artick*, which as it was moved, ftill raifed it felf at one end higher and higher, keeping the other end fixt to the *Terrella*; and when it had compleated it Journy to the very *Artick Points*, it ftood upright upon that *Point*; then he moved the other piece of *Needle* to the *Antartick Point*, which had its *Elevations* like the other, and when it came to the *Point*, it fixt it felf upon that *Point*, and ftood *upright*, and then taking the *Terrella* in my Hand, I could perfectly fee that the two *pieces* of *Needles* ftood fo exactly one againft the other, as if it had been one intire *long Needle* put through the *Terrella*, which made me give credit to thofe who held, That there is an *Aftral Influence* that *darts* it felf through the *Globe* of *Earth* from *North* to *South* (and is as the *Axel-Tree* to the *Wheel*, and fo called the *Axis* of the *World*) about which the *Globe* of the *Earth* is turned, by an *Aftral Power*, fo as what I thought *imaginary*, by this *Demonftration*, I found *real*."

Page 13, line 20.   Page 13, line 22.   The editions of 1628 and 1633 give a different woodcut from this: they fhow the terrella lined with meridians, equator, and parallels of latitude: and they give the compafs needle, at the top, *pointing in the wrong direction*.

Page 14, line 3.   Page 14, line 3.   The Berlin "facfimile" reprint omits the afterifk here.

Page 14, line 5.   Page 14, line 6.   *erectus* altered in ink in the folio to *erecta*.   But *erectus* is preferved in editions 1628 and 1633.   In Cap. IIII., on p. **14**, both thefe Stettin editions infert an additional cut reprefenting the terrella A placed in a tub or veffel B floating on water.

Page 14, line 34.   Page 14, line 39.   *variatione quadā*.   The whole of Book IIII. is devoted to a difcuffion of the variation of the compafs.

Page 16, line 28.   Page 16, line 34.   *aquæ.*—This curious ufe of the dative occurs alfo on p. **222**, line **8**.

Page 17, line 1.   Page 17, line 1.   *videbis.*—The reading *vibebis* of the 1633 edition is an error.

Page 18, line 24.   Page 18, line 27.   *Theamedem.*—For the myth about the alleged *Theamedes*, or repelling magnet, fee Cardan, *De Subtilitate* (folio ed., 1550, lib. vii., p. 186).

Pliny's account, in the Englifh verfion of 1601 (p. 587), runs:

" To conclude, there is another mountaine in the fame Æthyopia, and not farre from the faid Zimiris, which breedeth the ftone Theamedes that will abide no yron, but rejecteth and driveth the fame from it."

Martin Cortes, in his *Arte de Nauegar* (Seville, 1556), wrote:

" And true it is that Tanxeades writeth, that in Ethiope is found another kinde of this ftone, that putteth yron from it " (Eden's tranflation, London, 1609).

Page 21, line 24.   Page 21, line 25.   *Hic fegetes, &c.*—The Englifh verfion of thefe lines from Vergil's *Georgics*, Book I., is by the late Mr. R. D. Blackmore.

Page 22, line 18.   Page 22, line 19.   *quale*, altered in ink in the folio text to *qualis*.   The editions of 1628 and 1633 both read *qualis*.

Page 22, line 19.   Page 22, line 20.   *rubrica fabrili:* in Englifh *ruddle* or *reddle*.   See " Sir " John Hill, *A General Natural Hiftory*, 1748, p. 47. In the *De Re Metallica* of Entzelt (Encelius), Frankfurt, 1551, p. 134, is a paragraph headed *De Rubrica Fabrili*, as follows: " Rubrica fabrilis duplex eft. à Germanis aūt utraque dicitur rottel, röttelftein, wie die zimmerleüt vnd fteynmetzen brauchen. à Græcis μίλτος τεκτονική. Eft enim alia nativa, alia factitia. Natiua à Germanis propriè dicitur berckrottel. haec apud nos eft foffilis. . . . Porro factitia eft rubrica fabrilis, à Germanis braunrottel, quæ fit ex ochra ufta, ut Theophraftus et Diofcorides teftantur."

Page 22, line 19. Page 22, line 20. *In Suffexia Angliæ.*—In Camden's *Britannia* (1580) we read concerning the iron induftry in the villages in Suffex : " They are full of iron mines in fundry places, where, for the making and founding thereof, there be furnaces on every fide ; and a huge deal of wood is yearly burnt. The heavy forge-hammers, worked by water-power, ftored in hammer-ponds, ceafeleffly beating upon the iron, fill the neighbourhood round about, day and night, with continual noife."

Page 23, line 1. Page 22, line 44. *in libro Ariftotelis de admirandis narrationibus.*—The reference is to the work ufually known as the *De Mirabilibus Aufcultationibus*, Cap. XLVIII.: " Fertur autem peculiariffima generatio effe ferri Chalybici Amifenique, ut quod ex fabulo quod a fluviis defertur, ut perhibent certe, conflatur. Alii fimpliciter lotum in fornace excoqui, alii vero, quod ex lotura fubfedit, frequentius lotum comburi tradunt adjecto fimul et pyrimacho dicto lapide, qui in ifta regio plurimus reperiri fertur." (Ed. Didot, vol. ii., p. 87.) According to Georgius Agricola, the ftone pyrimachus is fimply iron pyrites.

Page 23, line 22. Page 23, line 23. *vt in Italia Comi,* &c.—This is moftly taken from Pliny. Compare the following paffage from Philemon Holland's tranflation (1601), p. 514:
" But the moft varietie of yron commeth by the meanes of the water, wherein the yron red-hot is eftfoones dipped and quenched for to be hardened. And verely, water only which in fome place is better, in other worfe, is that which hath ennobled many places for the excellent yron that commeth from them, as namely, Bilbilis in Spaine, and Taraffio, Comus alfo in Italie ; for none of thefe places have any yron mines of their owne, and yet there is no talke but of the yron and fteele that commeth from thence."
Bilbilis is Bambola, and Tariaffona the Tarazona of modern Spain.

Page 24, line 28. Page 24, line 27. *Quare vani funt illi Chemici.*—Gilbert had no faith in the alchemifts. On pp. **19** and **21** he had poked fun at them for declaring the metals to be conftituted of fulphur and quickfilver, and for pronouncing the fixed earth in iron to be fulphur. On p. **20** he had denied their propofition that the differences between filver, gold, and copper could arife from proportions of their conftituent materials ; and he likewife denounced unfparingly the fuppofed relation between the feven metals and the feven planets. He now denounces the vain dreams of turning all metals into gold, and all ftones into diamonds. Later he rejects as abfurd the magnetic curing of wounds. His detachment from the pfeudo-fcience of his age was unique if not complete.

Page 25, line 15. Page 25, line 16. *Petro-coriis, & Cabis Biturgibus.*—The Petro-corii were a tribe in the neighbourhood of Perigord ; the Cubi Biturges another in that of Bourges.

Page 25, line 21. Page 25, line 23. Pliny's account, as tranflated by P. Holland (ed. 1601, p. 515), runs thus:
" Of all mines that be, the veine of this mettall is largeft, and fpreadeth it felfe into moft lengths every way: as we may fee in that part of Bifcay that coafteth along the fea, and upon which the Ocean beateth : where there

is a craggie mountaine very fteep and high, which ftandeth all upon a mine or veine of yron. A wonderfull thing, and in manner incredible, howbeit, moft true, according as I have fhewed already in my Cofmographie, as touching the circuit of the Ocean."

Page 26, line 15. Page 26, line 12. *quas Clampas noftri vocant.*— The name *clamp* for the natural kiln formed by heaping up the bricks, with ventilating fpaces and fuel within the heap, is ftill current.

Page 26, line 39. Page 26, line 38. *Pluebat in Taurinis ferrum.*— The occurrence is narrated by Scaliger, *De Subtilitate*, Exercitat. cccxxiii. :

" Sed falfò lapidis pluviam creas tu ex pulvere haufto à nubibus, atque in lapidem condenfato. At ferrum, quod pluit in Taurinis, cuius fruftum apud nos extat, qua ex fodina fuftulit nubes ? Tribus circiter annis antè, quàm ab Rege provincia illa recepta effet, pluit ferro multis in locis, fed raris" (p. 434, Editio Lutetiæ, 1557).

" During the latter ages of the Roman Empire the *city* of Augufta Taurinorum feems to have been commonly known (as was the cafe in many inftances in Tranfalpine Gaul) by the name of the tribe to which it belonged, and is called fimply Taurini in the Itineraries, as well as by other writers, hence its modern name of Torino or Turin" (Smith's *Dictionary of Greek and Roman Geographies*, p. 1113).

There exifts a confiderable literature refpecting falls of meteors and of meteoric iron. Livy, Plutarch, and Pliny all record examples. See alfo *Remarks concerning ftones faid to have fallen from the clouds*, by Edward King (London, 1796); Chladni, *Ueber den Urfprung der von Pallas gefundenen und anderer ihr ähnlicher Eifenmaffen* (Riga, 1794); *Philofophical Tranf-actions*, vol. lxxviii., pp. 37 and 183; vol. lxxxv., p. 103; vol. xcii., p. 174; Humboldt's *Cofmos*, vol. i. (p. 97 of London edition, 1860); C. Rammelfberg, *Die chemifche Natur der Meteoriten* (Berlin, 1879); Mafkelyne, *Some lecture-notes on Meteorites* printed in *Nature*, vol. xii., pp. 485, 504, and 520, 1875. Mafkelyne denominates as *fiderites* thofe meteorites which confift chiefly of iron. They ufually contain from 80 to 95 per cent. of iron, often alloyed with nickel. This meteoric iron is fometimes fo pure that it can at once be forged by the fmith. An admirable fummary of the whole fubject is to be found in L. Fletcher's *An Introduction to the ftudy of Meteorites*, publifht by the Britifh Mufeum (Nat. Hift.), London, 1896.

Page 27, line 3. Page 26, line 41. *vt Cardanus . . . fcribit.*—The paffage runs :

" Vidimus anno MDX cum cecidiffet è cœlo lapides circiter MCC in agrum fluvio Abduæ conterminum, ex his unum CXX pondo, alium fexaginta delati fuerunt ad reges Gallorũ fatrapes, plurimi : colos ferrugineus, durities eximia, odor fulphureus" (Cardan, *De Rerum Varietate*, lib. xiiii., cap. lxxii.; Bafil., 1557, p. 545).

Page 27, line 9. Page 27, line 2. *aut ftannum, aut plumbum album.* Although moft authorities agree in tranflating *plumbum album* or *plumbum candidum* as "tin" (which is unqueftionably the meaning in fuch examples as Pliny's *Nat. Hift.*, xxxiv. 347, and iv. 16; or Strabo, iii. 147), neverthelefs it is certain that here *plumbum album* is not given as a fynonym of *ftannum* and therefore is not *tin*. That Gilbert meant either fpelter or pewter is pretty certain. He bafed his metallic terms mainly upon Encelius (Chriftoph Entzelt) whofe *De Re Metallica* was publifhed at Frankfurt in 1551. From this work are taken the following paffages:

p. 61. *De Plumbo candido.* Cap. XXXI.

" Veluti plumbum nigrũ uocatur à Germanis blei fimpliciter, od' fchwartz-blei : ita plumbũ candidũ ab his uocatur weifsblei, od' ziñ. Impropriè autem plumbum hoc noftrum candidum ziñ, ftannum dicitur. Et non funt idem, ut hactenus voluerunt, ftannum et plumbum candidum, unfer ziñ. Aliud eft ftannum, de quo mox agemus : et aliud plumbum candidum noftrum, unfer ziñ, quod nigro plumbo quafi eft quiddã purius et perfectius. . . ."

p. 62. *De Stanno.* Cap. XXXII.

" In præcedenti capite indicauimus aliud effe ftannum, aliud effe plumbũ candidũ. Illa ergo definitio plumbi candidi, defs zinnes, etiã apud chimiftas nõ de ftanno, fed de plumbo candido (ut mihi uidetur) intelligenda eft, cum dicunt : Stannum (es foll heyffen plumbum candidum) eft metallicum album, non purum, lividum. . . ."

p. 63. " Sic uides ftannum, fecundum Serapionem, metallicum effe quod reperitur in fua propria uena, ut forfitan apud nos bifemutũ : ecõtra noftrũ candidũ plumbũ, eft Plinij candidũ plumbũ, das zin, quod cõflatur ut plumbum nigrum, ex pyrite, galena, et lapillis nigris. Deinde uides ftannum Plinio effe quiddã de plumbo nigro, nempe primum fluorem plumbi nigri, als wann man vnfer bley ertz fchmeltzet, das erft das do fleüffet, zwäre Plinio ftannum. Et hoc docet Plinius adulterari plũbo candido, mit vnferm zinn, vnd wann du ihm recht nachdenckeft, daruon die kannen gemacht werden, das man halbwerck heift. . . . O ir lofen vngelerten, vnckenbrenner. Stannum proculdubio Arabis metallum eft preciofius noftro candido plumbo : ficuti apud nos bifemuthum quiddam plumbo preciofius."

Page 27, line 21. Page 27, line 17. *venas . . . venis.*—It is im-poffible to give in Englifh this play on words between veins of ore and veins of the animal body.

Page 28, line 23. Page 28, line 20. *quem nos verticitatem dicimus.*—See the notes on Gilbert's gloffary, *ante.* The word verticity remained in the language. On p. 140 of Jofeph Glanvill's *Vanity of Dogmatizing* (Lond., 1661) we read : " We believe the *verticity* of the *Needle*, without a Certificate from the *dayes of old.*"

Page 29, line 15. Page 29, line 16. *Nos verò diligentiùs omnia experientes.*—The method of carefully trying everything, inftead of accepting ftatements on authority, is characteriftic of Gilbert's work. The large afterifks affixed to Chapters IX. X. XI. XII. and XIII. of Book I. indicate that Gilbert confidered them to announce important original magnetical difcoveries. The electrical difcoveries of Book II., Chapter II., are fimilarly diftinguifhed. A rich crop of new magnetical experiments, marked with marginal afterifks, large and fmall, is to be found in Book II., from Chapter XV. to Chapter XXXIV.; while a third feries of experimental magnetical difcoveries extends throughout Book III.

Page 31, line 30. Page 31, line 25. *verticem.*—The context and the heading of the Chapter appear to require *verticitatem.* All editions, how-ever, read *verticem.*

Page 32, line 12. Page 32, line 9. *Gartias ab horto.*—The paffage from Gartias ab Horto runs as follows in the Italian edition of 1616, *Dell' Hiftoria dei Semplici Aromati.* . . . di Don Garzia dall' Horto, Medico Portughefe, . . . Venezia MDCXVI., p. 208.

" Nè meno è quefta pietra velenofa, fi come molti hanno tenuto; imperoche le genti di quefte bande dicono che la Calamita prefa per bocca, però in poca quantità, conferva la gioventù. La onde fi racconta, che il Re di Zeilan il vecchio' f'haveva fatto fare tutti i vafi, dove fi cocevano le vivăde per lui, di Calamita. Et quefto lo diffe à me colui proprio, che fu à quefto officio deftinato."

Page 32, line 29. Page 32, line 29. *Plutarchus & C. Ptolemæus.*—The garlick myth has already been referred to in the note to p. 1. The originals are Plutarch, *Quæftiones Platonicæ*, lib. vii., cap. 7, § 1; C. Ptolemæus, *Opus Quadripartitum*, bk. i., cap. 3. The Englifh tranflation of the latter, by Whalley (London, 1701), p. 10, runs: " For if the *Loadftone* be *Rubbed* with *Garlick*, the *Iron will not be drawn by it.*"

Page 32, line 32. Page 32, line 33. *Medici nonnulli.*—This is apparently a reference to the followers of Rhazes and Paracelfus. The argument of Gilbert as to the inefficacy of powdered loadftones is reproduced more fully by William Barlowe in his *Magneticall Aduertifements* (1616, p. 7), as follows:

" It is the goodneffe of the *Loadftone* ioyned with a fit forme that will fhew great force. For as a very good forme with bafe fubftance can doe but very litle, fo the fubftance of the *Loadftone* bee it neuer fo excellent, except it haue fome conuenient forme, is not auaileable. For example, an excellent *loadftone* of a pound waight and of a good fafhion, being vfed artificially, may take vp foure pounds of Iron; beate it into fmall pouder, and it fhall bee of no force to take vp one ounce of Iron ; yea I am very well affured that halfe an ounce of a Loadftone of good fafhion, and of like vertue will take vp more then that pound will doe being beaten into powder. Whence (to adde this by the way) it appeareth manifeftly, that it is a great error of thofe Phyfitions and Surgeons, which to remedy ruptures, doe prefcribe vnto their Patients to take the pouder of a *Loadftone* inwardly, and the fmall filing of iron mingled in fome plaifter outwardly : fuppofing that herein the *magneticall* drawing fhould doe great wonders."

Page 33, line 11. Page 33, line 8. *Nicolaus in emplaftrum divinum . . .*—Nicolaus Myrepfus is alfo known as Præpofitas. In his *Liber de compofitione medicamentorum* (Ingoldftat, 1541, 4to) are numerous recipes containing loadftone : for example, Recipe No. 246, called " efdra magna," is a medicine given for inflammation of the ftomach and for ftrangury, compounded of fome forty materials including " litho demonis " and " lapis magnetis." The *emplaftrum divinum* does not, however, appear to contain loadftone. In the Englifh tractate, *Præpofitas his Practife, a worke . . . for the better prefervation of the Health of Man. Wherein are . . . approved Medicines, Receiptes and Ointmentes. Tranflated out of Latin in to Englifh by* L. M. (London, 1588, 4to), we read on p. 35, " An Emplaifter of D. N. [Doctor Nicolaus] which the Pothecaries call Divinum." This contains litharge, bdellium, and " green braffe," but no loadftone.

Luis de Oviedo in his treatife *Methodo de la Coleccion y repoficion de las Medicinas fimples*, edited by Gregorio Gonçalez, Boticario (Madrid, 1622), gives (p. 502) the following : " Emplafto de la madre. *Recibe :* Nuezes mofcadas, clauos, cinamono, artemifia, piedraimon. De cada uno dos onças. . . . Entre otras differencias que ay de piedraiman fe hallan dos. Vna que por la parte que mira al Septentrion, atrae el hierro, por lo quel fe llama magnes ferrugineus. Y otra que atrae la carne, a la qual llaman magnes creaginus."

An " Emplaftrum fticticum " containing amber, mummy, loadftone, hæmatite, and twenty other ingredients, and declared to be "vulnerum ulcerumque telo inflictorum ſticticum emplaſtrum præſtantiſſimum," is deſcribed on p. 267 of the *Baſilica chimica* of Oſwaldus Crollius (Frankfurt, 1612).

Page 33, line 12. Page 33, line 9. *Auguſtani . . . in emplaſtrum nigrum. . . .*—Amongſt the phyſicians of the Augſburg ſchool the moſt celebrated were Adolphus Occo, Ambroſio Jung, and Gereone Seyler. This particular reference is to the *Pharmacopœia Auguſtana . . . a Collegio Medico recognita,* publiſhed at Augſburg, and which ran through many editions. The recipe for the "*emplaſtrum nigrum vulgo Stichpflaſter*" will be found on p. 182 of the ſeventh edition (1621-2). The recipe begins with oil of roſes, colophony, wax, and includes ſome ·twenty-two ingredients, amongſt them mummy, dried earthworms, and two ounces *lapidis magnetis præparati.* The recipe concludes: "Fiat Emplaſtrum ſecundùm artem. Perquàm efficax ad recentia vulnera et puncturas, vndè denominationem habet." The volume is a handſome folio not unlike Gilbert's own book, and bears at the end of the prefatory addreſs *ad Lectorem* identically the ſame *cul de lampe* as is found on p. **44** of *De Magnete.*

The contradictions as to the alleged medicinal virtues of loadſtone are well illuſtrated by Galen, who in his *De facultatibus* ſays that loadſtone is like hæmatite, which is aſtringent, while in his *De ſimplici medicina* he ſays it is purgative.

Page 33, line 14. Page 33, line 12. *Paracelſus in fodicationum emplaſtrum.*—Paracelſus's recipe for a plaſter againſt ſtab-wounds is to be found in *Wundt vund Leibartznei . . .* D. Theoph. Paracelſus (Frankf., 1555, pp. 63-67).

Page 33, line 17. Page 33, line 15. *Ferri vis medicinalis.*—This chapter on the medicinal virtues of iron is a ſummary of the views held down to that time. Thoſe curious to purſue the ſubject ſhould conſult Waring's *Bibliotheca Therapeutica* (London, 1878). Nor ſhould they miſs the rare black-letter quarto by Dr. Nicholas Monardus, of Seville, *Joyfull Newes out of the New-found Worlde,* tranſlated by John Frampton (London, 1596), in which are recited the opinions of Galen, Rhazes, Avicenna, and others, on the medicinal properties of iron. In addition to the views of the Arabic authors, againſt whom his arguments are directed, Gilbert diſcuſſes thoſe of Joannes Manardus, Curtius, and Fallopius. The treatiſe of Manardus, *Epiſtolarum medicinalium libri viginti* (Baſil., 1549), is a *réſumé* of the works of Galen and the Arabic phyſicians, but gives little reſpecting iron. Curtius (Nicolaus) was the author of a book, *Libellus de medicamentis præparatibus et purgantibus* (Gieſſæ Cattorum, 1614). The works of Fallopius are *De Simplicibus Medicamentis purgentibus tractatus* (Venet., 1566, 4to), and *Tractatus de Compoſitione Medicamentorum* (Venet., 1570, 4to).

Page 34, line 7. Page 34, line 3. *quorundā Arabum opiniones.*—The Arabian authorities referred to here or elſewhere by Gilbert are:

Albategnius (otherwiſe known as Machometes Aractenſis), Muhammad Ibn Jābir, *Al-Battānī.*
Avicenna (otherwiſe Abohali). Abou-'Ali al-'Hoſéin ben-'Abd-Allah Ibn-Sinâ, or, ſhortly, *Ibn Sina.*
Averroes. Muhammad Ibn Ahmed Ibn-Roſchd, *Abou Al-Walid.*
Geber. Abū Mūſā Jābir Ibn Haiyān, *Al-Tarſūſi.*
Hali Abas. 'Alí Ibn Al-'Abbás, *Al Majúſi.*

Rhazes, or *Rafis*.   Muhammad Ibn Zakarīyā.
Serapio.   Yuhanná Ibn Sarapion.
Thebit Ben-Kora (otherwife Thabit Ibn Corrah).   Abū Thabit Ibn Ḱurrah, *Al Harraṅī*.

Page 34, line 38. Page 34, line 40. *electuarium de fcoria ferri defcriptum à Raze.*—Rhazes or Rafis, whofe Arabic name was Muhammad Ibn Zakarīyā, wrote *De Simplicibus, ad Almanforem*. In Chap. 63 of this work he gives a recipe for a ftomachic, which includes fennel, anife, origanum, black pepper, cinammon, ginger, and iron flag. In the fplendid folio work of Rhazes publifht at Venice in 1542, with the title *Habes candide lector Continētem Rafis*, Libri ultimi, cap. 295, under the heading *De Ferro*, are fet forth the virtues of iron flag: " Virtus fcorie eft ficut virtus fcorie [a]eris fed debilior in purgãdo: et erugo ferri eft ftiptica: et cũ fuperpofitur retinet fluxus menftruorũ. . . . Ait Paulus: aqua in qua extinguitur ferrũ calens. . . . Dico: certificatus fum experientia q̃ valet contra emorryodas diabetem et fluxum menftruorum."

Page 35, line 16. Page 35, line 13. *Paulus.*—This is not Fra Paolo Sarpi, nor Marco Polo, nor Paulus Jovius the hiftorian, nor Paulus Nicolettus Venetus, but Paulus Aeginæ.

Page 35, line 29. Page 35, line 28. *Sed malè Avicenna.*—The advice of Avicenna to adminifter a draught containing powdered loadftone, reads as follows in the Giunta edition (Venice, 1608):

Lib. ii., cap. 470, p. 356. " Magnes quid eft? Eft lapis qui attrahit ferrum, quum ergo aduritur, fit hæmatites, & virtus ejus eft ficut virtus illius. . . . Datur in potu [ad bibitionem limaturæ ferri, quum retinetur in ventre fcoria ferri. Ipfe enim extrahit] ipfam, & affociatur ei apud exitum. Et dicitur, quando in potu fumuntur ex eo tres anulufat cum mellicrato, educit folutione humorem groffum malum."

The paffage is identical with that in the Venetian edition of 1486, in both of which the liquid prefcribed is mellicratus—mead. Gilbert fays that the iron is to be given in juice of *mercurialis*. Here he only follows Matthiolus, who, in his *Commentaries on Diofcorides*, fays (p. 998 of the Bafil. edition of 1598): " Sed (vt idem Auicenna fcribit) proprium hujufce ferrei pharmaci antidotum, eft lapis magnes drachmæ pondere potus, ex mercurialis, vel betæ fucco."

Serapio, in his *De Simplicibus Medicinis* (Brunfels' edition, Argentorati, 1531), p. 264, refers to Galen's prefcription of iron fcoriæ, and under the article *de lapide magnetis*, p. 260, quotes Diofcorides as follows: " Et uirtus huius lapidis eft, ut quãdo dantur in potu duo onolofat ex eo cũ melicrato, laxat humores groffos."

The original paffage in Diofcorides, *De Materia Medica*, ch. 147 (Spengel's edition of 1829) runs: Τοῦ δὲ μαγνήτου λίθου ἄριστός ἐστιν ὁ τὸν σίδηρον εὐχερῶς ἕλκων, καὶ τὴν χρόαν κυανίζων, πυκνός τε καὶ οὐκ ἄγαν βαρύς. Δύναμιν δὲ ἔχει πάχους ἀγωγὸν διδόμενος μετὰ μελικράτου τριωβόλου βάρος· ἔνιοι δὲ τοῦτον καίοντες ἀντὶ αἱματίτου πιπράσκουσιν."

In the Frankfurt edition of Diofcorides, tranflated by Ruellius (1543), the paffage is:

" Magnes lapis optimus eft, qui ferrum facile trahit, colore ad cœruleum uergente, denfus, nec admodum gravis. Datur cum aqua mulfa, trium obolorum pondere, ut craffos humores eliciat. Sunt qui magnetem crematũ pro hæmatite vendant. . . ."

In the *Scholia* of Joannes Lonicerus upon Diofcorides *In Diofcoridæ*

Anazarbei de re medica libros a Virgilio Marcello verſos, Scholia nova, Ioanne Lonicero autore (Marburgi, 1543, p. 77), occurs the following:

"*De recremento ferri.* Cap. XLIX.

"Σκωρία σιδήρου. ſcoria vel recrementum ferri. Quæ per ignem à ferro et cupro ſordes ſeparantur ac reijciuntur, et ab aliis metallis σκωρία uocantur. Omnis ſcoria, maxime uero ferri exiccat. Acerrimo aceto macerauit Galenus ferri ſcoriam, ac deinde excocto, pharmacum efficax confecit ad purulentas quæ multo tempore uexatæ erant, aures, admirando ſpectantium effectu. Ardenti ſcoria uel recrementum ἕλκυσμα, inquit Galenus."

See alſo the *Enarrationes eruditiſſimæ* of Amatus Luſitanus (Venet.,1597), pp. 482 and 507, upon iron and the loadſtone..

Page 36, line 27. Page 37, line 29. *eijcitur* for *ejicitur.*

Page 37, line 18. Page 37, line 22. *ut Cardanus philoſophatur.*— Cardan's nonſenſe about the magnet feeding on iron is to be found in *De Subtilitate*, lib. vii. (Baſil., 1611, p. 381).

Page 38, line 4. Page 38, line 7. *ferramenta . . . in uſum navigantium.* —Compare Marke Ridley's *A Short Treatiſe of Magneticall Bodies and Motions* (Lond., 1613), p. *a*2 in the *Preface Magneticall*, where he ſpeaks of the "iron-workes" uſed in building ſhips. The phraſeology of Marke Ridley throws much light on the Latin terms uſed by Gilbert.

Page 38, line 36. Page 38, line 42. *vruntur;* changed in ink to *vrantur* in the folio of 1600; but *uruntur* appears in the editions of 1628 and 1633.

Page 39, line 12. Page 39, line 12. *vtrumque;* altered in ink to *vtrunque* in all copies of the folio edition of 1600.

Page 40, line 32. Page 40, line 33. *ad tantos labores exantlandos.*— Pumping, as it was in mining before the invention of the ſteam engine, may beſt be realized by examining the woodcuts in the *De re metallica* of Georgius Agricola (Baſil., Froben, 1556).

Page 40, line 34. Page 40, line 36. *quingentas orgyas.*—Gilbert probably had in his mind the works of the Rörerbühel, in the diſtrict of Kitzbühl, which in the ſixteenth century had reached the depth of 3,107 feet. See Humboldt's *Coſmos* (Lond., 1860, vol. i., p. 149).

Page 43, line 34. Page 43, line 33. *glis.*—This word, here tranſlated *grit*, does not appear to be claſſical Latin; it may mean *ooze* or *ſlime.*

Page 45, line 25. Page 45, line 26. *Motus igitur . . . quinque.* The five kinds of magnetic motions correſpond in fact to the remaining ſections of the book; as follows : *Coitio*, Book II.; *Directio*, Book III.; *Variatio*, Book IV.; *Declinatio*, Book V.; and *Revolutio*, Book VI.

Page 46, line 7. Page 46, line 8. *Jofrancus Offuſius.*—The reference is to the treatiſe *De divina aſtrorum facultate* of Johannes Franciſcus Offuſius (Paris, 1570).

Page 47, line 15. Page 47, line 18. *Græci vocant* ἠλέκτρον, *quia ad ſe paleas trahit.* In this diſcuſſion of the names given to amber, Gilbert apparently conceives ἠλέκτρον to be derived from the verb ἑλκεῖν; which is manifeſtly a doubtful etymology. There has been much diſcuſſion amongſt philologiſts as to the derivation of ἠλέκτρον or ἤλεκτρον, and its poſſible connection with the word ἠλέκτωρ. This diſcuſſion has been ſomewhat obſcured by the circumſtance that the Greek authors unqueſtionably uſed ἤλεκτρον (and the Latins their word *electrum*) in two different ſignifications, ſome of them uſing theſe words to mean amber, others to mean a ſhining metal, apparently of having qualities between those of gold and silver, and probably some sort of alloy. Schweigger, *Ueber das Elektron der Alten* (Greifswald, 1848), has argued that this metal was indeed no other than platinum: but his argument partakes too much of special pleading. Those who desire to follow the question of the derivation of ἤλεκτρον may consult the following authorities: J. M. Gessner, *De Electro Veterum* (Commentt. Soc. Reg. Scientt. Goetting., vol. iii., p. 67, 1753); Delaunay, *Mineralogie der Alten*, Part II., p. 125; Buttmann, *Mythologus* (Appendix I., *Ueber das Elektron*), Vol. II., p. 355, in which he adopts Gilbert's derivation from ἕλκειν; Beckmann, *Ursprung und Bedeutung des Bernsteinnamens Elektron* (Braunsberg, 1859); Th. Henri Martin, *Du Succin, de ses noms divers et de ses variétés suivant les anciens* (Mémoires de l'Académie des Inscriptions et Belles-lettres, Tome VI., 1re série, 1re partie, 1860); Martinus Scheins, *De Electro Veterum Metallico* (Inaugural dissertation, Berlin, 1871); F. A. Paley, *Gold Worship in relation to Sun Worship* (Contemporary Review, August, 1884). See also Curtius, *Grundzüge der griechischen Etymologie*, pp. 656-659. The net result of the disputations of scholars appears to be that ἠλέκτωρ (he who shines) is a masculine form to which there corresponds the neuter form ἤλεκτρον (that which shines). Stephanus admits the accentuation used by Gilbert, ἠλέκτρον, to be justified from the *Timæus* of Plato; see Note to p. **61**.

Page 47, line 16.   Page 47, line 19.   ἅρπαξ *dicitur,* & χρυσοφόρον.—With respect to the other names given to amber, M. Th. Henri Martin has written (see previous note) so admirable an account of them that it is impossible to better it.   It is therefore given here entire, as follows:

" Le succin a reçu chez les anciens des noms très-divers.   Sans parler du nom de λυγκούριον, *lyncurium*, qui peut-être ne lui appartient pas, comme nous le montrerons plus loin, il s'est nommé chez les Grecs le plus souvent ἤλεκτρον au neutre,[1] mais aussi ἤλεκτρος au masculin[2] et même au féminin,[3] χρυσήλεκτρος,[4] χρυσοφόρος,[5] et peut-être, comme nous l'avons vu, χαλκολίθανον; plus tard σούχιον[6] ou σουχῖνος,[7] et ἠλεκτριανὸς λίθος;[8] plus tard encore βερενίκη, βερονίκη ou βερνίκη;[9] il s'est nommé ἅρπαξ chez les Grecs établis en Syrie;[10] chez les Latins *succinum, electrum,* et deux variétés, *chryselectrum* et *sualiterni-*

---

[1] Voyez Hérodote, III., 115; Platon, *Timée*, p. 80 c; Aristote, *Météor.*, IV., 10; Théophraste, *Hist. des plantes*, IX., 18 (19), § 2; *Des pierres*, § 28 et 29; Diodore de Sic., V., 23; Strabon, IV., 6, n° 2, p. 202 (Casaubon); Dioscoride, *Mat. méd.*, I., 110; Plutarque, *Questions de table*, II., 7, § 1; *Questions platoniques*, VII., 1 et 7; Lucien, *Du succin et des cygnes*; le même, *De l'astrologie*, § 19; S. Clément, *Strom.* II., p. 370 (Paris, 1641, in-fol.); Alexandre d'Aphr., *Quest. phys. et mor.*, II., 23; Olympiodore, *Météor.*, I., 8, fol. 16, t. I., p. 197 (Ideler) et l'abréviateur d'Etienne de Byzance au mot Ἡλεκτρίδες.

[2] Voyez Sophocle, *Antigone*, v. 1038, et dans Eustathe, sur l'*Iliade*, II., 865; Elien, *Nat. des animaux*, IV. 46; Quintus de Smyrne, V., 623; Eustathe, sur la *Périégèse* de Denys, p. 142 (Bernhardy), et sur l'*Odyssée*, IV., 73; et Suidas au mot νάλη.

[3] Voyez Alexandre, *Problèmes*, sect. 1, procœm., p. 4 (Ideler); Eustathe, sur l'*Odyssée*, IV., 73, et Tzetzès, *Chiliade* VI., 650.

[4] Voyez Psellus, *Des pierres*, p. 36 (Bernard et Maussac).

[5] Voyez Dioscoride, *Mat. méd.*, I., 110.

[6] Voyez S. Clément, *Strom.*, II., p. 370 (Paris, 1641, in-fol.).   Il paraît distinguer l'un de l'autre τὸ σούχιον et τὸ ἤλεκτρον, probablement parce qu'il attribue à tort au métal ἤλεκτρον la propriété attractive du succin.

[7] Voyez le faux Zoroastre, dans les *Géoponiques*, XV., 1, § 29.

[8] Voyez le faux Zoroastre, au même endroit.

[9] Voyez Eustathe, sur l'*Odyssée*, IV., 73; Tzetzès, *Chil.* VI., 650; Nicolas Myrepse, *Antidotes*, ch. 327, et l'*Etymol. Gud.* au mot ἤλεκτρον.   Comparez Saumaise, *Exerc. plin.*, p. 778.

[10] Voyez Pline, XXXVII., 2, s. 11, n° 37.

cum ou *fubalternicum;*[1] chez les Germains, *Glefs;*[2] chez les Scythes, *facrium;*[3] chez les Egyptiens, *facal;*[4] chez les Arabes, *karabé*[5] ou *kahraba;*[6] en perfan, *káruba.*[7] Ce mot, qui appartient bien à la langue perfane, y fignifie *attirant la paille*, et par conféquent exprime l'attraction électrique, de même que le mot ἅρπαξ des Grecs de Syrie. En outre, le nom de *haur roumi (peuplier romain)* était donné par les Arabes, non-feulement à l'arbre dont ils croyaient que le fuccin était la gomme, mais au fuccin lui-même. *Haur roumi*, tranf-formé en *aurum* par les traducteurs latins des auteurs arabes, et confondu mal à propos avec *ambar* ou *ambrum*, nom arabe latinifé de l'ambre gris, a produit le nom moderne d'*ambre*, nom commun à l'*ambre jaune* ou fuccin, qui eft une réfine foffile, et à l'*ambre gris*, concrétion odorante qui fe forme dans les inteftins des cachalots. On ne peut dire avec certitude fi le nom de baffe grécité βερνίκη eft la fource ou le dérivé de *Bern*, radical du nom allemand du fuccin (*Bernftein*). Quoi qu'il en foit, le mot βερνίκη a produit *vernix*, nom d'une gomme dans la baffe latinité, d'où nous avons fait *vernis.*[8]

Page 47, line 17. Page 47, line 20. *Mauri vero Carabem appellant, quià folebant in facrificijs, & deorum cultu ipfum libare. Carab enim fignificat offerre Arabicè; ita Carabe, res oblata; aut rapiens paleas, vt Scaliger ex Abohali citat, ex linguâ Arabicâ, vel Perficâ.*—The printed text, line **18**, has " Non rapiens paleas," but in all copies of the folio of 1600, the " Non " has been altered in ink into " aut," poffibly by Gilbert's own hand. Neverthelefs the editions of 1628 and 1633 both read " Non." There appears to be no doubt that the origin of the word *Carabe*, or *Karabe*, as affigned by Scaliger, is fubftantially correct. As fhown in the preceding note, Martin adopted this view. If any doubt fhould remain it will be removed by the following notes which are due to Mr. A. Houtum Schindler (member of the Inftitu-tion of Electrical Engineers), of Terahan.

Reference is made to the magnetic and electric properties of ftones in three early Perfian lapidaries. There are three ftones only mentioned, amber, loadftone, and garnet. The electric property of the diamond is not mentioned. The following extracts are from the *Tanfûk nâmah*, by Nafîr ed dîn Tûfi, A.D. 1260. The two other treatifes give the firft extracts in the fame words.

" *Kâhrubâ*, alfo *Kahrabâ* [Amber],

" Is yellow and tranfparent, and has its name from the property, which it poffeffes, of attracting fmall, dry pieces of ftraw or grafs, after it has been rubbed with cloth and become warm. [Note. In Perfian, Kâh = ftraw; rubâ = the robber, hence Kâhrubâ = the ftraw-robber.] Some confider it a mineral, and fay that it is found in the Mediterranean and Cafpian feas, floating on the furface, but this is not correct. The truth is that Kâhrubâ

[1] Voyez Pline, XXXVII., 2, s. 11-13, et Tacite, *Germanie*, ch. 45. La forme *fualiterni-cum*, dans Pline (s. 11, n° 33), eft donnée par le manufcrit de Bamberg et par M. Sillig (t. V., p. 390), au lieu de la forme *fubalternicum* des éditions antérieures.
[2] Voyez Tacite et Pline, *ll. cc.*
[3] Voyez Pline, XXXVII., 2, s. 11, n° 40, Comp. J. Grimm, *Gefch. der deutfch. Sprache*, Kap. x., p. 233 (Leipzig, 1848, in-8).
[4] Pline, *l. c.*
[5] Voyez Saumaife, *De homon. hyles iatricæ*, c. 101, p. 162 (1689, in-fol.).
[6] Voyez Sprengel, fur Diofcoride, t. II., pp. 390-391.
[7] Voyez M. de Sacy, cité par Buttmann, *Mythologus*, t. II., pp. 362-363.
[8] Voyez Saumaife, *Ex. plin.*, p. 778. Il n'eft pas probable que le mot βερνίκη ou βερενίκη, nom du fuccin dans la grécité du moyen âge, foit lié étymologiquement avec le nom propre βερενίκη, qui vient de l'adjectif macédonien βερένικος pour φερένικος.

E

is the gum of a tree, called jôz i rûmî [*i.e.*, roman nut ; walnut?], and that
moſt of it is brought from Rûm [here the Eaſtern Rome] and from the
confines of Sclavonia and Ruſſia.   On account of its bright colour and
tranſparency it is made into beads, rings, belt-buckles, &c. . . . &c.

. . . .

"The properties of attraction and repulſion are poſſeſſed by other ſubſtances
than loadſtone, for inſtance, by amber and bîjâdah,[1] which attract ſtraws,
feathers, etc., and of many other bodies, it can be ſaid that they poſſeſs the
power of attraction.   There is alſo a ſtone which attracts gold ; it has a pure
yellow colour.   There is alſo a ſtone which attracts ſilver from diſtances of
three or two yards.   There are alſo the ſtone which attracts tin, very hard,
and ſmelling like aſafœtida, the ſtone attracting hair, the ſtone attracting
meat, etc., but, latterly, no one has ſeen theſe ſtones : no proof, however,
that they do not exiſt."

Avicenna (Ibn Sinâ) gives the following under the heading of *Karabe*
(ſee *Canona Medicinæ*, Giunta edition, Venet., 1608, lib. ii., cap. 371,
p. 336):

"Karabe quid eſt ?   Gumma ſicut ſandaraca, tendens ad citrinitatem, &
albedinem, & peruietatem, & quandoque declinat ad rubedinem, quæ attrahit
paleas, & [fracturas] plantarum ad ſe, & propter hoc nominatur Karabe,
ſcilicet rapiens paleas, perſicè. . . . Karabe confert tremori cordis, quum
bibitur ex eo medietas aurei cum aqua frigida, & prohibet ſputum ſanguinis
valde. . . . Retinet vomitum, & prohibet materias malas a ſtomacho, &
cum maſtiche confortat ſtomachum. . . . Retinet fluxum ſanguinis ex
matrice, & ano, & fluxum ventris, & confert tenaſmoni."

Scaliger in *De Subtilitate, Exercitatio* ciii., § 12, the paſſage reterred to
by Gilbert ſays: "Succinum apud Arabas uocatur, Carabe : quod princeps
Aboali, rapiens paleas, interpretatur" (p. 163 *bis*, editio Lutetiæ, 1557).

Page 47, line 21.   Page 47, line 25.   *Succinum ſeu ſuccum.*—Dioſcorides
regarded amber as the inſpiſſated juice of the poplar tree.   From the
Frankfurt edition of 1543 (*De Medicinali materia, etc.*), edited by Ruellius,
we have, liber i., p. 53:

Populus.   Cap. XCIII.

". . . Lachrymam populorum commemorant quæ in Padum amnem
defluat, durari, ac coire in ſuccinum, quod electrum vocant, alii chryſophorum.
id attritu jucundum odorem ſpirat, et aurum colore imitatur. tritum potumque
ſtomachi ventriſque fluxiones ſiſtit."

To this Ruellius adds the commentary:

"Succinum ſeu ſuccina gutta à ſucco dicta, Græcis ἤλεκτρομ [ſic], eſſe

---

[1] *Bîjâdah* is claſſified by Muhammad B. Manſûr (A.D. 1470) and by Ibn al Mubârak
(A.D. 1520) under "ſtones reſembling ruby"; the Tanſûk nâmah deſcribes it in a ſeparate
chapter.   From the deſcription it can be identified with the almandine garnet, and the
method of cutting this ſtone *en cabochon*, with hollow back in order to diſplay its colour
better, is ſpecially mentioned.   The Tanſûk nâmah only incidentally refers to the electric
property of the *bîjâdah* in the chapter on loadſtone, but the other two treatiſes ſpecially refer
to it in their deſcription of the ſtone.   The one has : "*Bîjâdah*, if rubbed until warm,
attracts ſtraws and other light bodies juſt as amber does"; the other: "*Bîjâdah*, if rubbed on
the hair of the head, or on the beard, attracts ſtraws."   Surûri, the lexicographer, who
compiled a dictionary in 1599, conſiders the *bîjâdah* "a red ruby which poſſeſſes the property
of attraction."   Other dictionaries do not mention the attractive property, but ſome authors
confound the ſtone with amber, calling it *Kâhrubâ*, the ſtraw-robber.   The *bîjâdah* is not
rubellite (red tourmaline) for it is deſcribed in the lapidaries as common, whereas rubellite
(from Ceylon) has always been rare, and was unknown in Perſia in the thirteenth century.

lachryma populi albæ, vel etiam nigræ quibuſdam videtur, ab ejuſdem arboris reſina. Dioſcoridi et Galeno dicta differens et πτερυγοφόρος, id eſt paleas trahens, quoque vocatur, quantum ei quoque Galenus tribuit li. 37, ca. 9. Succinum ſcribit à quibuſdam pinei generis arboribus, ut gummi à ceraſis excidere autumno, et largum mitti ex Germania ſeptentrionali, et inſulis maris Germanici. quod hodie nobis eſt compertiſſimum : ad hæc liquata igni valentiore, quia à frigido intenſiore concrevit. pineam aperte olet, calidum primo gradu, ſiccum ſecundo, ſtomachum roborat, vomitum, nauſeam arcet. cordis palpitationi prodeſt. pravorem humorum generationem prohibet.

"Germani weiſs und gelbaugſtein et breñſtein.

"Galli ambra vocant: vulgo in corollis precariis frequens."

In the ſcholia of Johann Lonicer in his edition of Dioſcorides, we find, lib. i., cap. xcviii., *De nigra Populo :*

"αἴγειρος, populus nigra. . . . idem electrum vel ſuccinum αἰγείρου lachrymam eſſe adſeverat [Paulus], cui præter vires quæ ab Dioſcoride recenſentur, tribuit etiam vim ſiſtendi ſanguinis, ſi tuſum in potu ſumatur. Avicennæ Charabe, ut colligitur ex Joanne Jacobo Manlio, eſt electrum hoc Dioſcoridis, atteſtatur Brunfelſius. Lucianus planè nullum electrum apud Eridanum ſeu Padum inveniri tradit, quandoquidem ne populus quidem illa ab nautis ei demonſtrari potuerit. Plinius ruſticas transſpadanas ex electro monilia geſtare adfirmat, quum à Venetis primum agnoſcere didiciſſent adverſus nimirum vitia gutturis et tonſillarum. Num ſit purgamentum maris, vel lachryma populi, vel pinus, vel ex radiis occidentis ſolis naſcatur, vel ex montibus Sudinorum profluat, incertum etiam Eraſmus Stella relinquit. Sudinas tamen Boruſſiorum opes eſſe conſtat."

Matthiolus (in *P. A. Mattioli . . . Opera quæ extant omnia, hoc eſt Commentarii in vi libros P. Dioſcoridis de materia medica*, Frankfurt, 1596, p. 133) comments on the ſuggeſtion of Galen that amber came from the *Populus alba*, and alſo comments on the Arabic, Greek, and Latin names of amber.

The poplar-myth is commemorated by Addiſon (in *Italy*) in the lines :

> No interwoven reeds a garland made,
> To hide his brows within the vulgar ſhade ;
> But poplar wreathes around his temples ſpread,
> And tears of amber trickled down his head.

Amber is, however, aſſuredly not derived from any poplar tree: it comes from a ſpecies of pine long ago extinct, called by Göppert the *pinites ſuccini-fer.*

Gilbert does not go into the medicinal uſes, real or fancied, that have been aſcribed to amber in almoſt as great variety as to loadſtone. Pliny mentions ſome of theſe in his *Natural Hiſtorie* (Engliſh verſion of 1601, p. 609):

"He [Calliſtratus] ſaith of this yellow Amber, that if it be worne about the necke in a collar, it cureth feavers, and healeth the diſeaſes of the mouth, throat, and jawes: reduced into pouder and tempered with honey and oile of roſes, it is ſoveraigne for the infirmities of the eares. Stamped together with the beſt Atticke honey, it maketh a ſingular eyeſalve for to help a dim ſight: pulverized, and the pouder thereof taken ſimply alone, or elſe drunke in water with Maſticke, is ſoveraigne for the maladies of the ſtomacke."

Nicolaus Myrepſus (Recipe 951, *op. citat.*) gives a preſcription for dyſentery and diabetes confiſting chiefly of " Electri vel ſucci Nili (Nili ſuccum appellant Arabes Karabem)."

Page 47, line 22. Page 47, line 26. *Sudauienſes ſeu Sudini.*—Cardan in *De Rerum Varietate*, lib. iii., cap. xv. (Editio Baſil., 1556, p. 152), ſays of amber :

"Colligitur in quadam penè inſula Sudinorum, qui nunc uocātur Bruſci, in Pruſſia, nunc Boruſſia, juxta Veneticum ſinum, & ſunt orientaliores oſtiis Viſtulæ fluuii : ubi triginta pagi huic muneri deſtinati ſunt," etc. He rejects the theory that it conſiſts of hardened gum.

There exiſts an enormous literature concerning Amber and the Pruſſian amber induſtry. Amongſt the earlieſt works (after Theophraſtus and Pliny) are thoſe of Aurifaber (*Bericht über Agtſtein oder Börnſtein*, Königſberg, 1551); Goebel (*De Succino, Libri duo, authore Severino Gæbelio, Medico Doctore*, Regiomont., 1558); and Wigand (*Vera hiſtoria de Succino Boruſſico*, Jena, 1590). Later on Hartmann, P. J. (*Succini Pruſſici Phyſica et civilis Hiſtoria*, Francofurti, 1677); and the ſplendid folio of Nathaniel Sendel (*Hiſtoria Succinorum corpora aliena involventium*, Lipſiæ, 1742), with its wealth of plates illuſtrating amber ſpecimens, with the various included foſſil fauna and flora. Georgius Agricola (*De natura Foſſilium*, liber iv.), and Aldrovandi (*Muſæum Metallicum*, pp. 411-412) muſt alſo be mentioned. Bibliographies of the earlier literature are to be found in Hartmann (*op. citat.*), and in Daniel Gralath, *Elektriſche Bibliothek (Verſuche und Abhandlungen der Naturforſchenden Geſellſchaft in Danzig*, Zweiter Theil, pp. 537-539, Danzig and Leipzig, 1754). See alſo Karl Müllenhoff, *Deutſche Altertumſkunde*, vol. i., Zweites Buch, pp. 211-224, Zinn und Bernſteinhandel (Berlin, 1870), and Humboldt's *Coſmos* (Bohn's edition, London, 1860, vol. ii., p. 493).

The ancient Greek myth according to which amber was the tears of the Heliades, ſhed on the banks of the river Eridanus over Phaethon, is not alluded to by Gilbert. It is narrated in well-known paſſages in Ovid and in Hyginus. Thoſe intereſted in the modern handling of the myth ſhould refer to Müllenhoff (*op. citat.*, pp. 217-223, der Bernſteinmythus), or to that delightful work *The Tears of the Heliades*, by W. Arnold Buffum (London, 1896).

Page 47, line 30. Page 47, line 36. *quare & muſcos . . . in fruſtulis quibuſdam comprehenſos retinet.*—The occurrence of flies in amber was well known to the ancients. Pliny thus ſpeaks of it, book xxxvii., chap. iii. (p. 608 of P. Holland's tranſlation of 1601) :

"That it doth deſtill and drop at the firſt very clear and liquid, it is evident by this argument, for that a man may ſee diverſe things within, to wit, Piſmires, Gnats, and Lizards, which no doubt were entangled and ſtucke within it when it was greene and freſh, and ſo remain encloſed within as it waxed harder."

A locuſt embedded in amber is mentioned in the *Muſæum Septalianum* of Terzagus (Dertonæ, 1664).

Martial's epigram (*Epigrammata*, liber vi., 15) is well known :

Dum Phaethontea formica vagatur in umbra
Implicuit tenuem ſuccina gutta feram.

See alſo Hermann (Daniel), *De rana et lacerta Succino Boruſſiaco inſitis*

(Cracov., 1580; a later edition, Rigæ, 1600). The great work on *inclusa* in amber is, however, that of Nathaniel Sendel. See the previous note.

Sir Thomas Browne muſt not be forgotten in this connexion. The *Pſeudodoxia* (p. 64 of the ſecond edition, 1650) ſays:

"Laſtly, we will not omit what Bellabonus upon his own experiment writ from Dantzich unto Mellichius, as he hath left recorded in his chapter *De Succino*, that the bodies of Flies, Piſmires and the like, which are ſaid oft times to be included in Amber, are not reall but repreſentative, as he diſcovered in ſeverall pieces broke for that purpoſe. If ſo, the two famous Epigrams hereof in Martiall are but poeticall, the Piſmire of Braſſavolus Imaginary, and Cardans Mouſoleum for a flie, a meer phancy. But hereunto we know not how to aſſent, as having met with ſome whoſe reals made good their repreſentments." See alſo Pope's *Epiſtle to Dr. Arbuthnot*, line 169.

Page 47, line 34. Page 47, line 40. *Commemorant antiqui quod ſuccinum feſtucas et paleas attrahit.*—Pliny (book xxxvii., chap. ii., p. 606 of the Engliſh edition of 1601) thus narrates the point:

" Hee [*Niceas*] writeth alſo, that in Aegypt it [amber] is engendered. . . . Semblably in Syria, the women (ſaith hee) make wherves of it for their ſpindles, where they uſe to call it Harpax, becauſe it will catch up leaves, ſtraws, and fringes hanging to cloaths.'

p. 608. " To come to the properties that Amber hath, If it bee well rubbed and chaufed betweene the fingers, the potentiall facultie that lieth within, is ſet on work, and brought into actual operation, whereby you ſhall ſee it to drawe chaffe ſtrawes, drie leaves, yea, and thin rinds of the Linden or Tillet tree, after the ſame ſort as loadſtone draweth yron."

Page 47, line 36. Page 47, line 42. *Quod etiam facit Gagates lapis.* —The properties of Jet were well known to the mediæval writers. *Julius Solinus* writes in *De Mirabilibus*, chapter xxxiv., *Of Britaine* (Engliſh verſion of 1587 by A. Golding):

" Moreover to the intent to paſſe the large abounnance of ſundry mettals (whereof Britaine hath many rich mynes on all ſides), Here is ſtore of the ſtone called Geate, and yᵉ beſt kind of it. If ye demaund yᵉ beautie of it, it is a black Jewell: if the qualitie, it is of no weight: if the nature, it burneth in water, and goeth out in Oyle; if the power, rubbe it till it be warme, and it holdeth ſuch things as are laide to it; as Amber doth. The Realme is partlie inhabited of barbarous people, who even frõ theyr childhoode haue ſhapes of divers beaſtes cunninglye impreſſed and incorporate in theyr bodyes, ſo that beeing engraued as it were in theyr bowels, as the man groweth, ſo growe the marks painted vpon him . . .'

Pliny deſcribes it as follows (p. 589, Engliſh edition of 1601):

" The Geat, which otherwiſe we call Gagates, carrieth the name of a toune and river both in Lycia, called Gages: it is ſaid alſo, that the ſea caſteth it up at a full tide or high water into the Iſland Leucola, where it is gathered within the ſpace of twelve ſtadia, and no where elſe: blacke it is, plaine and even, of a hollow ſubſtance in manner of the pumiſh ſtone, not much differing from the nature of wood; light, brittle, and if it bee rubbed or bruiſed, of a ſtrong flavour." (Book xxxvi., chap. xviii.)

In the Commentary of Joannes Ruellius upon Dioſcorides, *Pedanii Dioſcoridis Anazarbei de medicinali materia libri ſex, Ioanne Ruellio Sueſſionenſi interprete* . . . (Frankfurt, 1543, fol., liber quintus, cap. xcii.) is the following deſcription:

"In Gagatarum lapidum genere, præferendus qui celeriter accenditur, et odorem bituminis reddit. niger eft plerunque, et fqualidus, cruftofus, per quam levis. Vis ei molliendi, et difcutiendi. deprehendit fonticum morbum fuffitus, recreatque uuluæ ftrangulationes. fugat ferpentes nidore. podagricis medicaminibus, et a copis additur. In Cilicia nafci folet, qua influens amnis in mare effunditur, proxime oppidum quod Plagiopolis dicitur. vocatur autem et locus et amnis Gagas, in cujus faucibus ii lapides inveniuntur.

"Gagates lapis colorė atro, Germanis Schwartzer augftein, voce parum depravata, dicitur. odore dum uritur bituminis, ficcat, glutinat, digerit admotus, in corollis precariis et falinis frequens."

And in the *Scholia* upon Diofcorides of Joannes Lonicer (Marpurgi, 1643, cap. xcvii., p. 80) is the following :

"*De Gagate Lapide.* Ab natali folo, urbe nimirum Gagae Lyciae nomen habet. Galenus fe flumen ifthuc et lapidem non inveniffe, etiamfi naui parua totam Lyciam perluftravit: ait, fe autem in caua Syria multos nigros lapides inveniffe glebofos, qui igni impofiti, exiguam flammam gignerent. Meminit hujus Nicander in Theriacis nempe fuffitum hujus abigere venenata."

There is alfo a good account of *Gagates* (and of *Succinum*) by Langius, *Epiftola* LXXV., p. 454, of the work *Epiftolarum medicinalium volumen tripartitum* (Francofurti, 1589).

Page 47, line 39. Page 47, line 45. *Multi funt authores moderni.*— The modern authors who raifed Gilbert's wrath by ignorantly copying out all the old tales about amber, jet, and loadftone, inftead of inveftigating the facts, were, as he fays at the beginning of the chapter, fome theologians, and fome phyficians. He feems to have taken a fpecial diflike to Albertus Magnus, to Puteanus (Du Puys), and to Levinus Lemnius.

Page 47, line 39. Page 47, line 46. *& gagate.*—The editions of 1628 and 1633 both read *ex gagate*.

Page 48, line 14. Page 48, line 16. *Nam non folum fuccinum, & gagates (vt illi putant) allectant corpufcula.*—The lift of bodies known to become electrical by friction was not quite fo reftricted as would appear from this paffage. Five, if not fix, other minerals had been named in addition to amber and jet.

(1.) *Lyncurium.* This ftone, about which there has been more obfcurity and confufion than about any other gem, is fuppofed by fome writers to be the tourmaline, by others a jacinth, and by others a belemnite. The ancients fuppofed it to be produced from the urine of the lynx. The following is the account of Theophraftus, *Theophraftus's Hiftory of Stones. With an Englifh Verfion* . . ., by "Sir" John Hill, London, 1774, p. 123, ch. xlix.-l. "There is fome Workmanfhip required to bring the Emerald to its Luftre, for originally it is not fo bright. It is, however, excellent in its Virtues, as is alfo the *Lapis Lyncurius*, which is likewife ufed for engraving Seals on, and is of a very folid Texture, as Stones are; it has alfo an attractive Power, like that of Amber, and is faid to attract not only Straws and fmall pieces of Sticks, but even Copper and Iron, if they are beaten to thin pieces. This Diocles affirms. The *Lapis Lyncurius* is pellucid, and of a fire Colour." See alfo W. Watfon in *Philos. Trans.*, 1759, L. i., p. 394, *Obfervations concerning the Lyncurium of the ancients.*

(2.) *Ruby.*

(3.) *Garnet.* The authority for both thefe is Pliny, *Nat. Hift.*, book xxxvii., chap. vii. (p. 617 of Englifh edition of 1601).

"Over and befides, I find other forts of Rubies different from thofe above-named; . . . which being chaufed in the Sun, or otherwife fet in a heat by rubbing with the fingers, will draw unto them chaffe, ftrawes, fhreads, and leaves of paper. The common Grenat alfo of Carchedon or Carthage, is faid to doe as much, although it be inferiour in price to the former."

(4.) *Jafper.* Affaytatus is the authority, in *Fortunii Affaitati Phyfici atque Theologi . . . Phyficæ & Aftronomicæ côfiderationes* (Venet., 1549), where, on p. 20, he fpeaks of the magnet turning to the pole, likening it to the turning of a " palea ab Ambro vel Iafpide et hujufcemodi lapillis lucidis."

(5.) *Lychnis.* Pliny and St. Ifidore fpeak of a certain ftone *lychnis*, of a fcarlet or flame colour, which, when warmed by the fun or between the fingers, attracts ftraws or leaves of papyrus. Pliny puts this ftone amongft carbuncles, but it is much more probably *rubellite*, that is to fay, red tourmaline.

(6.) *Diamond.* In fpite of the confufion already noted, *à propos* of *adamas* (Note to p. **47**), between loadftone and diamond, there feems to be one diftinct record of an attractive effect having been obferved with a rubbed diamond. This was recorded by Fracaftorio, *De fympathia et antipathia rerum* (Giunta edition, Venice, MDLXXIIII, chap. v., p. 60 *verfo*), " cujus rei & illud effe fignum poteft, cum confricata quædã vt Succinum, & Adamas fortius furculos trahunt." And (on p. 62 *recto*); " nam fi per fimilitudine (vt fupra diximus) fit hæc attractio, cur magnes non potius magnetem trahit, q̃ ferrum, & ferrum non potius ad ferrum movetur, quàm ad magnetem? quæ nam affinitas eft pilorum, & furculorum cum Electro, & Adamante? præfertim q̃ fi cum Electro affines funt, quomodo & cum Adamante affinitatem habebunt, qui diffimilis Electro eft?" An inconteftable cafe of the obfervation of the electrification of the diamond occurs in Gartias ab Horto. The firft edition of his *Hiftoria dei Semplici Aromati* was publifht at Goa in India in 1563. In chapter xlviii. on the Diamond, occur thefe words (p. 200 of the Venetian edition of 1616): "Quefto fi bene ho fperimentato io più volte, che due Diamanti perfetti fregati infieme, fi vnifcono di modo infieme, che non di leggiero li potrai feparare. Et ho parimente veduto il Diamante dopo di effer ben rifcaldato, tirare à fe le feftuche, non men, che fi faccia l'elettro." See alfo Aldrovandi, *Mufæum Metallicum* (Bonon., 1648, p. 947).

Levinus Lemnius alfo mentions the Diamond along with amber. See his *Occulta naturæ miracula* (Englifh edition, London, 1658, p. 199).

Page 48, line 16. Page 48, line 18. *Iris gemma.*—The name *iris* was given, there can be little doubt, to clear fix-fided prifms of rock-cryftal (quartz), which, when held in the fun's beams, caft a crude fpectrum of the colours of the rainbow. The following is the account of it given in Pliny, book xxxvii., chap. vii. (p. 623 of the Englifh verfion of 1601):

" . . . there is a ftone in name called Iris: digged out of the ground it is in a certaine Ifland of the red fea, diftant from the city Berenice three fcore miles. For the moft part it refembleth Cryftall: which is the reafon that fome hath tearmed it the root of Cryftall. But the caufe why they call it Iris, is, That if the beames of the Sunne ftrike upon it directly within houfe, it doth fend from it againft the walls that bee neare, the very refemblance both in forme and alfo in colour of a rainebow; and eftfoones it will chaunge the fame in much varietie, to the great admiration of them that behold it. For certain it is knowne, that fix angles it hath in manner of the Cryftall: but they fay that fome of them have their fides rugged, and the fame unequally angled: which if they be laid abroad againſt the Sunne in the open aire, do ſcatter the beames of the Sunne, which light upon them too and fro: alſo that others doe yeeld a brightnes from themſelves, and thereby illuminat all that is about them.   As for the diverſe colours which they caſt forth, it never happeneth but in a darke or ſhaddowie place: whereby a man may know, that the varietie of colours is not in the ſtone Iris, but commeth by the reverberation of the wals.   But the beſt Iris is that which repreſenteth the greateſt circles upon the wall, and thoſe which bee likeſt unto rainebowes indeed."

In the Engliſh tranſlation of Solinus's *De Mirabilibus* (*The excellent and pleaſant worke of Julius Solinus contayning the noble aſtions of humaine creatures, the ſecretes and providence of nature, the deſcriptions of countries . . . tr. by A. Golding, gent.*, Lond., 1587), chapter xv. on Arabia has the following:

"Hee findeth likewiſe the Iris in the Red ſea, ſixe cornered as the Cryſtall: which beeing touched with the Sunnebeames, caſteth out of him a bryght reflexion of the ayre like the Raynebowe."

Iris is alſo mentioned by Albertus Magnus (*De mineralibus*, Venet., 1542, p. 189), by Marbodeus Gallus (*De lapidibus*, Par. 1531, p. 78), who deſcribes it as "cryſtallo ſimulem ſexangulam," by Lomatius (*Artes of curious Paintinge*, Haydocke's tranſlation, Lond., 1598, p. 157), who ſays, ". . . the Sunne, which caſting his beames vpon the *ſtone Iris*, cauſeth the *raine-bowe* to appeare therein . . .," and by "Sir" John Hill (*A General Natural Hiſtory*, Lond., 1748, p. 179).

Figures of the Iris given by Aldrovandi in the *Muſæum Metallicum* clearly depiſt cryſtals of quartz.

Page 48, line 16.   Page 48, line 18.   *Vincentina, & Briſtolla* (*Anglica gemma ſiue fluor*).   This is doubtleſs the ſame ſubſtance as the *Gemma Vincentij rupis* mentioned on p. **54**, line **16** (p. 54, line 18, of Engliſh Verſion), and is nothing elſe than the ſo-called "Briſtol diamond," a variety of dark quartz cryſtallized in ſmall brilliant cryſtals upon a baſis of hæmatite. To the work by Dr. Thomas Venner (Lond., 1650), entitled *Via Reſta* or the *Bathes of Bathe,* there is added an appendix, *A Cenſure concerning the water of Saint Vincents Rocks neer Briſtol* (*Urbs pulchra et Emporium celebre*), in which, at p. 376, occurs this paſſage: "This Water of Saint *Vincents* Rock is of a very pure, cleare, cryſtalline ſubſtance, anſwering to thoſe cryſtalline Diamonds and tranſparent ſtones that are plentifully found in thoſe Clifts."

In the *Foſſils Arranged* of "Sir" John Hill (Lond., 1771), p. 123, is the following entry: "Black cryſtal.   Small very hard heavy gloſſy.   Perfeſtly black, opake.   Briſtol (grottos, glaſs)" referring to its uſe.

The name *Vincentina* is not known as occurring in any mineralogical book.   Prof. H. A. Miers, F.R.S., writes concerning the paſſage: "*Anglica gemma ſive fluor* ſeems to be a ſynonym for *Briſtolla,* or poſſibly for *Vincentina et Briſtolla*.   Both quartz and fluor are found at Clifton.   In that caſe Vincentina and Briſtolla refer to theſe two minerals, and if ſo one would expeſt Briſtolla to be the Briſtol Diamond, and Vincentina to be the comparatively rare Fluor ſpar from that locality."

At the end of the edition of 1653 of Sir Hugh Plat's *Jewel Houſe of Art and Nature,* is appended *A rare and excellent Diſcourſe of Minerals, Stones, Gums, and Roſins; with the vertues and uſe thereof,* By D. B. Gent. Here, p. 218, we read:

"We have in England a ſtone or mineral called a Briſtol ſtone (becauſe many are found thereabouts) which much refembles the Adamant or Diamond, which is brought out of Arabia and Cyprus ; but as it is wanting of the fame hardneffe, fo falls it fhort of the like vertues."

Page 48, line 18. Page 48, line 19. *Cryftallus.*—Rock-cryftal. Quartz. Pliny's account of it (Philemon Holland's verfion of 1601, p. 604) in book xxxvii., chap. ii., is:

" As touching Cryftall, it proceedeth of a contrarie caufe, namely of cold ; for a liquor it is congealed by extreame froft in manner of yce ; and for proofe hereof, you fhall find cryftall in no place els but where the winter fnow is frozen hard : fo as we may boldly fay, it is verie yce and nothing elfe, whereupon the Greeks have give it the right name Cryftallos, *i.* Yce. . . . Thus much I dare my felfe avouch, that cryftall groweth within certaine rockes upon the Alps, and thefe fo fteepe and inacceffible, that for the moft part they are conftrained to hang by ropes that fhall get it forth."

Page 48, line 18. Page 48, line 20. *Similes etiam attrahendi vires habere videntur vitrum . . . fulphur, maftix, & cera dura figillaris.* If, as fhown above, the electric powers of diamond and ruby had already been obferved, yet Gilbert was the firft beyond queftion to extend the lift of *electrics* beyond the clafs of precious ftones, and his difcovery that *glafs, fulphur,* and *fealing-wax* acted, when rubbed, like amber, was of capital importance. Though he did not purfue the difcovery into mechanical contrivances, he left the means of that extenfion to his followers. To Otto von Guericke we owe the application of fulphur to make the firft electrical machine out of a revolving globe ; to Sir Ifaac Newton the fuggeftion of glafs as affording a more mechanical conftruction.

Electrical attraction by natural products other than amber after they have been rubbed muft have been obferved by the primitive races of mankind. Indeed Humboldt in his *Cofmos* (Lond., 1860, vol. i., p. 182) records a ftriking inftance :

" I obferved with aftonifhment, on the woody banks of the Orinoco, in the fports of the natives, that the excitement of electricity by friction was known to thefe favage races, who occupy the very loweft place in the fcale of humanity. Children may be feen to rub the dry, flat and fhining feeds or hufks of a trailing plant (probably a *Negretia*) until they are able to attract threads of cotton and pieces of bamboo cane."

Page 48, line 23. Page 48, line 25. *arfenicum.*—This is *orpiment.* See the *Dictionary of metallick words* at the end of Pettus's *Fleta Minor.*

Page 48, line 23. Page 48, line 26. *in convenienti cælo ficco.*—The obfervation that only in a dry climate do rock-falt, mica, and rock-alum act as electrics is alfo of capital importance. Compare page **56**.

Page 48, line 27. Page 48, line 31. *Alliciunt hæc omnia non feftucas modò & paleas.*—Gilbert himfelf marks the importance of this difcovery by the large afterifk in the margin. The logical confequence was his invention of the firft *electrofcope*, the *verforium non magneticum*, made of any metal, figured on p. **49**.

Page 48, line 34. Page 48, line 36. *quòd tantum ficcas attrahat paleas, nec folia ocimi.*—This filly tale that bafil leaves were not attracted by amber arofe in the *Quæftiones Convivales* of Plutarch. It is repeated by Marbodeus and was quoted by Levinus Lemnius as true. Gilbert denounced it as nonfenfe. Cardan (*De Subtilitate*, Norimb., 1550, p. 132) had already contradicted the fable. " Trahit enim," he fays, " omnia levia, paleas, feftucas, ramenta

tenuia metallorum, & ocimi folia, perperam contradicente Theophrafto."
Sir Thomas Browne fpecifically refuted it. "For if," he fays, "the leaves
thereof or dried ftalks be ftripped into fmall ftrawes, they arife unto Amber,
Wax, and other Electricks, no otherwife then thofe of Wheat or Rye."

Page 48, line 34. Page 48, line 38. *Sed vt poteris manifeftè experiri* ...
Gilbert's experimental difcoveries in electricity may be fummarized as
follows :

1. The generalization of the clafs of *Electrics*.
2. The obfervation that damp weather hinders electrification.
3. The generalization that electrified bodies attract everything, including even metals, water, and oil.
4. The invention of the non-magnetic *verforium* or electrofcope.
5. The obfervation that merely warming amber does not electrify it.
6. The recognition of a definite clafs of *non-electrics*.
7. The obfervation that certain electrics do not attract if roafted or burnt.
8. That certain electrics when foftened by heat lofe their power.
9. That the electric effluvia are ftopped by the interpofition of a fheet of paper or a piece of linen, or by moift air blown from the mouth.
10. That glowing bodies, fuch as a live coal, brought near excited amber difcharge its power.
11. That the heat of the fun, even when concentrated by a burning mirror, confers no vigour on the amber, but diffipates the effluvia.
12. That fulphur and fhell-lac when aflame are not electric.
13. That polifh is not effential for an electric.
14. That the electric attracts bodies themfelves, not the intervening air.
15. That flame is not attracted.
16. That flame deftroys the electrical effluvia.
17. That during fouth winds and in damp weather, glafs and cryftal, which collect moifture on their furface, are electrically more interfered with than amber, jet and fulphur, which do not fo eafily take up moifture on their furfaces.
18. That pure oil does not hinder production of electrification or exercife of attraction.
19. That fmoke is electrically attracted, unlefs too rare.
20. That the attraction by an electric is in a ftraight line toward it.

Page 48, line 35. Page 48, line 39. *quæ funt illæ materiæ.*—Gilbert's
lift of electrics fhould be compared with thofe given fubfequently by Cabeus
(1629), by Sir Thomas Browne (1646), and by Bacon. The laft-named
lift occurs in his *Phyfiological Remains*, publifhed pofthumoufly in 1679; it
contains nothing new. Sir Thomas Browne's lift is given in the following
paffage, which is interefting as ufing for the firft time in the Englifh
language the noun *Electricities*:

"Many ftones alfo both precious and vulgar, although terfe and fmooth,
have not this power attractive; as Emeralds, Pearle, Jafpis, Corneleans,
Agathe, Heliotropes, Marble, Alablafter, Touchftone, Flint and Bezoar.
Glaffe attracts but weakely though cleere, fome flick ftones and thick glaffes
indifferently: Arfenic but weakely, fo likewife glaffe of Antimony, but
Crocus Metallorum not at all. Saltes generally but weakely, as Sal Gemma,
Alum, and alfo Talke, nor very difcoverably by any frication: but if gently
warmed at the fire, and wiped with a dry cloth, they will better difcover
their Electricities." (*Pfeudodoxia Epidemica*, p. 79.)

In the *Philofophical Tranfactions*, vol. xx., p. 384, is *A Catalogue of
Electrical Bodies* by the late Dr. Rob. Plot. It begins "Non folum fuccinum,"
and ends "alumen rupeum," being identical with Gilbert's lift except that
he calls "Vincentina & Briftolla" by the name "Pfeudoadamas Briftolienfis."

Page 49, line 25. Page 49, line 30. *non diffimili modo.*—The *modus* *operandi* of the electrical attractions was a subject of much discussion; see Cardan, *op. citat.*

Page 51, line 2. Page 51, line 1. *appellunt.*—This appears to be a misprint for *appelluntur.*

Page 51, line 22. Page 51, line 23. *smyris.*—Emery. This substance is mentioned on p. **22** as a magnetic body.

Page 52, line 1. Page 51, line 46. *gemmæ . . . vt Crystallus, quæ ex limpidâ concreuit.* See the note to p. **48.**

Page 52, line 30. Page 52, line 32. *ammoniacum.*—Ammoniacum, or Gutta Ammoniaca, is described by Dioscorides as being the juice of a ferula grown in Africa, resembling galbanum, and used for incense.

"*Ammoniack* is a kind of Gum like Frankincense; it grows in Lybia, where *Ammon's* Temple was." Sir Hugh Plat's *Jewel House of Art and Nature* (Ed. 1653, p. 223).

Page 52, line 38. Page 52, line 41. *duæ propositæ sunt causæ . . . materia & forma.*—Gilbert had imbibed the schoolmen's ideas as to the relations of matter and form. He had discovered and noted that in the magnetic attractions there was always a verticity, and that in the electrical attractions the rubbed electrical body had no verticity. To account for these differences he drew the inference that since (as he had satisfied himself) the magnetic actions were due to *form*, that is to say to something immaterial—to an "imponderable" as in the subsequent age it was called—the electrical actions must necessarily be due to *matter.* He therefore put forward his idea that a substance to be an electric must necessarily consist of a concreted humour which is partially resolved into an effluvium by attrition. His discoveries that electric actions would not pass through flame, whilst magnetic actions would, and that electric actions could be screened off by interposing the thinnest layer of fabric such as sarcenet, whilst magnetic actions would penetrate thick slabs of every material except iron only, doubtless confirmed him in attributing the electric forces to the presence of these effluvia. See also p. **65.** There arose a fashion, which lasted over a century, for ascribing to "humours," or "fluids," or "effluvia," physical effects which could not otherwise be accounted for. Boyle's tracts of the years 1673 and 1674 on "effluviums," their "determinate nature," their "strange subtilty," and their "great efficacy," are examples.

Page 53, line 9. Page 53, line 11. *Magnes vero . . .*—This passage from line **9** to line **24** states very clearly the differences to be observed between the magnetical and the electrical attractions.

Page 53, line 36. Page 53, line 41. *succino calefacto.*—Ed. 1633 reads *succinum*, in error.

Page 54, line 9. Page 54, line 11. *Plutarchus . . . in quæstionibus Platonicis.*—The following Latin version of the paragraph in *Quæstio sexta* is taken from the bilingual edition publisht at Venice in 1552, p. 17 *verso*, liber vii., cap. 7 (or, *Quæstio Septima* in Ed. Didot, p. 1230).

"Electrum uero quæ apposita sunt, nequaquàm trahit, quem admodum nec lapis ille, qui sideritis nuncupatur, nec quicquā à seipso ad ea quæ in propinquo sunt, extrinsecus assilit. Verum lapis magnes effluxiones quasdam tum graves, tum etiam spiritales emittit, quibus aer continuatus & iunctus repellitur. Is deinceps alium sibi proximum impellit, qui in orbem circum actus, atque ad inanem locum rediens, ui ferrum secum rapit & trahit. At Electrum uim quandam flammæ similem & spiritalem continet, quam quidem tritu fummæ partis, quo aperiuntur meatus, foras eijcit. Nam leuiffima corpufcula & aridiffima quæ propè funt, fua tenuitate atque imbecillitate ad feipfum ducit & rapit, cum non fit adeo ualens, nec tantum habeat ponderis & momenti ad expellendam aeris copiam, ut maiora corpora more Magnetis fuperare poffit & uincere."

Page 54, line 16.   Page 54, line 18.   *Gemma Vincentij rupis.*—See the note to p. **48** *fupra*, where the name *Vincentina* occurs.

Page 54, line 30.   Page 54, line 35.   *orobi.*—The editions of 1628 and 1633 read *oribi*.

Page 55, line 34.   Page 55, line 42.   *in euacuati.*—The editions of 1628 and 1633 read *inevacuati*.

Page 58, line 21.   Page 58, line 25.   *affurgentem vndam . . . declinat ab F.*—Thefe words are wanting in the Stettin editions.

Page 59, line 9.   Page 59, line 9.   *fluore.*—This word is conjectured to be a mifprint for *fluxu*, but it ftands in all editions.

Page 59, line 22.   Page 59, line 25.   *Ruunt ad eleĉtria.*—This appears to be a flip for *eleĉtrica*, which is the reading of the editions of 1628 and 1633.

Page 60, line 7.   Page 60, line 9.   *tanq̃ materiales radij.*—The fuggeftion here of material *rays* as the *modus operandi* of electric forces feems to fore-fhadow the notion of electric lines of force.

Page 60, line 10.   Page 60, line 12.   *Differentia inter magnetica & eleĉtrica.*—Though Gilbert was the firft fyftematically to explore the differences that exift between the magnetic attraction of iron and the electric attraction of all light fubftances, the point had not paffed unheeded, for we find St. Auguftine, in the *De Civitate Dei*, liber xxi., cap. 6, raifing the queftion why the loadftone which attracts iron fhould refufe to move ftraws.   The many analogies between electric and magnetic phenomena had led many experimenters to fpeculate on the poffibility of fome connexion between electricity and magnetifm.   See, for example, Tiberius Cavallo, *A Treatife on Magnetifm*, London, 1787, p. 126.   Alfo the three volumes of J. H. van Swinden, *Receuil de Mémoires fur l'Analogie de l'Eleĉtricité et du Magnétifme*, La Haye, 1784.   Aepinus wrote a treatife on the fubject, entitled *De Similitudine vis eleĉtricæ et magneticæ* (Petropolis, 1758).   This was, of courfe, long prior to the difcovery, by Oerfted, in 1820, of the real connexion between magnetifm and the electric current.

Page 60, line 25.   Page 60, line 31.   *Coitionem dicimus, non attraĉtionem.*—See the remarks, at the outfet of thefe Notes, on Gilbert's definitions of words.

Page 60, line 33.   Page 61, line 1.   *Orpheus in fuis carminibus.*—This paffage is in the chapter Λιθικά of Orpheus, verfes 301 to 327.   See Note to p. **11**, line **19**.

Page 61, line 15.   Page 61, line 19.   *Platonis in Timæo opinio.*—The paffage runs (edition Didot, vol. ii., p. 240, or Stephanus, p. 80, C.):

Καὶ δὴ καὶ τὰ τῶν ὑδάτων πάντα ῥεύματα ἔτι δὲ τὰ τῶν κεραυνῶν πτώματα καὶ τὰ θαυμαζόμενα ἠλέκτρων περὶ τῆς ἕλξεως καὶ τῶν Ἡρακλείων λίθων, πάντων τούτων ὁλκὴ μὲν οὐκ ἔστιν οὐδένι ποτε, τὸ δὲ κενὸν εἶναι μηδὲν περιωθεῖν τε αὐτὰ ταῦτα εἰς ἄλληλα, τό τε διακρινόμενα καὶ συγκρινόμενα πρὸς τήν αὐτῶν διαμειβόμενα ἕδραν ἕκαστα ἰέναι πάντα, τούτοις τοῖς παθήμασι πρὸς ἄλληλα συμπλεχθεῖσι τεθαυματουργημένα τῷ κατὰ τρόπον ζητοῦντι φανήσεται.

Page 61, line 30.   Page 61, line 38.   The Englifh verfion of the lines of Lucretius is from Bufby's tranflation.

Page 62, line 5. Page 62, line 7. *Iohannes Coſtæus Laudenſis.*— Joannes Coſta, of Lodi, edited Galen and Avicenna. He alſo wrote a *De univerſali ſtirpium Natura* (Aug. Taurin., 1578).

Page 63, line 3. Page 63, line 4. *Cornelius Gemma* 10. *Coſmocrit.*— This refers to the work *De Naturæ Divinis Charaĉteriſmis . . . Libri ii. Avĉtore D. Corn. Gemma* (Antv., 1575, lib. i., cap. vii., p. 123).

"Certè vt à magnete inſenſiles radij ferrum ad ſe attrahunt, ab echineide paruo piſciculo ſiſtuntur plena nauigia, à catoblepa ſpiritu non homines ſolùm, ſed & alta ſerpentum genera interimuntur, & ſaxa dehiſcunt."

See alſo Kircher's *Magneticum Naturæ Regnum* (Amſterodami, 1667, p. 172), Seĉtio iv., cap. iii., De Magnete Navium, quæ Remora ſeu Echeneis dicitur. See the note to p. **7**, line **21**.

Page 63, line 6. Page 63, line 7. *Guilielmus Puteanus.*—Puteanus (Du Puys) wrote a work *De Medicamentorum quomodocunque Purgantium Facultatibus*, Libri ii. (Lugd., 1552), in which he talks vaguely about the ſubſtantial "form" of the magnet, and quotes Ariſtotle and Galen.

Page 63, line 21. Page 63, line 25. *Baptiſtæ Portæ.*—The paſſage in the tranſlation is quoted from the Engliſh verſion of 1658, pp. 191, 192.

Page 64, line 4. Page 64, line 9. *Eruditè magis Scaliger.*—Gilbert pokes fun at Scaliger, whoſe "erudite" gueſs (that the motion of iron to the magnet was that of the offspring toward the parent) is to be found in his book *De Subtilitate, ad Cardanum*, Exercitatio CII. (Lutetiæ, 1557, p. 156 *bis*).

Page 64, line 7. Page 64, line 11. *Diuus Thomas.*—On p. **3** Gilbert had already ſpoken of St. Thomas Aquinas as a man of intelleĉt who would have added more about the magnet had he been more converſant with experiments. The paſſage here quoted is from the middle of Liber vii. of his commentaries on the *de Phyſica* of Ariſtotle, *Expoſitio Diui Thome Aquinatis Doĉtoris Angelici ſuper oĉto libros Phyſicorum Ariſtotelis*, etc. (Venice, Giunta edition, 1539, p. 96 *verſo*, col. 2).

Page 64, line 16. Page 64, line 24. *Cardinalis etiam Cuſanus.*— Cardinal de Cuſa (Nicolas Khrypffs) wrote a ſet of dialogues on Statics, *Nicolai Cuſani de ſtaticis experimentis dialogus* (1550), of which an Engliſh verſion appeared in London in 1650 with the title, *The Idiot in four books; the firſt and ſecond of wiſdom, the third of the minde, the fourth of ſtatick experiments. By the famous and learned C. Cuſanus.* In the fourth book *of ſtatick Experiments, Or experiments of the Ballance*, occurs (p. 186) the following:

"*Orat.* Tell me, if thou haſt any device whereby the vertues of ſtones may be weighed.

"*Id.* I thinke the vertue of the Load-ſtone might be weighed, if putting ſome Iron in one ſcale, and a Load-ſtone in the other, untill the ballance were even, then taking away the Load-ſtone, and ſome other thing of the ſame weight being put into the ſcale, the Load-ſtone were holden over the Iron, ſo that that ſcale wou'd begin to riſe; by reaſon of the Load-ſtones attraĉtion of the Iron, then take out ſome of the weight of the other ſcale, untill the ſcale wherein the iron is, doe ſinke againe to the æquilibrium, or equality ſtill holding the Load-ſtone unmovable as it was; I beleeve that by weight of what was taken out of the contrary ſcale, one might come proportionably to the weight of the vertue or power of the Load-ſtone. And in like manner, the vertue of a Diamond, might be found hereby, becauſe they say it hinders the Load-ſtone form drawing of Iron ; and ſo other vertues of other ſtones, conſideration, being alwayes had of the greatneſſe of the bodyes, becauſe in a greater body, there is a greater power and vertue."

In the 1588 edition of Baptiſta Porta's *Magiæ Naturalis Libri xx.*, in lib. vii., cap. xviii., occurs the deſcription of the uſe of the balance to which Gilbert refers.

Page 67, line 21. Page 67, line 22. *aëris rigore.*—All editions read thus, but the ſenſe ſeems to require *frigore*.

Page 67, line 27. Page 67, line 31. *Fracaſtorius.*—See his *De Sympathia*, lib. i., cap. 5 (Giunta edition, 1574, p. 60).

Page 68, line 5. Page 68, line 6. *Thaletis Mileſij.*—See the note to p. 11, line 26.

Page 68, line 30. Page 68, line 35. *Itâ coitio magnetica aſtus eſt magnetis, & ferri, non aſtio vnius.*—See the introductory remarks to theſe notes. There is a paſſage in Scaliger's *De Subtilitate ad Cardanum* (Exercitat. CII., cap. 5, p. 156 *op. citat.*) which may be compared with Gilbert's for its uſe of Greek terms : " Nã cùm uita dicatur aſtus animæ, acceptus eſt abs te aſtus pro aſtione. Sed aſtus ille eſt ἐντελέχεια, nõ autem ἔργον. At Magnetis attraſtio est ἔργον, non autẽ ἐντελέχεια." To which Gilbert retorts : " non aſtio unius, utriuſque ἐντελέχεια ; non ἔργον, συνεντελέχεια et conaſtus potius quam ſympathia." He returns on p. **70** to the attack on Scaliger's metaphyſical notions. There is a parallel paſſage in the *Epitome Naturalis Scientiæ* of Daniel Sennert (Oxoniæ, 1664), in the chapter *De Motu*.

Page 71, line 4. Page 71, line 8. *vt in 8. phyſicorum Themiſtius exiſtimat.*—See *Omnia Themiſtii Opera* (Aldine edition, 1533, p. 63), **Book** 8 of his Paraphraſe on Ariſtotle's *Phyſica.*

Page 71, line 9. Page 71, line 14. *Quod verò Fracaſtorius.*—Op. citat., lib. i., cap. 7, p. 62 *verſo.*

Page 73, line 2. Page 73, line 2. *ſi A borealis.*—The editions of 1628 and 1633 omit the twelve words next following.

Page 73, line 9. Page 73, line 11. *ex minera.*—*Minera* is not a recognized word, even in late Latin. It occurs again, p. **97**, line **12**.

Page 77, line 2. Page 77, line 2. *multo magis.*—This is an *à fortiori* argument. It is intereſting to find Gilbert comparing the velocity of propagation of magnetic forces in ſpace with the velocity of light. The parallel is completed in line 13 by the conſideration that as the rays of light require to fall upon an objeſt in order that they may become viſible, ſo the magnetic forces require a magnetic objeſt in order to render their preſence ſenſible.

Page 78, line 14. Page 78, line 16. *Orbem terrarum diſtinguunt.*— The editions of 1628 and 1633 here add a figure of a globe marked with meridians and parallels of latitude, but with an erroneous verſorium pointing to the ſouth. Theſe editions alſo both read *exiſtentiam* for the word *exiſtentium* in line **20**.

Page 83, line 5. Page 83, line 5. *magnes longior maiora pondera ferri attollit.*—Gilbert diſcovered the advantage, for an equal maſs of loadſtone, of an elongated ſhape. It is now well known that the ſpecific amount of magnetiſm retained by elongated forms exceeds that in a ſhort piece of the ſame material ſubjeſted to equal magnetizing forces.

Page 83, line 24. Page 83, line 28. *Non obſtant craſſa tabulata.*— Gilbert has ſeveral times referred (*e.g.*, on p. **77**) to the way in which magnetic forces penetrate ſolid bodies. The experimental inveſtigation in this chapter is the more interefting becaufe it fhows that Gilbert clearly perceived the fhielding action of iron to be due to iron conducting afide or diverting the magnetic forces.

Page 85, line 26.   Page 85, line 31.   *non conveniant.*—The editions of 1628 and 1633 both read *et conveniant.*

Page 86, line 3.   Page 86, line 3.   *illud quod exhalat.*—Literally, *that which exhales*, in the fenfe of that which efcapes : but in modern Englifh the verb exhale in the active voice is now not ufed of the fubftance that efcapes, but is ufed of the thing which emits it.   It muft therefore be rendered *that which is exhaled* (*i.e.*, breathed out).

Page 86, line 13.   Page 86, line 15.   *Ita tota interpofita moles terreftris.* —Gilbert's notion that the gravitational force of the moon in producing the tides acts *through* the fubftance of the earth may feem curioufly expreffed. But the underlying contention is effentially true to-day.   The force of gravity is not cut off or fcreened off by the interpofition of other maffes.   A recent inveftigation by Profeffor Poynting, F.R.S., has fhown that fo far as all evidence goes all bodies, even the denfeft, are tranfparent with refpect to gravitational forces.

Page 86, line 18.   Page 86, line 20.   *Sed de æftus ratione aliàs.*— There is no further difcuffion of the tides in *De Magnete*.   But a fhort account is to be found in Gilbert's pofthumous work *De Mundo noftro Sublunari Philofophia nova* (Amfterdam, Elzevir, 1651), in Lib. v., the part which in the manufcript was left in Englifh, and was turned into Latin by his brother. It comprifes about fifteen quarto pages, from Cap. X. to Cap. XIX. inclufive, beginning with a characteriftic diatribe againft Taifnier, Levinus Lemnius, and Scaliger.   But in affigning caufes he himfelf goes wide of the mark. Proceeding by a procefs of elimination he firft fhows that the moon's light cannot be the caufe that impels the tides.   "Luna," he fays, "non radio, non lumine, maria impellit. quomodo igitur?   Sane corporum confpiratione, atque (ut fimilitudine rem exponam) Magnetica attractione."   This cryptic utterance he proceeds to explain by a diagram, and adds : "Quare Luna non tam attrahit mare, quàm humorem & fpiritum fubterraneum ; nec plus refiftit interpofita terra, quàm menfa, aut quicquam aliud denfum, aut craffum, magnetis viribus."

Page 87, line 7.   Page 87, line 9.   *armatura.*—Here this means the cap or fnout of iron with which the loadftone was armed.   This is apparently the firft ufe of the term in this fenfe.

·In the *Dialogues of Galileo* (p. 369 of Salufbury's *Mathematical Collections*, Dialogue iii.), Sagredus and Salviatus difcufs the arming of the loadftone, and the increafed lifting power conferred by adding an iron cap.   Salviatus mentions a loadftone in the Florentine Academy which, unarmed, weighed fix ounces, lifting only two ounces, but which when armed took up 160 ounces.   Whereupon Galileo makes Salviatus fay: "I extreamly praife, admire, and envy this Authour, for that a conceit fo ftupendious fhould come into his minde. . . . I think him [*i.e.*, Gilbert] moreover worthy of extraordinary applaufe for the many new and true Obfervations that he made, to the difgrace of fo many fabulous Authours, that write not only what they do not know, but whatever they hear fpoken by the foolifh vulgar, never feeking to affure themfelves of the fame by experience, perhaps, becaufe they are unwilling to diminifh the bulk of their Books."

Page 87, line 12.   Page 87, line 15.   The reference to *lib.* 3 is a mifprint for *lib*. 2. It is corrected in the edition of 1633, but not in that of 1628.

Page 87, line 17. Page 87, line 21. *conactu.*—The editions of 1628 and 1633 read *conatu*.

Page 88, line 2. Page 88, line 3. *Coitio verò non fortior.*—This heading to chap. xix., taken with the feven lines that follow, and the contraft drawn between *unitio* and *coitio*, throw much light on the fundamental fenfe attached by Gilbert to the term *coitio*. It is here clearly ufed in the fenfe of *mutual tendency toward union*. Note alfo the contrafted ufe in chap. xx. of the verbs *cohære* and *adhære*. Adhærence connotes a one-fided force (an impoffibility in phyfics), cohærence a mutual force.

Page 90, line 9. Page 90, line 9. *nempè vt alter polus maius pondus arripiat.*—This acute obfervation is even now not as well known as it ought to be. Only fo recently as 1861 Siemens patented the device of faftening a mafs of iron to one end of an electromagnet in order to increafe the power of the other end. The fact, fo far as it relates to permanent magnets was known to Servington Savery. See *Philos. Tranfactions*, 1729, p. 295.

Page 92, line 3. Page 92, line 4. *Sufpendit in aëre ferrum Baptifta Porta.*—Porta's experiment is thus defcribed (*Natural Magick*, London, 1658, p. 204): " *Petrus Pellegrinus* faith, he fhewed in another work how that might be done : but that work is not to be found. Why I think it extream hard, I fhall fay afterwards. But I fay it may be done, becaufe I have now done it, to hold it faft by an invifible band, to hang in the air ; onely fo, that it be bound with a fmall thread beneath, that it may not rife higher : and then ftriving to catch hold of the ftone above, it will hang in the air, and tremble and wag itfelf."

Page 97, line 29. Page 97, line 33. *Sed quæri poteft . . . .*—The queftion here raifed by Gilbert is whether the lifting-power of magnets of equal quality is proportional to their weight. If a ftone weighing a drachm will lift a drachm, would a ftone that weighs an ounce lift an ounce ? Gilbert erroneoufly anfwers that this is fo, and that the lifting-power of a loadftone, whether armed or unarmed, is proportional to its mafs.

The true law of the tractive force or lifting-power of magnets was firft given in 1729 by James Hamilton (afterwards Earl of Abercorn) in a work entitled *Calculations and Tables Relating to the Attractive Virtue of Load-ftones . . . Printed* [at London ?] *in the Year* 1729. (See alfo a paper in the *Philos. Tranfactions*, 1729-30, vol. xxxvi., p. 245). This work begins thus :

" The Principle upon which thefe Tables are formed, is this : That if Two *Loadftones* are perfectly Homogeneous, that is, if their Matter be of the fame Specifick Gravity, and of the fame Virtue in all Parts of one Stone, as in the other ; and that Like Parts of their Surfaces are Cap'd or Arm'd with Iron ; then the Weights they fuftain will be as the Squares of the Cube Roots of the Weights of the *Loadftones* ; that is, as their Surfaces."

Upon lifting-power fee alfo D. Bernoulli, *Acta Helvetica*, iii., p. 223, 1758 ; P. W. Haecker, *Zur Theorie des Magnetifmus*, Nürnberg, 1856 ; Van der Willigen, *Arch. du Mufée Teyler*, vol. iv., Haarlem, 1878 ; S. P. Thompfon, *Philos. Magazine*, July, 1888.

In the book of James Hamilton, p. 5, he mentions a fmall terrella weighing 139 Englifh grains, which would fuftain no lefs than 23,760 grains, and was valued at £21 13s. 10¾d.

In the *Muſæum Septalianum* of Terzagus (Dertonæ, 1664, p. 42) is mentioned a loadſtone weighing twelve ounces which would lift ſixty pounds of iron.

Sir Iſaac Newton had a loadſtone weighing 3 grains, which he wore in a ring. It would lift 746 grains.

Thomſon's *Britiſh Annual*, 1837, p. 354, gives the following reference : " In the *Records of General Science*, vol. iii., p. 272, there is an intereſting deſcription of a very powerful magnet which was ſent from Virginia in 1776 by the celebrated Dr. Franklin to Profeſſor Anderſon, of Glaſgow. It is now in the poſſeſſion of Mr. Crichton. It weighs 2½ grains, and is capable of ſupporting a load of 783 grains, which is equivalent to 313 times its own weight."

Page 99, line 10. Page 99, line 11. *Manifeſtum eſt.*—In this, as in many other paſſages, Gilbert uſes this expreſſion in the ſenſe that *it is demonſtrable*, rather than meaning that *it is obvious :* for the fact here deſcribed is one that is not at all ſelf-evident, but one which would become plain when the experiment had been tried. For other inſtances of this uſe of *manifeſtum* ſee pages **144**, line **20** ; **158**, line **19** ; **162**, line **10**.

Page 100, line 20. Page 100, line 24. *ſi per impedimēta . . . pervenire poſſunt.*—All editions agree in this reading, but the ſenſe undoubtedly requires *non poſſint.* Compare p. **91**, line **21**.

Page 102, line 4. Page 102, line 4. *capite 4.*—This is a miſprint for *capite* 40, and is retained in the later editions. In the quotation from Baptiſta Porta, where the Engliſh verſion of 1658 is adhæred to, the words " & deturbat eam " have been omitted by the tranſlator.

Page 107, line 16. Page 107, line 18. *Cardanus ſcribit.*—The alleged perpetual motion machine is mentioned in *De rerum varietate, lib.* 9, cap. xlviii. (Baſil., 1581, p. 641). See alſo the Note to p. **223**. For Peregrinus and for Taiſnier, ſee the note to p. **5**, lines **8** and **12**.

Page 107, line 19. Page 107, line 21. *Antonij de Fantis.*—His work is : *Tabula generalis ſcotice ſubtilitatis octo Sectionibus vniuerſam Doctoris Subtilis Peritiā cōplectēs : ab excellentiſſimo doctore Antonio de Fātis taruiſino edita . . .* Lugd., 1530.

Page 108, line 26. Page 108, line 31. *Cuſani in ſtaticis.*—See the note to p. **64**, line **16**.

Page 108, line 33. Page 108, line 41. *Languidi . . . tardiùs acquieſcunt.*—The editions of 1628 and 1633 omit theſe ſeven words.

Page 109, line 11. Page 109, line 13. *halinitro.*—Either native carbonate of ſoda or native carbonate of potaſh might be meant, but not ſaltpetre. Scaliger, in his *De Subtilitate ad Cardanum* (Lutet., 1557, p. 164), *Exercitatio* CIII., 15, under the title, *Nitrum non eſt Salpetræ,* ſays : " More tuo te, tuaque confundis. Salpetræ inter ſalis foſſilis ponis hîc. Mox Halinitrum inter ſalis, & nitri naturam, ſpeciem obtinere."

" *Sal nitrum* is ſalt which is boiled out of the earth, eſpecially fat earth, as in ſtables, or any place of excrements." (*A Chymicall Dictionary explaining Hard Places and Words met withall in the Writings of Paracelſus* . . ., Lond., 1650.)

Page 109, line 20. Page 109, line 23. *arte ioculatoriâ.*—Edition 1628, *joculatoriâ ;* edition 1633, *jaculatoriâ.*

Page 110, line 11. Page 110, line 12. *qualis fuit Antonij denarius.*— The Elizabethan verſion of Pliny (book xxxiii., ch. ix., p. 479) runs thus :

" To come now unto thofe that counterfeit money. *Antonius* whiles hee was one of the three ufurping Triumvirs, mixed yron with the Romane filver denier. He tempered it alfo with the brafen coine, and fo fent abroad falfe and counterfeit money."

Georgius Agricola (*De Natura Foffilium*, p. 646) fays:

" Sed ea fraus capitalis eft, non aliter ac eorum qui adulterinas monetas cudunt, argento mifcentes multam plumbi candidi portionem, aut etiam ferri, qualis fuit Antonii denarius, ut Plinius memoriæ tradidit. Nunc dicam de candido plumbo, nam majoris pretii eft quàm aes. In quod plumbum album, inquit Plinius, addita aeris tertia portione candidi adulteratur ftannum."

Page 111, line 3. Page 111, line 3. *Meminerunt Chatochitis lapis Plinius, atque Iulius Solinus.*—The paffage in Pliny (Englifh verfion of 1601, book xxxvii., ch. x., p. 625) runs:

" Catochitis is a ftone proper unto the Ifland Corfica: in bigneffe it exceedeth ordinarie pretious ftones: a wonderfull ftone, if all be true that is reported thereof, and namely, That if a man lay his hand thereon, it will hold it faft in manner of a glewie gum."

Page 111, line 7. Page 111, line 7. *Sagda vel Sagdo.*—Albertus Magnus in *De Mineralibus* (Venet., 1542, p. 202) fays:

" Sarda quem alij dicunt Sardo lapis eft qui fe habet ad tabulas ligni ficut magnes ad ferrũ, et ideo adhæret ita fortiter tabulis nauium quòd euelli nõ poffit, nifi abfcindatur cum ipfo ea pars tabulæ cui inhæferit, eft autẽ in colore puriffimus nitens."

And Pliny (*op. citat.*, p. 629):

" Sagda is a ftone, which the Chaldeans find fticking to fhips, and they fay it is greene as Porrets or Leekes."

Page 111, line 8. Page 111, line 8. *Euace.*—Evax, king of the Arabs, is faid to have written to Nero a treatife on the names, colours, and properties of ftones. See the note on Marbodæus, p. **7**, line **20**.

Page 113, line 14. Page 113, line 19. *repulfus fit.* The words read thus in all editions, but the fenfe requires *repulfa fint.*

Page 113, line 23. Page 113, line 29. *Electrica omnia alliciunt cuncta, nihil omninò fugant vnquam, aut propellunt.* This denial of electrical repulfion probably arofe from the fmallnefs of the pieces of electric material with which Gilbert worked. He could hardly have failed to notice it had he ufed large pieces of amber or of fealing-wax. Electrical repulfion was firft obferved by Nicolas Cabeus, *Philofophia Magnetica*, Ferrara, 1629; but firft fyftematically announced by Otto von Guericke in his treatife *Experimenta Nova (ut vocantur) Magdeburgica, de Vacuo Spatio* (Amftel., 1672).

Page 113, line 29. Page 113, line 37. *cùm de calore quid fit difputabimus.*—The difcuffion of the nature of heat is to be found in Gilbert's *De Mundo noftro Sublunari* (Amftel., 1651), lib. i., cap. xxvi., pp. 77-88.

Page 115, line 23. Page 115, line 23. *trium vel quatuor digitorum.*—Here as in all other places in Gilbert, *digitus* means a finger's breadth, fo that three or four digits means a length of two or three inches, or from fix to eight centimetres.

Page 117, line 26. Page 117, line 25. *ille Thebit Bencoræ trepidationis motus.*

" Trepidation in the ancient Aftronomy denotes a motion which in the Ptolemaic fyftem was attributed to the firmament, in order to account for feveral changes and motions obferved in the axis of the world, and for which they could not account on any other principle." (Barlow's *Mathematical Dictionary*.)

Page 118, line 10. Page 118, line 8. *cufpis aut lilium*.—Gilbert ufes *cufpis* or *lilium* always of the North-pointing end of the needle. Sir Thomas Browne fpeaks of " the lilly or northern point"; but he differs from Gilbert in faying " the *cufpis* or Southern point" (*Pfeudodoxia Epidemica*, 1650, p. 46). Only in one place (p. **101**, line **5**) does Gilbert fpeak of *cufpis meridionalis*. Everywhere elfe the fouth-pointing end is called the *crux*.

Page 118, line 15. Page 118, line 13. *nam æquè potens eft*.—Later obfervation fhowed this view to be incorrect. The horizontal component of the earth's magnetic field is not equally ftrong all over the globe, and the fluggifhnefs of the needle's return to its pofition of reft is not due to the fupporting pin becoming blunt with wear. The value of the horizontal component is zero at the north magnetic pole, and increafes toward the magnetic equator. It is greateft near Singapore and in Borneo, being there more than twice as great as it is at London. (See Captain Creak in *Report of Voyage of H.M.S. Challenger, Phyfics and Chemiftry*, vol. ii., part vi., 1889.)

Page 119, line 5. Page 119, line 2. *lapis*.—Both Stettin editions read *lapidis*.

Page 119, lines 9-11. Page 119, lines 7-9. The gift of the whole book is fummarized in thefe lines. They furnifh a cardinal example of that inductive reafoning which was practift by Gilbert, and of which Bacon fubfequently pofed as the apoftle. Compare pages **41** and **211**.

Page 120, line 8. Page 120, line 5. *dicturi fumus*.—Change of verticity is treated of in book iii., chap. x., pp. **137** to **140**.

Page 125, line 24. Page 125, line 29. *appofitam*.—All editions give this word, though the fenfe requires *appofitum*.

Page 128, line 9. Page 128, line 11. *non nimis longum*.—The editions of 1628 and 1633 read (wrongly) *minus* inftead of *nimis*.

Page 130, line 12. Page 130, line 14. The word *hunc* in the folio of 1600 is corrected in ink to *tunc*, and the Stettin editions both read *tunc*.

Page 132, line 9. Page 132, line 10. *minimus & nullius ponderis*.— The editions of 1628 and 1633 both wrongly read *eft* for *&*.

Page 132, line 28. Page 133, line 1. *nutat*.—The editions of 1628 and 1633 both wrongly read *mutat*.

Page 134, line 22. Page 134, line 25. *in rectâ fphærâ*.—The meaning of the terms a *right* or *direct fphere*, an *oblique fphere* and a *parallel fphere* are explained by Moxon on pages 29 to 31 of his book *A Tutor to Aftronomy and Geography* (Lond., 1686):

" A *Direct Sphere* hath both the *Poles* of the *World* in the Horizon . . . It is called a *Direct Sphere*, becaufe all the *Celeftial* Bodies, as *Sun*, *Moon*, and *Stars*, &c. By the *Diurnal* Motion of the *Primum Mobile*, afcend directly Above, and defcend directly Below the *Horizon*. They that Inhabit under the *Equator* have the *Sphere* thus pofited."

" An *Oblique Sphere* hath the *Axis* of the *World* neither *Direct* nor *Parallel* to the *Horizon*, but lies aflope from it."

" A *Parallel Sphere* hath one *Pole* of the *World* in the *Zenith*, the other in the *Nadir*, and the *Equinoctial* Line in the *Horizon*."

Page 136, line 1. Page 136, line 1. *præfenti*.—The editions of 1628 and 1633 read *fequenti*, to fuit the altered pofition of the figure.

Page 137, line 24. Page 137, line 28. *atque ille ftatim.*—The Stettin editions both wrongly read *illi.*

Page 139. There is a curious hiftory to this picture of the blackfmith in his fmithy ftriking the iron while it lies north and fouth, and fo magnetizing it under the influence of the earth's magnetifm. Woodcuts containing human figures are comparatively rare in Englifh art of the fixteenth century; a notable exception being Foxe's *Acts and Monuments* with its many crude cuts of martyrdoms. The artift who prepared this cut of the fmith took the defign from an illuftrated book of Fables by one Cornelius Kiliani or Cornelius van Kiel entitled *Viridarium Moralis Philofophiæ, per Fabulas Animalibus brutis attributas traditæ, etc.* (Coloniæ, 1594). This rare work, of which there is no copy in the Britifh Mufeum, is illuftrated by fome 120

fine copper-plate etchings printed in the text. On p. 133 of this work is an etching to illuftrate the fable *Ferrarii fabri et canis*, reprefenting the fmith fmiting iron on the anvil, whilft his lazy dog fleeps beneath the bellows. The cut on p. **139** of Gilbert gives, as will be feen by a comparifon of the pictures, juft the fame general detail of forge and tools; but the pofition of the fmith is reverfed right for left, the dog is omitted, and the words *Septentrio* and *Aufter* have been added.

In the Stettin edition of 1628 the picture has again been turned into a copper-plate etching feparately printed, is reverfed back again left for right, while a compafs-card is introduced in the corner to mark the north-fouth direction.

In the Stettin edition of 1633 the artift has gone back to Kiliani's original plate, and has re-etched the defign very carefully, but reverfing it all right for left. As in the London verfion of 1600, the dog is omitted, and the words *Septentrio* and *Aufter* are added. Some of the original details—for example, the vice and one pair of pincers—are left out, but other details, for inftance, the cracks in the blocks that fupport the water-tub, and the drefs of the blackfmith, are rendered with flavifh fidelity.

It is perhaps needlefs to remark that the twelve copper-plate etchings in the edition of 1628, and the twelve completely different ones in that of 1633, replace certain of the woodcuts of the folio of 1600. For example, take the woodcut on p. **203** of the 1600 edition, which reprefents a fimple dipping-needle made by thrufting a verforium through a bit of cork and floating it, immerfed, in a goblet of water. In the 1633 edition this appears, flightly reduced, as a fmall inferted copper-plate, with nothing added; but in the 1628 edition it is elaborated into a full-page plate (No. xi.) reprefenting the interior, with fhelves of books, of a library on the floor of which ftands the goblet—apparently three feet high—with a globe and an armillary fphere; while befide the goblet, with his back to the fpectator, is feated an aged man, reading, in a carved armchair. This figure and the view of the library are unqueftionably copied—reverfed—from a well-known plate in the work *Le Diverfe & Artificiofe Machine* of Agoftino Ramelli (Paris, 1558).

In the Emblems of Jacob Cats (*Alle de Wercken*, Amfterdam, 1665, p. 65) is given an engraved plate of a fmith's forge, which is alfo copied—omitting the fmith—from Kiliani's *Viridarium*.

Page 140, line 2. Page 140, line 2. *præcedenti.*—This is fo fpelled in all editions, though the fenfe requires *præcedente*.

Page 141, line 21. Page 141, line 24. *quod in epiftolâ quâdam Italicâ fcribitur.*—The tale told by Filippo Cofta of Mantua about the magnetifm acquired by the iron rod on the tower of the church of St. Auguftine in Rimini is hiftorical. The church was dedicated to St. John, but in the cuftody of the Auguftinian monks. The following is the account of it given by Aldrovandi, *Mufæum Metallicum* (1648, p. 134), on which page alfo two figures of it are given:

"Aliquando etiam ferrum fuam mutat fubftantiam, dum in magnetem conuertitur, & hoc experientia conftat, nam Arimini fupra turrim templi S. Ioannis erat Crux a baculo ferreo ponderis centum librarum fuftentata, quod tractu temporis adeò naturam Magnetis eft adeptum, vt, illivs inftar, ferrum traheret: hinc magna admiratione multi tenentur, qua ratione ferrum, quod eft metallum in Magnetem, qui eft lapis tranfmutari poffit; Animaduertendum eft id à maxima familiaritate & fympathia ferri, & magnetis dimanare cum Ariftoteles in habentibus fymbolum facilem tranfitum femper admiferit. Hoc in loco damus imaginem frufti ferri in Magnetem tranfmutati, quod clariffimo viro Vlyffi Aldrouando Iulius Caefar Moderatus diligens rerum naturalium inquifitor communicauit; erat hoc fruftum ferri colore nigro, & ferrugineo, crufta exteriori quodammodo albicante." And further on p. 557.

"Preterea id manifeftiffimum eft; quoniam Arimini, in templo Sancti Ioannis, fuit Crux ferrea, quæ tractu temporis in magnetem conuerfa eft, & ab vno latere ferrum trahebat, & ab altero refpuebat." See alfo Sir T. Browne's *Pfeudodoxia Epidemica* (edition of 1650, p. 48), and Boyle's tract, *Experiments and Notes about the Mechanical Production of Magnetifm* (London, 1676, p. 12).

Another cafe is mentioned in Dr. Martin Lifter's *A Journey to Paris* (Lond., 1699, p. 83). "He [Mr. Butterfield] fhewed us a Loadftone fawed off that piece of the Iron Bar which held the Stones together at the very top of the Steeple of *Chartres*. This was a thick Cruft of Ruft, part of which was turned into a ftrong Loadftone, and had all the properties of a Stone dug out of the Mine. *Mons. de la Hire* has Printed a Memoir of it ; alfo Mons. *de Vallemont* a Treatife. The very outward Ruft had no Magnetic Virtue, but the inward had a ftrong one, as to take up a third part more than its weight unfhod." Gaffendi and Grimaldi have given other cafes.

Other examples of iron acquiring ftrong permanent magnetifm from the earth are not wanting. The following is from Sir W. Snow Harris's *Rudimentary Magnetifm* (London, 1872, p. 10).

"In the *Memoirs of the Academy of Sciences* for 1731, we find an account of a large bell at Marfeilles having an axis of iron : this axis refted on ftone blocks, and threw off from time to time great quantities of ruft, which, mixing with the particles of ftone and the oil ufed to facilitate the motion, became conglomerated into a hardened mafs : this mafs had all the properties of the native magnet. The bell is fuppofed to have been in the fame pofition for 400 years."

Page 142, line 13. Page 142, line 15. *tunc planetæ & corpora cœleftia.*—Gilbert's extraordinary detachment from all metaphyfical and ultra-phyfical explanations of phyfical facts, and his continual appeal to the teft of experimental evidence, enabled him to lift the fcience of the magnet out of the flough of the dark ages. This paffage, however, reveals that he ftill gave credence to the *nativities* of judicial Aftrology, and to the fuppofed influence of the planets on human deftiny.

Page 144, line 14. Page 144, line 14. *ijdem.*—The editions of 1628 and 1633 erroneoufly read *iifdem*.

Page 147, line 27. Page 147, line 29. *ex optimo aciario.*—Gilbert recommended that the compafs-needle fhould be of the beft fteel. Though the diftinction between iron and fteel was not at this time well eftablifhed, there is no reafon to doubt that by *aciarium* was meant edge-fteel as ufed for blades. Barlowe, in his *Magneticall Aduertifements* (Lond., 1616), p. 66, gives minute inftructions for the fafhioning of the compafs-needle. He gives the preference to a pointed oval form, and defcribes how the fteel muft be hardened by heating to whitenefs and quenching in water, fo that it is "brickle in a manner as glaffe it felfe," and then be tempered by reheating it over a bar of red hot iron until it is let down to a blue tint. Savery (*Philos. Trans.*, 1729) appears to have been the firft to make a fyftematic examination of the magnetic differences between hard fteel and foft iron.

Inftructions for touching the needle are given in the *Arte de Nauegar* of Pedro de Medina (Valladolid, 1545, lib. vi., cap. 1).

Page 149, line 8. Page 149, line 9. *per multa fæcula.*—Compare Porta's affertion (p. 208, Englifh edition) "iron once rubbed will hold the vertue a hundred years." Clearly not a matter within the actual experience of either Porta or Gilbert.

Page 153, line 2. Page 153, line 2. *Cardani ab ortu ftellæ in cauda vrfæ.*—What Cardan faid (*De Subtilitate, Edit. citat.*, p. 187) was: "ortum ftellæ in cauda urfæ minoris, quæ quinque partibus orientalior eft polo mundi, refpicit."

Page 153, line 21. Page 153, line 26. *fequitur quod verfus terram magnam, fiue continentem . . . à vero polo inclinatio magnetica fiat.*—Gilbert goes on to point out how, at that date, all the way up the weft European coaft from Morocco to Norway, the compafs is deflected eaftward, or toward the elevated land. He argued that this was a univerfal law.

In *Purchas his Pilgrimes* (Lond., 1625), in the Narrative, in vol. iii., of Bylot and Baffin's Voyage of 1616, there is mentioned an ifland between Whale-Sound and Smith's Sound, where there had been obferved a larger variation than in any other part of the world. Purchas, in a marginal note, comments on this as follows: " Variation of the Compafs 56° to the Weft, which may make queftionable D. Gilbert's rule, tom. I., l. 2, c. 1, that where more Earth is more attraction of the Compafs happeneth by variation towards it. Now the known Continents of Afia, &c., muft be unfpeakably more than here there can be, & yet here is more variation then about Jepan, Brafil, or Peru, &c."

Gilbert's view was in truth founded on an incomplete fet of facts. At that time, as he tells us, the variation of the compafs at London was $11\frac{1}{3}$ degrees eaftward. But he did not know of the fecular change which would in about fifty-feven years reduce that variation to zero. Still lefs did he imagine that there would then begin a weftward variation which in the year 1816 fhould reach 24° 30', and which fhould then fteadily diminifh fo that in the year 1900 it fhould ftand at 16° 16' weftward. For an early difcuffion of the changes of the variation fee vol. i. of the *Philofophical Tranfactions* (Abridged), p. 188. Still earlier is the claffical volume of Henry Gellibrand, *A Difcovrfe Mathematical on the Variation of the Magneticall Needle* (Lond., 1635). Gilbert heads chapter iii. of book iiii. (p. **159**) with the affertion *Variatio uniufcuiufque loci conftans eft*, declaring that to change it would require the upheaval of a continent. Gellibrand combats this on p. 7 of the work mentioned. He fays :

"Thus hitherto (according to the Tenents of all our *Magneticall* Philofophers) we have fuppofed the variations of all particular places to continue one and the fame. So that when a Seaman fhall happly returne to a place where formerly he found the fame variation, he may hence conclude he is in the fame former *Longitude*. For it is the Affertion of *Mr. Dr. Gilberts. Variatio vnicuiufq; Loci conftans eft*, that is to fay, the fame place doth alwayes retaine the fame variation. Neither hath this Affertion (for ought I ever heard) been queftioned by any man. But moft diligent magneticall obfervations have plainely offred violence to the fame, and proved the contrary, namely that the variation is accompanied with a variation."

In 1637 Henry Bond wrote in the *Sea-Mans Kalendar* that in the year 1657 the variation would be zero at London. Compare Bond's *Longitude Found* (Lond., 1676, p. 3).

As to inconftancy of the variation in one place fee further Fournier's *Hydrographie* (Paris, 1667, liv. xi., ch. 12, p. 413), and Kircher, *Magnes* (Colon. Agripp., 1643, p. 418).

Page 157, line 4. Page 157, line 5. *perfecto.*—Though this word is thus in all editions, it ought to ftand *perfectâ*, as in line **10** below.

Page 157, line 11. Page 157, line 13. *varietas*, for *variatio*.

Page 160, line 20. Page 160, line 23. *in Borrholybicum.*—This name for the North-weft, or North-North-Weft, is rarely ufed. It is found on the chart or windrofe of the names of the winds on pp. 151 and 152 of the *Mécometrie de l'Eyman* of G. Nautonier (1602). Here the name *Borrolybicus* is given as a fynonym for *Nortoueft Galerne*, or Ὀλυμπιάς, while the two winds on the points next on the weftern and northern fides refpectively are called *Upocorus* and *Upocircius*.

In Swan's *Specvlvm Mundi* (Camb., 1643, p. 174) is this explanation: "Borrholybicus is the North-weſt wind."

In Kircher's *Magnes* (Colon. Agripp., 1643, p. 434) is a table of the names of the thirty-two winds in ſix languages, where *Borrolybicus* is given as the equivalent of *Maeſtro* or *North-Weſt*.

Page 161, line 2. Page 161, line 2. *Inſula in Oceano variationem non mutat.*—The concluſions derived from the magnetic explorations of the Challenger expedition, 1873-1876, are briefly theſe: That in iſlands north of the magnetic equator there is a tendency to produce a local perturbation, attracting the north-ſeeking end of the needle downwards, and horizontally towards the higher parts of the land; while ſouth of the magnetic equator, the oppoſite effects are obſerved. (See *Challenger Reports, Phyſics and Chemiſtry*, vol. ii., part vi., *Report on the Magnetical Reſults* by Staff-Commander Creak, F.R.S.)

Page 162, line 2. Page 162, line 3. *quarè & reſpectiuum punctum . . . excogitauit.*—The paſſage referred to is in *The newe Attractiue* of Robert Norman (Lond., 1581), chap. vi.

" Your reaſon towards the earth carrieth ſome probabilitie, but I prove that there be no *Attractive*, or drawing propertie in neyther of theſe two partes, then is the *Attractive* poynt loſt, and falſly called the poynt *Attractive*, as ſhall be proved. But becauſe there is a certayne point that the Needle alwayes reſpecteth or ſheweth, being voide and without any *Attractive* propertie: in my judgment this poynt ought rather to bee called the point Reſpective . . . This Poynt *Reſpective*, is a certayne poynt, which the touched Needle doth alwayes *Reſpect* or ſhew . . ."

Page 165, line 2. Page 165, line 2. *De pyxidis nauticæ vſitatæ compoſitione.*—Gilbert's deſcription of the uſual conſtruction of the mariner's compaſs ſhould be compared with thoſe given by Levinus Lemnius in *The Secret Miracles of Nature* (London, 1658); by Lipenius in *Navigatio Salomonis Ophiritica* (Witteb., 1660, p. 333); and with that given in Barlowe's *Navigators Supply* (London, 1597). See alſo Robert Dudley's *Dell' Arcano del Mare* (Firenze, 1646).

Page 165 deals with the conſtruction; the proceſs of magnetizing by the loadſtone had already been diſcuſſed in pp. **147** to **149**. It is intereſting to ſee that already the magnetized part attached below the compaſs-card was being ſpecialized in form, being made either of two pieces bent to meet at their ends, or of a ſingle oval piece with elongated ends. The marking of the compaſs-card is particularly deſcribed. It was divided into thirty-two points or " winds," preciſely as the earlier " wind-roſe " of the geographers, diſtinguiſht by certain marks, and by a lily—or fleur-de-lys—indicating the North. Stevin in the *Havenfinding Art* (London, 1599), from which work the paſſage on p. **167** is quoted, ſpeaking on p. 20 of " the Inſtrument which we call the Sea-directorie, ſome the nautical box, . . . or the ſea compaſſe," mentions the " Floure de luce " marking the North.

The legend which aſſigns the invention of the compaſs to one Goia or Gioja of Amalfi in 1302 has been already diſcuſſed in the Note to page **4**. Gilbert generouſly ſays that in ſpite of the adverſe evidence he does not wiſh to deprive the Amalfians of the honour of the conſtruction adopted in the compaſſes uſed in the Mediterranean. But Baptiſta Porta the Neapolitan, who wrote forty years before Gilbert, diſcredited the legend. " *Flavius* ſaith, an Italian found it out firſt, whoſe name was *Amalphus*, born in our

Campania. But he knew not the Mariners Card, but ftuck the needle in a reed, or a piece of wood, crofs over; and he put the needles into a veffel full of water that they might flote freely." (Porta's *Natural Magick*, Englifh tranflation, London, 1658, p. 206.) See alfo Lipenius (*op. citat.*, p. 390).

The pivotting of the needle is expreffly defcribed in the famous *Epiftle* on the Magnet of Peter Peregrinus, which was written in 1269. Gaffer's edition, *Epiftola Petri Peregrini . . . de magnete*, was printed in Augfburg in 1558. In Part II., cap. 2, of this letter, a form of inftrument is defcribed for directing one's courfe to towns and iflands, and any places in fact on land or fea. This inftrument confifts of a veffel like a turned box (or *pyxis*) of wood, brafs, or any folid material, not deep, but fufficiently wide, provided with a cover of glafs or cryftal. In its middle is arranged a flender axis of brafs or filver, pivotted at its two ends into the top and the bottom of the box. This axis is pierced orthogonally with two holes, through one of which is paffed the fteel needle, while through the other is fixed fquare acrofs the needle another ftylus of filver or brafs. The glafs cover was to be marked with two crofs lines north-fouth and eaft-weft; and each quadrant was to be divided into ninety degrees. This the earlieft defcribed pivotted compafs was therefore of the crofs-needle type, a form claimed as a new invention by Barlowe in 1597. The firft fuggeftion of fufpending a magnetic needle by a thread appears to be in the *Speculum Lapidum* of Camillus Leonardus (Venet., 1502, fig. k ij, lines 25-31): "Nã tacto ferro ex una p̄te magnetis ex oppofita eius p̄te appropinquato fugat: ut expiĕtia docet de acu appenfo filo."

The earlieft known examples of the " wind-rofe" are thofe in certain parchment charts preferved in the Biblioteca Marciana in Venice. Thefe go back to 1426 or 1436, the beft being afcribed to Andrea Bianco. They have the North indicated by a fleur-de-lys, a trident, a fimple triangle, or a letter T; while the Eaft is diftinguifht by a crofs. The Weft is marked with a P. (fee Fincati, *op. citat.*). The eight marks in order, clockwife, run thus,

   ⚜ (or T).   G.   ✠ (or L)   S.   O.   A (or L).   P.   M.

The letters correfpond to the Italian names of the principal winds:

Tramontano	North.
Greco	North-Eaft.
Levante	Eaft.
Sirocco	South-Eaft.
Oftro	South.
Africo or Libeccio	South-Weft.
Ponente	Weft.
Maeftro	North-Weft.

Wind-rofes marked with the names of the minor winds are found in Nautonier's *Mécometrie de l'Eyman* (Vennes, 1602-1604, pp. 151-152), and Kircher's *Magnes Siue de Arte Magnetica* (Colon. Agripp., 1643, p. 432). The defcription above given of the early Venetian wind-rofes *exactly* defcribes the compafs-card as depicted by Pedro de Medina in his *Arte de Nauegar* (Valladolid, 1545, folio lxxx.), in the fixth book entitled " las aguias de navegar"; while in the *Breve compendio de la fphera* of Martin Cortes (Sevilla, 1551, cap. iii., *de la piedrayman*) a fimilar wind-rofe, without the letters, is found.

In the *De Ventis et navigatione* of Michaele Angelo Blondo (Venet., 1546, p. 15) is given a wind-rofe, defcribed as " Pixis uel Buxolus inftrumentum et dux nauigantium," having twenty-fix points infcribed with the names of the winds, there being fix between north and eaft, and fix between fouth and weft, and only five in each of the other quadrants. In the middle is a fmaller wind-rofe exactly like the early Italian ones juft mentioned.

In the *Della Guerra di Rhodi* of Jacobo Fontano (Venet., 1545, pages 7*-74) is a chapter *Dei Venti, e della Bvffola di nauicare di Giovanni Quintino*, giving a wind-rofe, and a table of the names of the winds, the north being indicated by a pointer, at the cufp of which are feven ftars, and the weft by an image of the fun. The other cardinal points are marked with letters.

Barlowe, in *The Navigators Supply* (Lond., 1597), fpeaks thus:

"The merueilous and diuine Inftrument, called the *Sayling Compaffe* (being one of the greateft wonders that this World hath) is a Circle diuided commonly into 32. partes, tearmed by our Seamen Windes, *Rumbes*, or Points of Compaffe."

It is a difputed point with whom the method of naming the winds originated. Some afcribe it to Charlemagne. Michiel Coignet (*Inftruction novvelle . . . touchant l'art de naviguer*, Anvers, 1581, p. 7) afcribes it to Andronicus Cyrrheftes. See Varro, *De Re Ruftica*, iii., 5, 17, and Vitruvius, i., 6, 4.

Gilbert's complaint of the evil practice of fetting the needles obliquely beneath the card, with the intention of allowing for the variation, is an echo of a fimilar complaint in Norman's *Newe Attractiue*. In chapter x. of this work Norman thus enumerates the different kinds of compaffes:

" Of thefe common Sayling Compaffes, I find heere (in *Europa*) five fundry fortes or fets. The firft is of *Levant*, made in *Scicile, Genoüa*, and *Venice*: And thefe are all (for the moft parte) made Meridionally, with the Wyers directlye fette under the South, and North of the Compaffe: And therefore, duely fhewing the poynt *Refpective*, in all places, as the bare Needle. And by this Compaffe are the Plats made, for the moft part of all the *Levants* Seas.

"Secondly, there are made in *Danfke*, in the Sound of *Denmarke*, and in *Flanders*, that have the Wyers fet at 3 quarters of a point to the Eaftwards of the North of the compaffe, and alfo fome at a whole point: and by thefe Compaffes they make both the Plats and Rutters for the Sound.

"Thirdly, there hath beene made in this Countrey particulary, for Saint *Nicholas* and *Rufcia*, Compaffes fet at 3 feconds of a point, and the firft Plats of that Difcoverie were made by this Compaffe.

"Fourthly the Compaffe made at *Sevill, Lifbone, Rochell, Bourdeaux, Roan*, and heere in *England*, arc mofte commonly fet at halfe a point: And by this Compaffe are the Plats of the Eaft and Weft *Indies* made for their Pylotes, and alfo for our Coaftes neere hereby, as *France, Spayne, Portugall*, and *England*: and therefore beft of thefe Nations to bee ufed, becaufe it is the moft common forte that is generally ufed in thefe Coaftes."

Beffard (*op. citat.*, pages 22 and 48) gives cuts of compaffes fhowing the needle difplaced one rumbe to the Eaft.

Gallucci, in his *Ratio fabricandi horaria mobilia et permanentia cum magnetica acu* (Venet., 1596), defcribes the needle as inclined 10 degrees from the fouth toward the fouth-weft.

The frontifpiece of the work of Pedro Nuñez, *Inftrumenta Artis Navigandi*, Bafil., 1592, depicts a compafs with the lily fet one point to the eaft.

Reibelt, *De Phyficis et Pragmaticis Magnetis Myfteriis* (Herbipolis, 1731), depicts the compafs with the needle fet about 12 degrees to the Eaft of North. See alfo Fournier, *Hydrographie* (Paris, 1667); De Lanis, *Magifterium Natvræ et Artis* (Brixiæ, 1684); Milliet Defchales, *Curfus feu Mundus*

Mathematicus (Lugd., 1674). Both the latter works give pictures of the compafs-cards as ufed in South Europe, and in North Europe, and of the various known fhapes of needles.

Page 168, line 29. Page 168, line 33. *Directio igitur inualidior eft propè polos.* Here as in many paffages *direction* means *the force which directs.* A fimilar ufage prevails with the nouns *variation* and *declination,* meaning frequently the force caufing variation or declination refpectively.

Page 172, line 13. *perquirere.* The edition of 1633 reads *perquirero,* in error.

Page 172, line 29. Page 172, line 33. *Ad pyxidis nauticæ veræ & meridionalis formam . . . fiat inftrumentum.*—An excellent form of portable meridian compafs, provided with fights for taking aftronomical obfervations, is defcribed by Barlowe (*The Navigators Supply,* London, 1597), and is depicted in an etched engraving. An identical engraving is repeated in Dudley's *Arcano del Mare* (Firenze, 1646). Gilbert's new inftrument was confiderably larger.

Page 174, line 19. Page 174, line 21. *addendo vel detrahendo proftaphærefin.*—"Profthaphærefis, conflata dictione, ex additione et fubtractione fpeciebus logiftices, nomen habet ab officio, quia vt in femicirculo altero ad æquabilem motum adijcitur, ita in altero fubtrahitur, vt adparens motus ex æquabili taxetur: atque hinc fit, quòd quæ Profthaphærefis dicitur Ptolemæo, ea vulgò æquatio vocetur." (Stadius, *Tabulæ Bergenfes,* Colon. Agripp., 1560, p. 37.)

Page 174, line 28. Page 174, line 31. *Stellæ Lucidæ.*—According to Dr. Marke Ridley (*Magneticall Animadverfions,* London, 1617, p. 9), this chapter xii. of book iv., with the Table of Stars, was written by Edward Wright, the author of the Prefatory Epiftle of *De Magnete.* Wright was Lecturer on Navigation to the Eaft India Company, and author of fundry treatifes on Navigation.

Page 187, line 14. Page 187, line 16. *hic qui verfus boream conftitit . . . meridionalis eft, non borealis, quem antè nos omnes exiftimabant effe borealem.*—Earlier on, on pages **15** and **125,** Gilbert had mentioned this point. His infiftence caufed Barlowe (*Magneticall Aduertifements,* 1616, p. 4) to fpeak of the fouth-pointing end of the needle as the "true North," and thereby drew on himfelf the animadverfions of Marke Ridley.

Page 188, line 15. Page 188, line 16. *in rectâ fphærâ.*—See note to p. **134.**

Page 190, line 14. Page 190, line 19. *declinans in Borealibus.*—Dipping as it does in northern regions; that is, with the north-feeking or true-fouth pole downward.

Page 195, line 20. Page 195, line 24. *multa maiora pondera.*—Many greater weights. All editions read *multa,* but the fenfe requires *multo:* "much greater weights."

Page 196, line 10. Page 196, line 12. *conftans eft.*—This muft not be read "is conftant," for it is conftant only in any given latitude.

Page 196, line 15. Page 196, line 18. *De proportione declinationis pro latitudinis ratione.*—Gilbert here announces, and proceeds in the next feven pages to develop, the propofition that to each latitude there correfponds a conftant dip to a particular number of degrees. If this were accurately fo, then a traveller by merely meafuring the dip would be able to afcertain, by calculation, by reference to tables, or by aid of fome geometrical appliance, the latitude of the place.   In this hope Gilbert fought to perfect the dipping-needle; and he alfo worked out, on pages **199** and **200**, an empirical theory, and a diagram.   This theory was ftill further developed by him, and given to Thomas Blundevile (fee the Note to p. **240**).   Briggs of Grefham College, on Gilbert's fuggeftion, calculated a table of Dip and Latitude on this theory. It was found, however, that the obferved facts deviated more or lefs widely from the theory.   Kircher (*Magnes*, 1643, p. 368) gives a comparative table of the computed and obferved values.   Further difcovery fhowed the method to be impracticable, and Gilbert's hope remained unfulfilled.

Page 197, line 18.   Page 197, line 21. *progreſſionis centri.*—Note Gilbert's precifion of phrafe.

Page 200, line 12.   Page 200, line 11. *ſubintelligŭtur.*—This is printed *ſubintelligitur*, and is altered in ink in all copies of the folio edition. The editions of 1628 and 1633 read *ſubintelliguntur*.   Similarly in line **14** the word *ducit* has had a fmall *r* added in ink, making it read *ducitur*, as alfo the other editions.

Page 203.   This figure of the experiment with the fimple dipping needle fufpended in water in a goblet is due to Robert Norman.   In his *Newe Attractiue* (London, 1581, chap. vi.) he thus defcribes it:

"Then you fhall take a deepe Glaffe, Bowle, Cuppe, or other veffell, and fill it with fayre water, fetting it in fome place where it may reft quiet, and out of the winde.   This done, cut the Corke circumfpectly, by little and little, untill the wyre with the Corke be fo fitted, that it may remain under the fuperficies of the water two or three inches, both ends of the wyer lying levell with the fuperficies of the water, without afcending or defcending, like to the beame of a payre of ballance beeing equalie poyfed at both ends.

"Then take out of the fame the wyer without mooving the Corke, and touch it with the *Stone*, the one end with the South of the *Stone*, and the other end with the North, and then fet it againe in the water, and you fhall fee it prefentlie turne it felfe upon his owne Center, fhewing the aforefay'd *Declining* propertie, without defcending to the bottome, as by reafon it fhould, if there were any *Attraction* downewards, the lower part of the water being neerer that point, then the fuperficies thereof."

Page 212, line 7.   Page 212, line 8. *ex altera parte.*—The fenfe feems to require *et altera parte*, but all editions read *ex*.

Page 213, line 1.   Page 213, line 2.   The paffage here quoted from Dominicus Maria Ferrarienfis, otherwife known as the aftronomer Novara, does not occur in any known writing of that famous man.   It is, however, quoted as being by Novara in at leaft three other writings of the fame epoch. See the *Tabulæ ſecvndorum mobilium coeleſtium* of Maginus (Venet., 1585, p. 29, line 19 to p. 30, line 11); the *Eratoſthenes Batavvs* of Willebrord Snell (Lugd. Batav., 1617, pp. 40-42); and the *Almageſti novi* (*Pars Poſterior*) of Riccioli (Bonon., 1651, p. 348).   The original document appears to have perifht.   See a notice by M. Curtze in Boncompagni's *Bullettino di Bibliografia*, T. iv., April, 1871.

Page 214, line 26.   Page 214, line 31. *Philolaus Pythagoricus.*

"Philolaüs a le premier dit que la terre fe meut en cercle; d'autres difent que c'eſt Nicétas de Syracufe."

"Les uns prétendent que le terre eſt immobile; mais Philolaüs le pythagoricien dit qu'elle fe meut circulairement autour du feu (central) et fuivant un cercle oblique, comme le foleil et la lune."—(Chaignet, *Pythagore et la Philoſophie pythagoricienne*, Paris, 1873.)

It appears that the firft of thefe *dicta* is taken from Diogenes Laërt., viii. 85; and the fecond from Plutarch, *Placit. Philos.*, III. 7.   The latter paffage may be compared with Ariftotle, *De Coelo*, II. 13, who, referring to the followers of Pythagoras, fays : " They fay that the middle is fire, that the earth is a ftar, and that it is moved circularly about this centre; and that by this movement it produces day and night."

Page 214, line 34. Page 214, line 42. *Copernicus.*—His work is *De revolutionibus orbium coeleftium, libri vi.* (Bafil., 1566).

Page 215, line 27. Page 215, line 24. *quæ . . . in cælo varijs diftantijs collocata funt.*—This remark appears to be Gilbert's one contribution to the fcience of Aftronomy; the ftars having previoufly been regarded as fixed in the eighth fphere all at the fame diftance from the central earth, around which it revolved.

Page 220, line 6. Page 220, line 6. *quem nyēthemeron vocamus.*—The 1628 and 1633 editions read *nyēlemoron*.

Page 221, line 10. Page 221, line 11. *poli verè oppofiti fint.*—For *verè*, the 1628 and 1633 editions read *reēlæ*. All editions read *fint*, though *funt* feems to make better fenfe.

Page 223, line 7. Page 223, line 8. *ad telluris conformitatem.*—The word *conformitas* is unknown in claffical Latin.

Page 223, line 16. Page 223, line 17. *Omitto quod Petrus Peregrinus conftanter affirmat, terrellam fuper polos fuos in meridiano fufpenfam, moveri circulariter integrâ revolutione 24 horis: Quod tamen nobis adhuc videre non contingit ; de quo motu etiam dubitamus.*

This ftatement that a fpherical loadftone pivotted freely with its axis parallel to the earth's axis will of itfelf revolve on its axis once a day under the control of the heavens, thus fuperfeding clocks, is to be found at the end of chap. x. of Peregrinus's *Epiftola De Magnete* (Augfb., 1537).

Gilbert, who doubted this experiment becaufe of the ftone's own weight is taken to tafk by Galileo, in the third of his Dialogues, for his qualified admiffion.

" I will fpeak of one particular, to which I could have wifhed that *Gilbert* had not lent an ear; I mean that of admitting, that in cafe a little Sphere of Loadftone might be exactly librated, it would revolve in it felf; becaufe there is no reafon why it fhould do fo " (p. 376 of Salufbury's *Mathematical Collections*, London, 1661). The Jefuit Fathers who followed Gilbert, but rejected his Copernican ideas, pounced upon this pfeudo-experiment, as though by difproving it they had upfet the Copernican theory.

Page 227, line 6. Page 227, line 7. This line is left out in the 1628 edition. In the 1633 edition it was alfo left out by the printer, and fubfequently printed in in the margin, being page 219 of that edition.

Page 234, line 35. Page 234, line 40. *vt poli telluris refpeēlus à polis.*—If it may be permitted to read *refpeēlu* for *refpeēlus* the fenfe is improved, and the paffage may then be tranflated thus: " that juft as it was needful . . . that the poles of the Earth as to direction fhould be 23 degrees and more from the poles of the Ecliptick; fo now, &c."

Page 237, line 19. Page 237, line 22. *vt motus quidem obfcuri faluarentur.*—It has been conjectured that *quidem* is here a mifprint for *quidam*, but the adverb *quidem* adds a fatirical flavour to his argument againft the folly of thofe who held the doctrine of the moving fpheres. The verb *falvare* does not occur in claffical Latin.

Page 240, line 13. Page 240, line 17. *à Copernico (Aftronomiæ inftauratore).*—Gilbert was the firft in England to uphold the doctrines of

Copernicus as to the motion of the earth on its axis and its revolution around the fun.   He confidered that his magnetic obfervations brought new fupport to that theory, and his views are quoted with approbation by Kepler, *Epitome Aftronomiæ Copernicanæ* . . . Authore Ioanne Keplero . . . (Francofurti, 1635); and by Galileo, *Dialogus de Syftemate Mundi* (Auguftæ Treboc., 1635), an Englifh tranflation of which appeared in Salufbury's *Mathematical Collections and Tranflations* (London, 1661, pp. 364 to 377).

For this the book *De' Magnete* was confidered by many as heretical. Many of the copies exifting in Italy are found to be either mutilated or elfe branded with a crofs.   For example, the copy in the library of the Collegio Romano in Rome has book VI. torn out.   Galileo ftates that the Book of Gilbert would poffibly never have come into his hands " if a Peripatetick Philofopher, of great fame, as I believe to free his Library from its contagion, had not given it me."   In England Barlowe, in his *Magneticall Aduertifements* (1616), expreffly repudiated Gilbert's Copernican notions, while praifing his difcoveries in magnetifm.   Marke Ridley, while upholding Gilbert's views, in his *Magneticall Animadverfions* (1617) did not confider him " fkilfull in Copernicus."   The Jefuit writers, Cabeus, Kircher, Fonfeca, Grandamicus, Schott, Leotaudus, Millietus, and De Lanis, one and all, who followed Gilbert in their magnetic writings, repudiated the idea that the magnetifm of the globe gave fupport to the heretical modern Aftronomy.

The works referred to are:

Cabeus, *Philofophia Magnetica, in qua Magnetis natura penitus explicatur . . . auctore Nicolao Cabeo Ferrarenfi Soc. Jefv.* (Ferrariæ, 1629).

Kircher, *Magnes, Siue de Arte Magnetica, Libri tres, Authore Athanafio Kirchero . . . e Soc. Iefv.* (Romæ, 1641).

Grandamicus, *Nova Demonftratio immobilitatis terræ petita ex virtute magnetica* (Flexiæ, 1645).   This work is moft beautifully illuftrated with copper-plate etchings of cupids making experiments with terrellas.

Schott, Gafpar, *Thaumaturgus Phyficus* (Herbipolis, 1659).

Leotaudus, *R. P. Vincentinii Leotavdi Delphinatis, Societ. Iefv., Magnetologia; in qva exponitvr Nova de Magneticis Philofophia* (Lvgdvni, 1668).

Millietus (Milliet Defchales), *Curfus feu Mundus Mathematicus* (Lugd., 1674), *Tomus Primus, Tractatus de Magnete.*

De Lanis, *Magifterium Natvræ et Artis.   Opus Phyfico-Mathematicvm P. Francifci Tertii de Lanis, Soc. Jesv.* (Brixiæ, 1684).

Page 240, line 24.   Page 240, line 31.   *hîc finem & periodum imponimus.*

On February 13 [1601] Gilbert wrote to Barlowe (fee *Magneticall Aduertifements*, p. 88) :

" I purpofe to adioyne an appendix of fix or eight fheets of paper to my booke after a while, I am in hand with it of fome new inventions, and I would haue fome of your experiments, in your name and inuention put into it, if you pleafe, that you may be knowen for an augmenter of that arte."

This he never did.   Perhaps his appointment (in February, 1601) as chief phyfician in perfonal attendance on the Queen interfered with the project; or his death, of the plague, in 1603, intervened before his intention had been carried into effect.   But it is probable that the fubftance of the propofed additions is to be found in the chapter, publifht in Gilbert's lifetime, in Blundevile's *Theoriques of the feuen Planets* (London, 1602), thus defcribed in the title-page of the work : " There is alfo hereto added,

The making, defcription, and vfe, of two moft ingenious and neceffarie Inftruments for Sea-men, to find out thereby the latitude of any Place vpon the Sea or Land, in the darkeft night that is, without the helpe of Sunne, Moone, or Starre. Firft inuented by M. Doctor Gilbert, a moft excellent Philofopher, and one of the ordinarie Phyficians to her Maieftie: and now here plainely fet downe in our mother tongue by Mafter Blundeuile."

Of thefe two inftruments the firft confifts of a mechanical device, with movable quadrants, to be cut out in cardboard, to be ufed in connection with the diagram of fpiral lines which Gilbert had given as a folding plate between pages **200** and **201** of *De Magnete*. The intention was that the Sea-man having found by experiment with a dipping-needle the amount of the dip at any place, fhould by applying this diagram and its moving quadrants, afcertain the latitude, according to the theory expounded in book V., chap. VII.

The fecond inftrument is a fimplified portable dipping-needle, having the degrees engraved on the inner face of a cylindrical brafs ring.

Blundevile adds a Table, calculated by Briggs, and "annexed to the former Treatife by *Edward Wright*, at the motion of the right Worfhipful M. Doctor *Gilbert*." This gives the values of the dip for different latitudes, as calculated from Gilbert's empirical theory.

The other work, *De Mundo noftro Sublunari Philofophia Nova*, which Gilbert left in manufcript at his death, does not contain any additional matter on the magnetical inveftigations. Though it contains feveral direct references to the *de Magnete*, and particularly to Book VI. on the rotation of the earth, it is doubtful whether it was written after or before the publication of *de Magnete*. On pages 137 to 144 of the pofthumous edition (Amfterdam, 1651) Gilbert refers to Peregrinus's alleged perpetually revolving fphere, and denies its poffibility. The greater part of the work is an anti-Ariftotelian difcuffion on Air, Meteorology, Aftronomy, the Winds, Tides, and Springs.

INDEX TO AUTHORITIES

1

CHISWICK PRESS: CHARLES WHITTINGHAM AND CO.
TOOKS COURT, CHANCERY LANE, LONDON.